PRENTICE-HALL INTERNATIONAL SERIES IN MANAGEMENT

HOLT, MUTH, MODIGLIANI, AND SIMON   *Planning Production, Inventories, and Work Force*

MILLER AND STARR   *Executive Decisions and Operations Research*

PFIFFNER AND SHERWOOD   *Administrative Organization*

PRENTICE-HALL, INC.

PRENTICE-HALL INTERNATIONAL, INC., UNITED KINGDOM AND EIRE

PRENTICE-HALL OF CANADA, LTD., CANADA

EDITORE FRANCO ANGELI, ITALY

J. H. DE BUSSY, LTD., HOLLAND AND FLEMISH-SPEAKING BELGIUM

DUNOD PRESS, FRANCE

MARUZEN COMPANY, LTD., FAR EAST

C. BERTELSMANN VERLAG, WEST GERMANY AND AUSTRIA

EXECUTIVE

and

DAVID W. *(Wendell)* MILLER

Graduate School of Business, Columbia University

MARTIN K. *(Kenneth)* STARR

Department of Industrial and Management Engineering, Columbia University; Martin K. Starr Associates, of New York

PRENTICE-HALL, INC.

DECISIONS

OPERATIONS

RESEARCH

Englewood Cliffs, N. J.

To

PROFESSOR SEBASTIAN B. LITTAUER

Mentor, colleague, and friend

Current printing (last digit):
16 15 14 13 12 11 10 9

EXECUTIVE DECISIONS AND OPERATIONS RESEARCH

DAVID W. MILLER & MARTIN K. STARR

© 1960, *by* PRENTICE-HALL, INC., *Englewood Cliffs, N. J.*

Library of Congress Card Number: 60–10194

Printed in the United States of America

29439—C

Preface

WE REJECT the approach that identifies operations research with a heterogeneous assortment of mathematical techniques. Operations research is an executive responsibility. We believe that the relationship of operations research to executive responsibility can be presented meaningfully only in terms of a basic decision-theory foundation and orientation. In our conception of it, operations research is a continuum of methods resulting from a fundamental program of model-building within the decision theory framework. This continuum embraces the gamut running from crude qualitative models to highly refined mathematical models.

This book examines executive decision problems in terms of a decision theory formulation. Within this framework operations research receives its due emphasis and the reader gains the means by which to determine when an operations research problem exists, how the problem should be approached, when it may be worthwhile to seek specialized assistance, how the results may be evaluated, and so forth. The reader is given an overview of the wide range and value of the many tools which have been developed in recent years to aid the executive in his decision problems.

Part 1 develops the theme of the relation of the executive to decision-making. Part 2 outlines the relationship of operations research and decisions, and provides the necessary basis for the treatment of the numerous decision problem paradigms which are presented in Part 3. Part 4 completes the triangle by presenting the relation of the executive to operations research and by analyzing the executive's special problems of evaluation, implementation, and control of the solution.

We have classified the problems analyzed in Part 3 not by the techniques of analysis used (linear programming, queuing theory, and the like) but by the business area in which the problem arises: marketing, production, or administration. The reader will be familiar with this traditional business classification and with the kinds of decision problems that arise in each area. Thus, he can devote his full attention to the methods used in attacking the problems. One soon discovers that seemingly different problems in widely dissimilar areas are susceptible to similar formulations and methods of solution.

This book has been designed to meet the needs of the executive who is not expected to spend his time and energy developing mathematical models and solving statistical problems. Therefore, only a minimum of mathematics is utilized. Those who lack extensive formal training in mathematics can get from this book the insights presently available only from highly technical treatments of operations research.

v

We have bent every effort to present a clear, unified, and comprehensive approach to business decision problems. The executive must make decisions, that is his function. It is our hope that this book will enable the reader to utilize the rich resources which are available to help him achieve optimal decisions.

We express our gratitude to Dr. Peter Langhoff, Vice President and Director of Research of Young & Rubicam, Inc., for permission to use in Chapter 9 marketing material which was developed in conjunction with the Research Department of Young & Rubicam, Inc. We wish particularly to express our gratitude to Chris Kentera for far surpassing the requirements of his editorship in offering us guidance in the writing of this book. He offered a great number of cogent suggestions which were always helpful and encouraging to the authors. We also thank William Beranek for his careful reading of part of the manuscript.

DAVID W. MILLER
MARTIN K. STARR

Contents

PART 1   THE EXECUTIVE AND DECISIONS

PART 3   DECISION-PROBLEM PARADIGMS

PART 4   THE EXECUTIVE AND OPERATIONS RESEARCH

PART 1

THE EXECUTIVE
AND DECISIONS

Chapter one

History of the Managerial Function

Management, as defined by *Webster's New International Dictionary*, is the "judicious use of means to accomplish an end." This definition places a great multitude of situations within the province of management. Most of us, however, think of management in more limited terms. We don't think that managing our own and family affairs is comparable with the managing of corporations and other large business organizations. There is even some reluctance to acknowledge that governments, hospitals, and libraries require a management team.

Suppose we redefine management as the judicious use of means to accomplish the ends *of business*. Still our concept is limited; what we think of is business as we know it—business in our terms and in our style. For example, consider the Dobuan Islander of the South Pacific who speculates in shell necklaces from the southern islands and arm-shells from the northern islands. Using *wabuwabu*, the strategy of a good businessman, the Dobuan accumulates his fortune while maintaining the movement of shell necklaces in a clockwise direction and arm-shells in a counter-clockwise direction through the Kula ring of islands. A modern-day businessman, no matter how well trained or experienced in his own kind of management, would feel like a fish out of water if he tried to negotiate on Dobuan terms. Similarly, in Burma where the accumulation of capital was not an objective of business, and where the pleasure of bargaining was far more important than the achievement of profit, we would find the term management awkward if not impossible to apply.

Clearly, then, when we consider management it is in terms of a limited number of ends to which we are accustomed in our own business practices. Our concept of management is a narrow one. What is the effect of this narrowness?

1. CHANGING CONCEPTS OF MANAGEMENT

Our restricted conception of ends or goals has obscured the search for those elements of management which are transferable to any management situation. A great deal of business-school training appears to be concentrated on special situations, specific techniques, and the propagation of customs, traditions, and attitudes.

An analysis of the evolution of management thinking shows, however, that two currents run side by side. One line of development emphasizes the necessary mastery of business methods as they exist at any given time. The other is devoted to the determination of those elements which are common to all management situations. Progress in the latter direction has been consistent and significant for many years. Our modern-day businessman is, in fact, better equipped to tackle Dobuan or Burmese business practice than he suspects.

Decision theory and operations research are the present-day culmination of management's evolution. At least at the moment they are the most advanced developments available for generalizing all management situations. They are—surprisingly enough—equally applicable to Dobu, Burma, Afghanistan, and the United States of America.

Operations research is a development of management. It is not something that appeared by chance in another context and was then absorbed by management. Military management was the first to consciously use O.R.; this was one of many developments that appeared in wartime when the urgency of the situation accelerated normal rates of progress.

2. EARLY TRAINING PROGRAMS AND BUSINESS PUBLICATIONS

Looking back into the history of business and executive training we are not surprised to find that in Babylonian times the institutions for business education were the households or small merchants' shops. Formal training programs not connected with apprenticeship appeared as early as 1478. At that time a book on arithmetic for business was printed at Treviso, Italy. At the end of the seventeenth century a book was written in France by Jacques Savary: *Le parfait négociant; ou Instruction générale pour ce qui regarde le commerce de tout sorte de marchandises.* This book was well received and was reprinted several times. Savary, treating personnel problems, wrote that if a master gives orders in anger then the apprentice should not obey immediately but wait for a second command, and if the apprentice feels that an order is to his master's disadvantage, he should pretend not to have heard the order and ask instead if his master had ordered something else. In England, William Scott wrote an *Essay of drapery, or The compleate citizen, trading justly, pleasingly, profitably.* At about the same time Jan Impyn completed the first Dutch book on accounting. His instructions were that the accounting journal should begin with the prayer, "May God our merciful Saviour vouchsafe me grace to make a profit and preserve me from all bad fortune."

These early works were important for the interest that they generated and because they led to a process of searching and self-questioning which management has not yet completed. Some of the earliest questioning can be traced to Thomas Watts who conducted a business school on Abchurch Lane in London. Watts called for the development of principles and the comparison of principles with practice. In Watts' writing, *An Essay on the Proper Method of Forming the Man of Business* (1716), we find the interplay of generalization with specific prescription. Watts emphasized arithmetic, accounting, mathematics including algebra and geometry, and mensuration. The last point is particularly interesting because it seems to have been forgotten after Watts' time. Not until the early part of the twentieth century did business reawaken to the problems and importance of measurement theory. The reawakening has been gradual, and we cannot help but wonder if a session or two in Thomas Watts' class on Mensuration would not prove helpful to all of us. Watts stressed principles, generalization, and mathematics, which are the progenitors of decision theory and operations research in our present day. To quote from Watts:

The several parts of the Mathematicks are of that extensive Use and Benefit to Mankind, that hardly anything is to be done without them; Consequently, the Man of Business can have no small Share in these Sciences: For he that has a thorough Knowledge in them, must have the best Foundation laid, and a Mind exquisitely furnish'd for the undertaking of any Business.

3. COLLEGE TRAINING PROGRAMS AND SCIENTIFIC MANAGEMENT

In September 1890 Edmund James, Professor of Public Finance and Administration at the Wharton School of Finance and Economy of the University of Pennsylvania, read a paper presenting the plan and curriculum of the Wharton School. James urged the establishment of other such schools for the higher education of businessmen. The Wharton School, established in 1881, was the first university-level business school in the United States. Wharton was followed by the University of Chicago and the University of California, both of which set up business schools in 1898. It was not until 1908 that the Harvard School of Business was founded, 272 years after Harvard College was begun. In 1926 the Columbia University School of Business came into existence. The purpose in giving these dates is to show how recent the development of modern institutions of management training is.

Business schools are the best evidence that business and industrial organizations support and encourage management training and management research. Management is always looking for better ways to do things. In the early 1900's Frederick W. Taylor concerned himself with the problems of production management and demonstrated that management could improve the means they used to accomplish ends. Some of his results were so startling that his methods swept across the United States. This movement, known as Scientific Management, was later developed into time and motion studies and work-simplification methods. Taylor was responsible for the rebirth of interest in measurement. Probably, Taylor's work also played an important part in creating interest in management training. If business and industry had not recognized the importance of method and general procedure it is very doubtful that business schools would have grown to the pre-eminent position that they occupy today. Similarly, if the quality of an executive were determined by his knowledge of ritual, custom, and tradition, apprenticeship training would have been more attractive than business-school training.

4. ACCOUNTING AND CONTROL

One of the first general methodologies management discovered was accounting. Accounting was neither limited to a specific industry nor restricted to a particular area of business. The history of modern accounting starts with a book by Pacioli, *Summa de arithmetica,* published in Italy in 1494. Pacioli's writing contains a descriptive statement of double-entry bookeeping methods. Apparently the system did not originate with him since he referred to it as the Venetian system. It was 1543, a half-century later, when Hugh Oldcastle wrote the first description in English of the methods of bookkeeping. Thomas Watts referred to this method of keeping accounts as his "darling science" and he had only contempt for those who kept single-entry books.

Interest in accounting methods grew rapidly in the nineteenth century. James Bennett of New York wrote *The American System of Practical Bookkeeping* in 1824. Eighteen years later 19 editions had been published. Bennett used his book as a text for classes which he conducted for business students from his house at 97 John Street in New York City. At about the same time, Mr. Thomas Jones founded the New York Commercial Academy at 183 Broadway in New York City, and published his book *Principles and Practices of Bookkeeping.*

Our purpose in stressing accounting in this brief summary of the development of management training may not be entirely clear. Accounting is important not only as one of the first generalized methods of business. It is also significant as a quantitative method. The importance of accounting to a business enterprise was so great that it tended to crystallize in definite forms so that it could be put to work on specific applications. However, underlying accounting problems were problems of observation and measurement, systems analysis, model construction, and decision theory. Certainly, operations research is not an offshoot of accounting. But the forces that brought accounting practices to the fore were not unlike the forces that have introduced operations research to the business world.

5. CHANGE IN OWNER-MANAGER RELATIONSHIP

Perhaps what we have been lacking in our definition of management is some phrase relating to the delegation of authority. The end of the nineteenth century and the beginning of the twentieth was the period of enormous expansion of industry in the United States which is credited to the Captains of Industry. These Captains with gigantic reserves of personal vitality directed their companies' fortunes in the capacity of the owner-manager which was familiar to smaller businesses. Gradually, as business began to move from its highly competitive position to a more cooperative-competitive attitude, the individual owner-manager began to disappear. In his place, an organizational structure evolved with the capacity to delegate authority for decisions and responsibility for the entire range of administrative tasks. Scientific management in Taylor's terms was hardly in a position to cope with the problems which organizational structure produced. In the first place, personnel problems appeared as a result of the complex, hierarchical arrangements of organization. Social developments emphasized the uniqueness of labor, management, the consumer, and the stockholder. At the same time, legal involvements and governmental controls raised new problems which the management team had to solve.

6. DEVELOPMENT OF SPECIALISTS

The answer was—and continues to be—specialization. The demands of organizational growth were incontestable. Specialization set the pattern for the traditional areas of management. Specialists were required for production, marketing, finance, personnel, real estate, business law, and so on. Then within each of these areas further specialization was required so that we had time standards, quality control, foundry, press shop, advertising, sales promotion, public relations, building codes, patent law, and the rest.

7. DEVELOPMENT OF GENERALISTS

And is the operations-research practitioner a specialist? Most certainly he is. However, he occupies the unique position of being a specialist in generalization. That is why top management prefers to locate the operations-research function high up on the organizational structure.

The twentieth century saw research and technological development spurt ahead with such impact that organizational identity could hardly be maintained. Faced with swift and startling developments, management had to question whether it had an existence above and beyond the products it made or the services it offered. At the same time, the separation of owner and manager engendered an executive tradition which permitted management people to shift from one organization to another. Consequently, management had to ask itself whether it had an identity that was independent of any or all of the individuals who composed the management group.

The answer to modern management's problems was the development of the executive-generalist. Such executives could maintain the company's existence no matter what product was made. They could develop abstract organizational forms which were independent of the individuals who at any time happened to compose the management group. They could coordinate the contributions of all of the specialists of an organization. Their task required the ability to employ structure before content in coping with the extreme diversity of information produced by the organization.

8. MANAGEMENT SCIENCE

Management recognized that its role had changed. Management required generalists. Individuals so trained could effectively operate in business, industry, city or federal government, hospitals, the armed forces, and schools, and could deal with behavioral scientists, research physicists, tax lawyers, and production foremen. To meet this challenge business schools have broadened their curriculums and have supported research in management problems. More and more they are seeking independence from prescribed means and prescribed ends. Operations research and the decision-theory framework are part of a current, world-wide *management science* movement. They provide one important avenue for increasing the executive's ability to generalize. As such, they are a logical development in the evolutionary process of the managerial function.

Management science differs from Taylor's scientific management in many ways. It is not primarily concerned with production tasks and the efficiency of men and machines. Rather, it views efficiency as a secondary achievement which should follow adequate planning. In other words, poor decisions can be implemented in an efficient way. A company can manufacture a high-quality product at minimum cost, but the product might not be the best choice for the company's objectives.

Management science is concerned with both short- and long-range planning. It attempts to establish whatever relationships exist between a company's objectives and the company's resources. In this way, it cuts across the traditional areas of management.

Management science neither avoids nor overlooks the effects of behavioral problems, even though such problems cannot always be formulated or solved. Management science is essentially quantitative; however, important problems that cannot be quantified are handled qualitatively. Whether quantitative or qualitative methods are applied, operations research is used to produce rational decisions and logical plans of action.

Chapter two

The Modern View of the Executive

Notions of evolution are applicable to organizations as well as species. Thriving organizations can find themselves unable to adapt to environmental and competitive changes. Unsuitable structures show up as marginal industries, and eventually such organizations enter receivership where reorganization takes place.

The ability of an organization to succeed in its environment and to adapt to change, or even capitalize on change, is basically in the hands of management. The discussion in Chapter 1 indicates that management's view of itself has not remained constant. Present-day management has redefined the executive role to improve the organization's flexibility and responsiveness.

9. THE EXECUTIVE IS A DECIDER AND NOT A DOER

The major function of the executive is not indicated by the strict derivation of the word. "Executive" derives from a Latin word meaning "to do," and the Oxford dictionary defines it in terms of "the action of carrying out or carrying into effect." Neither of these approaches would suggest that the main responsibility and function of the executive is to make decisions. Yet in modern business and industry this is precisely what is expected of him. He is rewarded and evaluated in terms of his success in making decisions.

This does not mean that the typical executive has nothing to do but make decisions. On the contrary, he has to do many other things. But most organizations make continual attempts to relieve the executive of his more or less routine doing so that he will have time for the more important deciding. This conception of the executive definitely does not diminish the importance of doing. Organizational structure is set up as the means for doing something. However, crucial questions of what, when, where, and how are prior to the doing. These are the decision problems with which the executive must deal. To the extent that he is involved in the doing he will have less time to devote to the deciding.

The distinction we are making between doing and deciding is certainly a drastic oversimplification. One simply cannot make such a neat distinction. A decision initiates a doing which in turn will generate the need for new decisions. The process is a never-ending one, and the executive is immersed to some degree in both parts. Nonetheless, a conceptual separation of the two permits concentration on those aspects of the decision part of the process which may yield us some useful insights.

When we concentrate on the decision side of the total process, we cannot afford to ignore the interaction with the doing. If deciding and doing are *completely* interrelated, in fact, it can be totally misleading even to try to separate them. This possibility must be considered before we proceed to analyze the decision problem separately.

10. THE ORGANIZATION AS A COMMUNICATION NETWORK

In order to clarify the relationship between doing and deciding it will be useful to introduce a *model* of the organization as a communication network.

One of the purposes of this book is to demonstrate the value of studying different models of organizations. A model is a simple way of thinking about an organization by abstracting only a few aspects of the organization. A full discussion of models will be given later in the book. For our present purposes it is enough to state that a model, if valid, is at best a partial truth. The reason for isolating or abstracting certain characteristics of an organization in the form of a model is to gain an understanding of the effect of the abstracted characteristics on the total organization. The risk involved in such abstraction is that other characteristics of the organization may be so important that ignoring them invalidates the model. The test of experience is the only final arbiter as to the successfulness of a specific model.

A communication network is simply a collection of points between which information is transmitted. Any telephone system provides a good example of a communication network. As a matter of fact, it was primarily problems of the sort that arise in connection with such communication networks as telephone systems that led to the development of a theory of these networks and the closely related information theory.

When we consider an organization as a communication network we are ignoring all of its characteristics except those represented by the existence and transmission of information between persons and places. This is certainly a rather severe abstractive simplification of an organization, but it is not quite as extreme as it might appear. The definition of "information" is not limited to standard forms of communication. Written memoranda and verbal exchanges are only one form of information. Blueprints, budgets, part numbers, and the like are another form. Materials and parts flowing through the factory or warehouse are legitimate units of information. In fact, any characteristic of an operation that can be observed and recorded constitutes potential information for the communication network. From this standpoint the production of an item is represented by the transmission of the information that that item has been added to inventory. The sale of an item is represented by the transmission of the information that that item has left inventory. At a later point, there is the transmission of information that a certain sum of money has been added to the organization's bank account. Similarly, most of the routine activities of the organization will have their information-flow analogs.

Viewed in this way any large organization is a tremendously intricate system of communication links through which an enormous amount of different kinds of information is constantly flowing.

11. INPUT-OUTPUT AND THE BLACK BOX

One important distinction between the kinds of information that are transmitted arises from the fact that the organization is embedded in its environment. This outside world consists of suppliers, buyers, competitors, tax and regulatory agencies, and other groups. The information that comes into the organization from the outside world is the *input* to the company. In response to the input the company buys material, hires labor, prices its products, advertises, floats stock issues, and so forth. The organizational responses are the *outputs*.

It is useful at times to treat the organization as though it were covered by a black box and therefore completely unobservable. The "black box" is a convenient term to describe a system (organism or mechanism) whose structure is unknown—either because it cannot be observed or because it is too complex to be understood. (The notion of the black box has been borrowed by systems analysts from electrical engineering where it is used to denote unspecified circuitry.) How well can the contents of the organizational black box be inferred from a knowledge of the inputs and outputs? Can reasonable predictions be made of the outputs that would occur for some hypothetical set of inputs if the contents of the black box cannot be inferred? The answers to both of these questions are a qualified "yes," the qualification depending upon the inherent structure of the information that appears in the inputs and outputs.

From an executive's point of view the black box does not cover his own organization, and he hardly likes to think that it covers his behavior [as in Figure 2.1(a)]. Instead, he thinks of the black box as covering the outside world [as in Figure 2.1(b)]. The output shown in Figure 2.1(a)

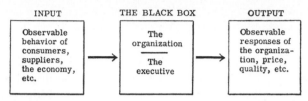

Figure 2.1(a)   Input-output model of the organization.

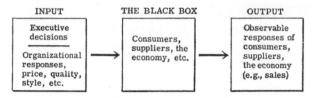

Figure 2.1(b)   Input-output model of executive control.

is transformed into the input of Figure 2.1(b), where management controls the inputs. When the black box covered the organization, only the organizational output could be observed. This output was all doing and contained no deciding to do. In fact, deciding was the circuitry that was hidden by the black box. By transforming to Figure 2.1(b), we have exposed the decision process to bring it into the realm of observable information.

From the standpoint of a communication network a decision consists of instructions from one point in the network to other points. As a result of the decision these other points will process the information they receive in a different manner or will change the rate of flow of information passing through them. Or, of course, the decision may result in the establishment of new points in the communication network.

12. INFORMATION STORAGE AND MEMORY

A specific decision will depend on the analysis, interpretation, and evaluation of the information available to the decision-maker.

Part of the information that comes to a decision-maker comes to him from storage. Every organization has a memory, or rather memories, in which data can be stored. The most obvious example of these memories are file-cases filled with information. Other storehouses of organizational knowledge are the brains of the persons comprising the organization. The access time required to obtain information stored in files is in some applications prohibitively high. The brain is not a reliable storage, memory being perhaps its weakest faculty. Therefore, computer memories have particular advantages under certain conditions for the storage of information.

It is quite apparent that the decision-maker can be deluged with information if he does not know how to select information that is pertinent to his problem. For this reason, information must be carefully categorized. Decision problems exist as to what information should be collected and in what form; where and how long it should be stored; when and by whom it should be called for; how it should be evaluated; when it should be supplemented, and so on. Information models provide some help in answering these questions, which are representative of the *deciding* activities of the executive. *Doing* would be the collecting, recording, dispatching, and storing of the information, and it is quite clear that management prefers to minimize executive time spent in this way.

Since the greatest part of this book is devoted to the procedure of making decisions we need not concern ourselves at the moment with that procedure. It is sufficient for our present purposes that the decision-maker does reach his decision on the basis of the information available to him.

13. INFORMATION FEEDBACK CHANNELS

Any decision that has been made may be countermanded or supplemented by subsequent decisions. Any such change will, presumably, be based on additional information. And, finally, this additional information may result from the changes that stem from the implementation of the decision or it may result from sources extraneous to the implementation of the decision. To the degree that it is the former, the decision process is closely entangled with the doing. To the degree that it is the latter, the decision process is more independent of the doing.

To make this distinction clearer, we must add an additional element to the input-output model. The new factor is called a *feedback* channel. (This term is also derived from electrical engineering where it is used to denote an electrical output which is fed back into the circuit from which it emanated.) Figure 2.2 illustrates two different feedback connections, (IV) and (V).

We can now examine the implications of the feedback links assuming that the executive occupies the position of the black box. For our purposes, the black box is not so opaque as to entirely hide the operations of the executive. Feedback channel IV indicates the executive's ability to call for certain inputs and to specify the form in which these inputs

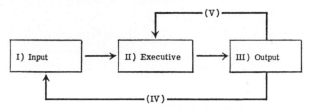

Figure 2.2 Input-output model of the organization with feedback channels.

should arrive. This matter was previously discussed in connection with memories and information storage. Basically, there are three types of inputs: (a) inputs that cannot be controlled, (b) inputs that are controlled by an outside agency with intelligence, and (c) inputs that our executive can control.

Link IV is the channel through which the executive exercises whatever control he has over the inputs. In all cases there is a decision and an action to effectuate control. Whenever feedback channel IV operates, we see that doing and deciding are implicitly bound together in a sequence: DECIDE → DO → DECIDE → DO, and so on. The nature of organizational control requires that most outputs should be fed back for inspection, evaluation, and follow-up.

On the other hand, the executive responds to a great range of inputs that do not arrive via feedback channel IV. These are the maneuvers of competitors, the changing situation of the economy, and a variety of factors that are essentially random events of importance to the company. Inputs that do not arrive via the feedback link pose a major challenge to executive decision-making ability; these inputs are examples of situations in which deciding and doing are separate.

Feedback channel V is required to show that an executive decision can result in an output that is capable of modifying the future behavior of the executive. That is, the executive can *decide to decide* in a certain way in the future. A decision can alter attitudes and values of the decision-maker. In this case, the output does not affect inputs but symbolically achieves a rewiring of the not entirely opaque black box. The importance of *deciding how to decide* is not trivial, as the reader will learn as he progresses with this book. There are no pat solutions to this problem but there is a methodology to help decision-makers. To whatever extent the executive devotes his time and attention to this executive problem, he is relegating doing to other areas of the organization. In consequence, we can say that only when channel IV is operating are doing and deciding bound together within the executive province.

The input-output feedback model has helped to indicate the nature of the decision process and the limitations involved in separating it from other organizational processes.   Let us consider a few practical examples of typical decisions in terms of the distinction between deciding and doing.

1. The lathe operator who decides to start his lathe will promptly reverse this decision if one of the cutting tools breaks.   Clearly, his decision is completely bound up with his doing.

2. The decision to build a new plant might be countermanded because of unforeseen difficulties in financing or because of unexpected changes in the over-all situation, but these are extraneous to the implementation of the decision.   So this sort of decision could be legitimately treated separately from the doing.

3. A decision to increase production might be revoked because of a sudden slump in sales, which is extraneous to the implementation, but it might also be countermanded because of production-line difficulties, which are directly tied to the implementation.   Here the validity of a separate consideration of the decision problem would depend on the point of view taken.   In most organizations the decision-maker would be two different people, or at least it would be one man acting in the two different capacities of production and marketing management.

This example should suffice to show that no one model is adequate to describe and categorize all decisions.   But it was not framed with this end in view.   It does confirm that a considerable number of important decisions are more nearly independent of the doing and, so, can be considered independently of their implementation.

14. CYBERNETIC SYSTEMS

When the input-output model with feedback links is fully developed we enter the domain of integrated control systems.   Many controls can be automatic and self-monitoring.   The study of such control systems has been named *cybernetics,* and is a rapidly growing field of research.

The classic example of a cybernetic system is the thermostat arrangement that controls the temperature of many houses.   The furnace produces heat which is measured by the thermostat which, in turn, controls the furnace.   In short, the thermostat feeds back to the furnace instructions which are based upon a comparison of the furnace's output and a criterion for the system's performance.   This idea of regulating feedback in terms of deviations from the objectives of a system (or in terms of error measurement and correction of the error), is at the heart of cybernetic theory. It is clear that the development of cybernetic systems can include a variety of management functions which involve feedback.

Previously, we acknowledged that the inherent circularity of such feedback systems would make the separation of decisions from actions purely arbitrary. In other words, the deciding and the doing are too closely related to permit a valid distinction between them. However, the cybernetic model permits the separation of deciding and doing by calling for decisions which are made only once and which determine the design of the organizational process. It can be recognized that the inputs arriving via the feedback channel become repetitive and that many of these inputs call for repeat decisions which should not require executive time. Many organizational designs permit these feedback inputs to by-pass the executive and to pass instead across an assistant's desk.

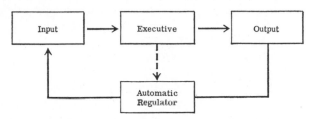

Figure 2.3 *Automatic decision-making by-passes the executive but carries out his instructions.*

In Figure 2.3 we see that the executive transmits decision criteria and operational requirements for the construction of an automatic decision-maker (or regulator). After that, the executive is relieved of the responsibility of employing the same decision criteria every time a given situation repeats itself. Of course, automatic decision-makers are seldom available except in specialized and highly instrumented process industries. Nevertheless, by transmitting decision instructions to subordinates in the form of policy and operating rules, the executive achieves almost the same degree of freedom.

In the case of the simple thermostat the basic decision criteria are:

1. The desired temperature gradients in the heated space.
2. The allowable fluctuations in temperature under conditions of steady demand, or sudden changes in demand (such as a door opening).
3. The location of the thermostat to deliver the required temperatures.
4. The cost of the installation.
5. The reliability of the error-sensing device.

6. The cost of maintaining the installation.

7. The element under control (fuel or heat valve or whatever).

In spite of the relative simplicity of the thermostat example many decisions must be made. Complex systems require many more decisions. Such decisions treated in cybernetic terms are not directly bound up with doing, even though they are based on feedback links that exist to control inputs. So we see that it will be legitimate to treat decisions separately from their implementation.

Consideration of different sorts of decisions that are made in business organizations indicates that those decisions which are most clearly separate from their implementation are the ones that are made by persons who are high in the organizational hierarchy. This is in accord with the fact that most organizations make special efforts to formulate and communicate policy which can relieve their top executives of doing. A separate treatment of the decision process may, therefore, not be adequate for all of the decisions within an organization, but it will certainly be relevant to the most important decisions.

15. THE NATURE OF A DECISION

What, then, is a decision? The word "decision" covers such a multitude of cases that it almost becomes one of the omnibus words which semanticists warn us about. There is general dictionary agreement that a decision is a conclusion or termination of a process. However, the end point of one process can also be viewed as the starting point of another. This brings us into a hall of mirrors where each mirror reflects its image onto an adjoining mirror in a seemingly endless progression of transformations. Consequently, when we decide to decide ... and so forth, we have left the realm of dictionary definition and have become entangled in a maze of reflective properties which defy analysis and interpretation. There are, of course, other words and phrases with similar properties, such as the will to will ..., to try to try ..., thinking about thinking about thinking. This reflexive property of decisions is not illusory. The organizational question of what triggers decisions is another way of asking: What causes the executive to decide to decide? In addition to this complication, the class of operations called decisions is so far-reaching and contains such great variety that the use of a simplified definition of decision can create confusion instead of adding intelligence.

Obviously, the executive has no monopoly on decisions. Everyone has to make all kinds of decisions throughout his life. What school to attend, what profession to choose, what job to take, whom to marry, how to plan for retirement—these are some of the many crucial decisions which each person must make. It is precisely the ubiquity of the decision problem which has led so many persons in so many fields to attempt to analyze it. Philosophers, psychologists, economists, sociologists, logicians, and mathematicians have all attempted to deal with the decision problem.

What, then, is the decision problem?   Simply the determination of how people should proceed in order to reach satisfactory or best decisions. In other words, what methods can be used; what questions should be asked; what steps should be taken; what are best decisions, and so forth. Let us consider some conclusions of the many specialized thinkers who have studied the decision problem.

16. PHILOSOPHERS AND DECISIONS

Philosophers have concerned themselves mainly with the question of what constitutes a "good" decision, which is the major concern of ethics. Mostly they have dealt with the problem of the individual: How should I act so as to lead a good life?   From this they have generalized to the question: What is a good life?   Philosophers approach the problem in two ways: either by defining "good" and considering a variety of values as aspects of it, or by summing up acceptable values and considering the totality to represent "good."   Many philosophers have conceived this "good" to have a kind of objective, real existence.   Other philosophers have maintained that values are simply those things which a particular person wants to have, and that such values are subjective and cannot be established in concrete terms.   In either case, the philosophers were dealing with a particular conception of the individual's decision problem— that of the free, untrammeled person who has chosen the values he wishes to achieve and who makes rational decisions in order to obtain his objectives.

17. ECONOMISTS AND DECISIONS

Typically, the values with which philosophy has dealt have been non-quantitative. How, for example, can happiness be quantified? Yet there are a whole range of human values that seem to be already quantified.   These are all of the goods and services that are offered and purchased in the market place. That these things have value is apparent from the fact that people want them and are willing to sacrifice time and effort in order to get them. And, of course, these values are already quantified in terms of money.

The classical philosophers were cognizant of these market-place values but they relegated them to a definitely subordinate and inferior position as compared to those other values which they held constituted the "good." Adam Smith was trained in philosophy and one of his first works was on ethics.   But despite his background in dealing with the higher values, it was one of his merits as an economist that he defined economics strictly in terms of the market-place values.   Smith believed that these economic values played a sufficiently important role in everyone's life to justify their scientific investigation.   But he also felt that such an investigation could only be successful if the higher, nonquantitative values were excluded from the province of economics.

The subsequent development of economics remained for a long time circumscribed within the limits established by Smith.   The decision problems with which economists have tried to deal have been on both sides of the supply-and-demand relationship.   How much of a commodity will a producer produce at a given price?   How much of a commodity will a consumer buy at a given price?   These and similar questions lead naturally to the prior question: What is the objective of the consumer (or of the producer)?   The economists' answer to this question has been framed in terms of the utility which the commodity will provide to the consumer or which the production of the commodity will give to the producer.   (*Utility* is defined as the power to satisfy human wants.)   The objective of the individual is held to be the maximization of the total utility he can achieve with his limited resources of time, effort, and money.   The rationality of the individual is defined in terms of the utilization he makes of his scarce resources to achieve this end of maximization of utility.

18. SOCIAL SCIENTISTS AND DECISIONS

Contemporary developments in economics have emphasized the lack of realism of the assumption that individuals act so as to maximize their utility.   There has not been an attack on the proposition that individuals should act so as to achieve a maximization of their utility.   Rather, there has been sufficient evidence and supporting reasons to show that they do not act in this way.   Among the reasons suggested have been the following: the inability of most people to duplicate the rather recondite mathematics which economists have used to solve the problem of maximization of utility; the existence of other values (the higher values originally excluded by Smith) which, though not readily quantifiable, do cause divergences from the maximization of utility in the market place; the effect of habit; the influence of social emulation; the effect of social institutions.   Many economists have been attempting to take these various factors into account in constructing economic theories which they feel will show a closer correspondence to the real world.

By introducing such factors, economists have been trying to incorporate aspects of behavior into choice or decision situations. This has also been the concern of psychologists and sociologists. The work of psychologists would certainly tend to confirm the assertion that human beings have a variety of diverse motivations which do not lend themselves to maximization of utility—at least so long as utility is defined in terms of the satisfactions resulting from market-place phenomena. Freudian theory is only one example of a conceptualization of human motivation that relegates rational calculations in decisions to a relatively minor role. Similarly, sociologists have accumulated considerable evidence to demonstrate the enormous influence of social institutions, habit, and tradition on the choices and decisions made by individuals. The effect of these psychological and sociological factors is, of course, to lead individuals to make decisions and to take actions without recourse to maximization of utility in the classical economic sense. Alternatively phrased, it can be said that these factors cause people to act irrationally—but it should be noted that this is simply a matter of definition, rationality having been defined as maximization of utility.

Thanks to the subjective definition of utility, it is possible for economists to maintain that all of these factors can be, or have been, incorporated in economic theory. If, for example, an individual's market decisions are affected by his desire for dignity, then it can simply be said that he is maximizing utility and he ascribes a utility to dignity. The difficulty, however, remains. The utility an individual gains from a commodity can be measured to some degree by observable market phenomena—for example, how much of the commodity he will buy at different prices. But there is no convenient measuring unit where utility for such an intangible as dignity is involved. Therefore, even if these other factors can be theoretically expressed in terms of utility, the difficulties involved in measuring the utilities prevent the theory from satisfactorily explaining observed behavior and decisions.

19. LOGIC AND DECISIONS

Many different approaches to the decision problem converge on one particular model of the decision situation. Indeed, it is hard to avoid this logical construction of the decision model once we ask ourselves how to describe the general decision situation.

To begin with, we want to know why decisions must be made. The answer is fairly obvious. The decision-maker wants to achieve something—call it his goal, purpose, objective, or use any other synonymous word. There is, in short, some state of affairs that he wishes to achieve. Of course, this state of affairs may be the same one as exists for him at the time of his decision. He may simply be striving for maintenance of the *status quo*. But, in either case, his decision is taken because he wants to achieve some state of affairs.

Now, what will the decision involve? Generally the decision-maker will choose an action which he believes will help him obtain his objective. This action will take the form of some kind of utilization of his own efforts and any resources that he controls. If there is only one course of action available to him we do not usually speak of a decision problem because the word "decision" implies some kind of choice. Therefore, his decision will consist of the specific utilization of particular resources that he controls, selected from among all resources that are available to him. For convenience we will call any such specific utilization of resources under the decision-maker's control a *strategy*. His decision, then, will consist of the selection of one of his available strategies.

Recognition of the notorious fact that we do not always achieve our objectives, despite our best efforts in that direction, leads to a final question: Why may the decision-maker not achieve his objective? The answer is immediately evident. Certain factors that affect the achievement of objectives are outside the control of the decision-maker.

There are two main classes of such factors. The first is the frequent intransigence of society and nature. For example, an umbrella manufacturer, faced with the decision problem of how many umbrellas to make for the coming season, knows that the final outcome of his decision will depend in large measure on the weather conditions that occur—a factor outside his control. Similarly, the executive of a small company that uses a basic raw material can scarcely influence the eventuality of a strike in the suppliers' industry which might close down the company. Generally, there are a great number of possible combinations of natural, uncontrollable factors that can occur. For simplicity, we will refer to any specific one of these combinations as a *state of nature.*

The second class of uncontrollable factors is the competition of rational opponents. For example, the final outcome of an executive's decision to capture a larger share of the market will usually be affected by actions his competitors take to frustrate his hopes. There are usually a great number of different possible competitive actions. Since the specific one that does occur is usually the result of a rational decision process on the part of the competition, it will be convenient to treat these uncontrollable factors as *competitive strategies,* rather than as states of nature. Many, if not most, executive decision problems involve both kinds of factors simultaneously.

Our logical analysis of the decision problem has suggested that there are at least three aspects to consider. We can now formulate the decision problem in these terms: *The decision-maker wishing to achieve some objective selects a* STRATEGY *from among those available to him. This strategy, together with the* STATE OF NATURE *that exists, and the* COMPETITIVE STRATEGY *that occurs, will determine the degree to which his objective is obtained.*

20. THE DECISION PROBLEM

If this theoretical skeleton of the decision situation is at all reasonable, then it should fit the flesh of actual decision problems. Does it? Let us consider some simple (but realistic) decision problems in terms of our logical analysis.

A farmer has a plot of land and he has the objective of achieving the largest profit from it. His available strategies might consist of a variety of crops, any of which he can plant—wheat, corn, soybeans, oats, sugar beets, no crop. His selection from among these strategies is wholly within his control and will, in fact, constitute his decision. Further, it is clear that the profit he will actually obtain will depend not only on the crop he plants but also on a number of factors that are outside his control. Weather is one extremely important example and market price is another, although governmental supports diminish the importance of this factor to a considerable degree. It seems that the farmer's decision problem fits our model without too much forcing.

The decision problem of an executive responsible for raw-materials inventory is similar. He might have the same objective as the farmer, which is to attain the largest possible amount of profit. His strategies would include the various possible amounts of inventory he could maintain. Numerous important factors that will determine the amount of profit he actually achieves are outside his control: future availability and price of the raw materials, demand for the finished products, competitive actions, general state of the economy, and so on. His success will depend on the strategy he selects and the state of nature and competitive strategy that actually occur. It appears, again, that the simple framework we have so far developed does seem to fit some actual decision problems.

Up to this point we have simply tried to discover a suitable framework by means of which we can describe the general decision problem. In quest of this framework we have examined the input-output model and we have briefly reviewed a number of approaches to the decision problem that have been used by different fields of study. We have not yet considered the basic question: How should the decision-maker select the one strategy he will use from among all the strategies that he is considering? In other words, how does he make his decision?

21. OBJECTIVES AND UTILITY

The notion of utility which was introduced by the economist proved to have general appeal to decision theorists. When utility is used as a measurement of the degree to which satisfaction is obtained, then, at least in theory, a number of alternatives can be compared to determine which choice yields the greatest amount of utility. Since satisfaction is not easily measured, a convenient transformation of terms changes the word "satisfaction" into the word "objective." This results in the statement that utility is a measurement of the degree to which an objective is obtained. If the objective can be stated in quantitative terms, then alternative choices can be compared with each other. Of course, the supposition is that satisfaction is directly proportional to the degree of attainment of the objective.

Some objectives are either attained or they aren't—with no intermediate possibilities. Good examples can be found in many games. The objective in the game of chess, for example, is to win, and, as the saying goes, "Close only counts in horseshoes." But the more general—and less frivolous—decision problems usually have objectives of such nature that there are vast numbers of different degrees of achieving them. This is certainly true of such business objectives as profit, or share of market. An executive may well have the objective of attaining $1 million gross profit. Naturally, he will be delighted to actually achieve $1.2 million and he may not be too disappointed if he only gets $950,000. Clearly, in such a case as this, there are an enormous number of possible amounts of profit which he might obtain. Further, the fact that his objective is expressed in dollars makes it simple to measure the degree to which the objective is achieved. In many cases the actual dollar profit obtained will be a good measure of the degree. Similar remarks obviously can be made in the case of the objective of achieving some specific share of the market.

Now, of course, not all business objectives are of this nature—some are like the game of chess. For example, management involved in a proxy fight for control can have numerous available strategies and there may be many possible states of nature and competitive strategies that affect the final outcome—in short, it is a genuine decision problem as we have depicted them. Yet there is only a "yes" or a "no" in terms of achievement of objective. Either management succeeds in retaining control, or it fails. There are no significant intermediary possibilities.

On the other hand, many business objectives are clearly of the sort that have numerous degrees of achievement and yet there is no straightforward measure for it. For example, a business objective in some de-cision problems may be to achieve good labor relations. Obviously there are degrees of goodness in labor relations, but how can they be meas-ured? An executive may have the personal objective of maximum job security. This clearly has degrees also. But how can they be measured?

There are, thus, a range of possibilities. At one extreme, the objective may be such that it is either achieved or not, with no other possibilities. At the other extreme, there are objectives that permit a whole range of possible degrees of achievement. For some objectives there are natural ways of measuring the degree of achievement; for others there does not seem to be any obvious way to measure this degree.

22. PREDICTION AND CONTROL

We have observed from the input-output model that certain elements (or variables) can be controlled by the decision-maker. The decision-maker's strategy is a plan of control for these variables. The only reason for controlling variables is to attempt to achieve objectives. Obviously, a good strategy includes the right variables, which means those variables which determine the degree of attainment of the objective. There are many examples of situations in which either the wrong variables are con-trolled, or not enough of the right ones are considered.

The fact that a large number of variables do not fall under the control of the executive does not mean that he should ignore them. On the con-trary, it is the decision-maker's responsibility to examine all noncon-trollable variables that affect his attaining the objectives. Although he can exercise no control over these variables, he can make predictions about them. The farmer can analyze weather records in order to esti-mate the kind of weather he is likely to experience. The executive in charge of the raw-material inventory can read reports, talk to informed people, observe the actions of other companies that stock the same raw material, and study the history of strikes in the industry that concerns him. Usually both states of nature and competitive strategies can be studied and estimates made to indicate that certain occurrences are more likely than others. Therefore, a good strategy must not only include good control of the right controllable variables, but it must also be based on good predictions of the right noncontrollable variables. Good predic-tions are hard to make, nor can the methods for obtaining predictions be quickly explained. Nevertheless, since prediction is such a basic re-quirement of decision-making, and such a fundamental procedure of op-erations research, we must prepare to delve deeper into this subject as the book progresses.

23. FUNCTIONS AND DISTRIBUTIONS

The decision-maker's objective is a variable, but it is a particular kind of a variable. It must be a variable since if it were a constant, with only one possible value, then the decision-maker would have no choice of a value for the objective and no problem to solve. The objective is called a *dependent* variable because the value that it takes depends on the values of the other variables in the system. These other variables, which are called *independent* variables, are the many controllable and noncontrollable factors which we have previously discussed. The mathematical representation of this situation is $y = f(x, z)$ where x stands for independent controllable variables, z stands for independent noncontrollable but predictable variables, and y stands for the dependent variable which is the objective. (f is used to represent the fact that y is a function of x and z.)

For example, we can choose profit as our objective. We know that total profit $(p) = f$[unit sales price (s); unit cost (c); number of items sold (n)]. $p = f(s, c, n)$. In this case, we know the exact function: $p = n(s - c)$. On the face of it, unit sales price and unit cost are controllable while the number of items sold is noncontrollable. Actually, we can exercise some control over the number of items sold since the number of items sold $= f$(unit sales price). Since we can control unit sales price, we can control to some extent the number of items sold. Looking at unit cost, we find that there is a threshold below which we cannot even manufacture an item. Above the threshold, there comes a point at which we can only cut cost by impairing quality. Lower quality may result in a smaller number of items sold. That is, quality $= f$(unit cost); number of items sold $= f$(unit cost). It is apparent from our example of the profit function that dependencies exist between the independent variables. The achievement of an objective requires the full consideration of the interrelationships between variables as well as direct relationships.

Degree of control is strongly affected by degree of predictability. We may, at best, have the notion that as price goes up the number of items sold goes down. (Of course this is not an inflexible rule since there are cases of items that increase in sales volume with increasing price.) Over a period of time, the decision-maker may have accumulated enough data to plot the relationship between sales price and sales volume. Figure 2.4 depicts a strong relationship with sales volume decreasing as price goes up.

The problem here is that each point represents a different month so that some points occur in the spring, which may be the best selling time. If seasonal variation is important, that would obscure the relationship between sales price and sales volume. Similarly, competitors' prices in each month may have affected the number of items sold. Many other factors could influence the relationship under study. The ability to pre-

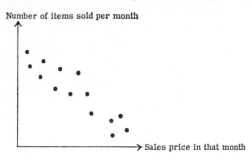

Figure 2.4 *Data from past observations indicate that sales volume tends to decrease as price increases.*

dict sales volume as a function of sales price is determined by the extent to which all the pertinent factors can be taken into account. But even then, we can seldom expect to obtain an exact relationship.

Variables that are essentially noncontrollable can be studied by means of a simple frequency distribution. The use of such distributions can result in surprisingly good predictions. For example, an executive has the hypothetical data in Table 2.1 concerning absenteeism tabulated and plotted.

Table 2.1

Number of times a worker is absent for a single day in a summer month or winter month	Number of workers with the given number of absences	
	SUMMER MONTH	WINTER MONTH
0	2	368
1	21	368
2	136	184
3	341	61
4	362	15
5	120	3
6	17	1
7	1	0

The shapes of these curves are well known, the summer chart illustrating a normal distribution and the winter chart showing a Poisson distribution. Many characteristics of these distributions have been carefully studied by the methods of mathematical statistics, and this large body of knowledge can be put to work to achieve useful predictions of future expectations.

One additional characteristic of a variable must be examined before we can indicate how measures of utility, objectives, variables, functions, and distributions can be put together in an integrated decision-theory

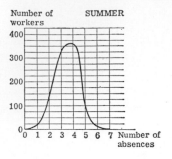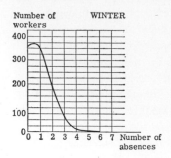

Figure 2.5 *A comparison of the number of times a worker is absent for a single day in a summer month and a winter month.*

framework. Data that are used to make predictions are always assumed to be derived from a stable process. In other words, the distribution is said to describe a particular situation that holds constant throughout the period in which the data are collected. Sometimes a frequency distribution gives evidence that a change took place during the period of observation. For example, the bimodal distribution shown in Figure 2.6 could, in fact, come from a process that produces a bimodal distribution. On the other hand, it could represent two normal distributions where a shift took place during the period of observation. Predictions based on unstable processes where this fact is not known can lead to serious mistakes.

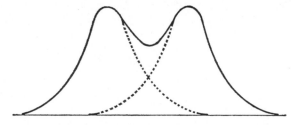

Figure 2.6 *The bimodal distribution can arise from an unstable process.*

The importance of stability in prediction is its vital contribution to stability in control.

24. MAXIMIZATION PRINCIPLES

We are now prepared to examine the decision-maker's sequence of operations up to this point.

1. Choose the objective and specify its value.

2. Isolate all of the variables that are pertinent to the attainment of the objective value, i.e., the independent variables.

3. Develop the relationships that the independent variables have to each other.

4. Separate controllable variables, which can be part of the strategy, from the noncontrollable variables, which will be part either of the state of nature or of the competitive strategies.

5. Develop predictions for the noncontrollable variables separating those variables which have intelligence behind them from those variables which are nature's contribution.

6. Determine whether or not the predictions are based on stable processes.

7. Determine the function that relates the independent variables to the dependent objective variable.

8. State the restrictions that limit the possible values of controllable variables.

9. Choose those values of the controllable variables (i.e., that strategy) which maximizes the degree of attainment of the objective, within the limits set by the restrictions.

In point (1) above, we stated that a specific value should be chosen for the objective. For example, our objective may be profit, and the chosen value of profit might be $500,000. Frequently it is not feasible to select a numerical value for the objective, and sometimes it is not even desirable. For such cases the alternative is to substitute for the numerical value the condition of "best possible," or *optimal* value. Where the objective is a variable measured along a continuous scale, the distinguishing property of an optimal value will be direction. In other words, optimal will sometimes be the greatest possible value or *maximal* value while at other times it will be the least possible value or *minimal* value. Although it may be reasonable to select $500,000 as our profit objective, the decision-maker would be overlooking the possibility that his company's profits could be greater. It is a perfectly reasonable decision problem to choose that strategy which will result in $500,000 profit, but it is not an optimal decision procedure. Optimal decision procedures are, in reality, always maximization procedures. The quantity that is always being maximized is the degree of attainment of the objective. Consequently, if we wish to minimize the cost of selling a given product, as we lower the cost we increase the degree of attainment. The minimum cost for the product is the maximum attainment of the objective.

It is quite clear that the minimum possible cost is zero cost. But zero cost, under normal circumstances, means no product can be made at all.

Therefore, minimization of cost is not a sensible objective unless restrictions are placed on the means for obtaining it. In the same way, maximum dollar profit is seldom desired at the expense of goodwill, future profits, or a jail term.

Restrictions are a part of a complex objective. All objectives are complex, because they never involve just one variable. Whenever we say that we wish to attain some end, we do so with all kinds of if's, and's, and but's. However, it isn't an easy matter to visualize the total set of objectives and to set them down at the very beginning of a problem. As much as possible, point (1) should specify multiple objectives, but point (8) takes into consideration the fact that certain restrictions become apparent only after the full set of relationships among variables has been investigated.

Generally speaking, degree of attainment for only one objective can be maximized. In other words, if we wish to maximize sales volume we cannot maximize profit at the same time. That is why we speak of an *objective* and *restrictions*. For example, we can maximize sales volume subject to the restriction that profit does not fall below p_1, or subject to the restriction that profit falls between p_1 and p_2.*

Point (5) requires that variables belonging to states of nature should be separated from variables belonging to intelligent competitors. The reason for this is that all decision-makers are trying to maximize their respective degrees of attainment. Therefore, if it is possible for a company to determine the objectives of its competitors, it can then predict the nature and consequences of optimal decisions made by the competitors. This approach is particularly important when competitors are striving for identical objectives, e.g., brand share. In any case, it is important to remember that other decision-makers are trying to achieve maximization. We are not alone in choosing strategies.

PROBLEMS

1. Develop the input-output model for an electric typewriter. How does this differ from a mechanical typewriter? What control is exercised over the inputs? What feedback exists? Transform the output into the input of a corresponding system.

2. Develop the input-output model for a warehouse. Assume that the decision to reorder is made by an executive in the company's main office which is 300

---

* In linear programming problems, the objective variable has a symmetric relationship with another, different variable which is automatically minimized when the objective is maximized, and vice versa. This characteristic is known as *duality;* it will be discussed in conjunction with linear programming. The meaning of the dual variable is not always apparent, but interestingly enough, it sometimes sheds light on an aspect of the problem that would not ordinarily be considered.

miles away from the warehouse. Design an automatic regulator to relieve management of this reorder function. How will exceptions to the procedure be handled?

3. Management has three brand names picked out for a new product, four different package designs, and four different advertising campaigns. How many different strategies are being considered? What possible states of nature could affect the choice? To what extent can competitive strategies be taken into account?

4. Using the data of Table 2.1 and Figure 2.5, draw the distribution that would apply to the fall season if the change between seasons were regular and continuous. Under these assumptions would spring and fall be the same? How many extra workers would you hire in the summer if demand for the product were constant throughout the year? How do these considerations relate to the decision framework?

5. Insofar as possible, apply the nine steps of the decision-maker's sequence to the following situations: management must either build a new plant or expand their present facilities; a company must replace the sales manager who is retiring; repeated complaints of bad service are received by a department store; top management requests a full report on the possibilities of bidding for government contracts.

6. A company which has one plant produces a variety of items for sale to the public. Their situation can be conceptualized thus:

The responsible executive establishes policies which determine when an order shall be transmitted to production which will require the production of a specific item. The system then functions very much like the furnace-thermostat system discussed in the text. The policies established usually require such an order when the inventory of an item falls to a certain level and the policy also usually establishes how much shall be produced. In analogy to the furnace-thermostat example these two levels are equivalent to the temperatures at which the furnace will turn on and off.

a. What objectives are involved in the decisions setting these two levels?

b. Suppose demand for some item has large fluctuations around an average which is constant for a long period of time. How does this affect the levels?

c. Suppose demand has very small fluctuations around its average but that the average is increasing steadily. How does this affect the levels?

d. Suppose one item has extremely high labor costs. How does this affect the levels?

e. Under what conditions will the inventory be essentially eliminated?

7. Classify the following objectives according to whether there are degrees of attainment and whether the degree of attainment is measurable:

a. A salesman's objective of increasing his sales enough to win a company prize.

b. A financial executive's objective of obtaining a $1,000,000 bank loan.

c. A salesman's objective of obtaining a large customer.

d. A salesman's objective of making a large non-repeat sale to a customer.

e. A company objective of achieving a required minimum percentage of employee participation in an health insurance program.

f. A plant manager's objective of achieving the lowest labor turnover of any plant in his company.

8. How many business situations can you think of which involve feedback?

9. How many different objectives can you think of which a sales manager might have? How many are quantifiable with regard to degree of attainment?

10. From the standpoint of advertising policies the totality of potential customers constitutes a black box. We have advertising as input and demand as output. Thus:

ADVERTISING→ BLACK BOX →DEMAND

The effect of advertising depends on the unknown circuitry of the black box. In order to determine advertising policies we would like to know something about the effect of the input, advertising, on the output, demand. If we really know nothing about the black box circuitry we can only get information by varying the input and then observing the output.

a. We can change the input or not change it and the output can either change or not change. Thus, there are four possible combinations. Without saying anything about the size or the direction of the changes involved, what can you conclude, if anything, from each of the four possible cases?

b. Suppose the output changes in the same direction as the input but that very large input changes produce only small output changes. What does this imply?

c. Suppose the circuitry is very complicated and there is a considerable time delay before changes in input show up in the form of output changes. Suppose, further, that this time delay is unknown. What effect does this have on our reasoning? What mistakes might it produce?

(Consider the analogy of controlling water temperature when taking a shower. Suppose the pipes leading to the shower are so long that ten seconds are required before a change in the amount of hot water reaches the shower. Now suppose you are impatient and only wait five seconds. What will happen?)

d. In terms of this model, what is wrong with the policy of setting a regional monthly advertising budget as a percentage of the preceding month's sales for the region?

Chapter three

Executive Objectives

As we have seen in the preceding chapter, any attempted rational approach to the decision problem depends directly on the objective of the decision-maker. The entire formulation of the problem stems from the answer to the question: Why make a decision at all? As we have seen, the reason for making the decision is the desire of the decision-maker to achieve some future state of affairs—his objective. The choice of one particular strategy from a number of alternatives can be made only in terms of the objective. Thus, the precise formulation of the objective is the first major problem facing the decision-maker. So our first concern is a careful consideration of the difficulties and problems involved in formulation of objectives.

We have already suggested that some objectives seem to be easily quantifiable, some are definitely not quantifiable, and a great number appear to be in the middle ground between these two types. These differences are important because the analysis of a decision problem in the terms we have been developing requires a measurement to describe each possible strategy. Only in this way can alternative strategies be compared. But quite apart from this consideration there are a number of major problems concerning objectives which require careful discussion in order to delimit the possibilities of a rational approach to the decision problem. The various ambiguities and difficulties involved in objectives will be presented in some detail in this chapter.

25. GOALS, PURPOSES, AND RATIONAL BEHAVIOR

The question of the formulation of objectives is very closely related to some of the major ethical questions. This might be expected since, after all, the classical philosophers were interested in discovering the steps that an individual should take in order to achieve the good life. And what is the idea of the good life if not an objective to be achieved?

As a matter of fact, the classical conception of rationality was defined in terms of the ability to select means to achieve goals or objectives. In other words, rationality was construed to be the same thing as the ability to pursue objectives. This line of reasoning was subsequently subjected to serious questioning.

First, the extension of this definition of rationality led to the interpretation of everything in terms of the purpose it fulfilled. Thus, the argument ran, if one saw a watch one could infer the existence of a watchmaker. Similarly, if one sees an ear one must infer the existence of a designer of that ear so that it could achieve its purpose of hearing. Reasoning of this sort is called teleological reasoning. The interpretation of events in these terms was what Aristotle called the "final causes" of the things. Such arguments have their place in religion and philosophy but are likely to impede scientific analysis. Thus, one of Darwin's major contributions was the demonstration of the fact that a remarkable adaption to environment could result from the interplay of a great number of essentially random factors. In short, he showed that it was unnecessary to assume final causes in order to understand the adaptation of living things to their environments.

A second argument against this kind of approach arose from the positivistic movement in science. A human being can introspect and believe that he has purposefully selected means to achieve his objectives. It is an easy step, then, to assume a similar purposefulness in the behavior of a white rat that is hungry. However, it is clearly not necessarily the same with a white rat as it is with a human being. As a matter of fact, modern psychology throws some doubt on human purposefulness in at least some situations where humans think they are being purposeful. In any event, positivism in science led to a desire to base scientific conclusions only on observable evidence. In psychology this took the form of the ruthless elimination of introspection as a source of valid scientific information. The school of psychology that carried this out to the fullest extreme is known as *behaviorism,* from the fact that only the observable behavior of the subject is studied. The net effect of the positivistic movement was to strongly prejudice scientists against ascribing rationality to goal-seeking or objective-seeking behavior.

26. OPEN SYSTEMS

Recent developments in science serve to confirm the fact that rationality cannot be identified with purposeful selection of means to achieve desired ends. A biologist, Ludwig von Bertalanffy, has introduced and extensively analyzed a new concept of a system, which he calls open systems. There are a number of highly interesting characteristics of such systems. For our purposes the most interesting characteristic is the fact that such a system will seem to seek objectives without being, in any possible sense of the word, "rational." A number of examples of such systems can be found in various kinds of chemical solutions but von Bertalanffy has found more interesting examples in living creatures and, possibly, even in higher systems which are composed of living creatures— for example, human society. The reason that the system appears to be goal-seeking, although there is no rationality behind it, is that the system is so set up that it has an equilibrium among its component parts. Any disturbance of this equilibrium initiates compensating reactions which immediately lead to the establishment of a new equilibrium. In other words, the system will search for equilibrium or stasis every time its equilibrium is disturbed. Now, since a great many human objectives can be easily redefined in terms of equilibrium it becomes very interesting to discover to what degree the search by humans for objectives (equilibrium) can be understood in terms of the dynamic process of open systems.

That this reasoning about open systems is not purely theoretical was demonstrated nicely by W. Ross Ashby, who designed and built an electrical device which he named the Homeostat. This is a complicated piece of electrical circuitry which will hunt for equilibrium whenever it is disturbed. Further, it will find a new equilibrium which was not intentionally built into the device by its maker. Therefore, when the device has achieved a new equilibrium no one, including the designer, will know what circuits it has completed in order to achieve the equilibrium. Other similar devices have now been constructed by many different people. Some of them show the most disconcertingly "lifelike" behavior when in pursuit of their objective. And yet there is simply no rationality in any of them. It has become quite clear, in short, that the existence of seemingly rational searches for some kinds of objectives by no means implies that rational choice dictated the selection of means used to attempt to achieve the given objective.

These remarks may seem singularly irrelevant to any study of organizational objectives. However, they are not really so far-fetched. The conclusion that one could reach from the arguments about open systems is that an open system will find equilibrium by itself. If the process by which the system achieves equilibrium is continually disturbed by "rational" efforts it may well produce an inherent instability and the equilibrium may never be achieved. For example, the United States national economy is an enormously complex organization which may well have many of the characteristics of open systems. A national economic objective is frequently stated as being the achievement of prosperity without inflation. Since the quantity of money in circulation plays a fundamental role in the national economy the Federal Reserve system uses its control over the money supply to attempt to achieve the national objective. The means it uses, such as changes in the discount rate, are given wide publicity and are well known. It is therefore interesting that a number of economists maintain that the rational efforts of the Federal Reserve system are of no avail and perhaps worse than useless. One point of view holds that a policy which is fixed in advance should be adhered to by the Federal Reserve system and that no changes should be made in this policy because of the changing economic situation. If, indeed, the national economy is an open system, then it would adapt itself to the new policy maintaining the national objectives as part of its own search for equilibrium. Consequently, our national objectives would have a better chance of being achieved. Similar possibilities exist in the case of business organizations.

It will be worthwhile to present a brief illustration of a business system that regains equilibrium after it has been disturbed. Consider the case of a mail-order company which solicits new customers by means of direct mail. (For the sake of clarity and to avoid obscuring the main point of this example we have not introduced random variation in the hypothetical data.) The company mails 800 letters each week and obtains orders from 1 per cent of the mailing. The repeat-order rate is constant. One-half of each week's new customers reorder in the second week, one-fourth reorder in the third week, one-eighth reorder in the fourth week, and so on. Table 3.1 shows how the generation of orders, composed of new-customer orders and repeat orders, reaches an equilibrium value of 15 orders per day. In the eighth and ninth weeks the company experiences an unusually heavy response. This raises the total orders for a period of six weeks. At the end of that time, by the fourteenth week, total orders have returned to equilibrium. Figure 3.1 shows how the system gradually returns to equilibrium.

In actuality, a system of this type is always being disturbed by random variation in both the number of new customers and the reorder rates. However, if the random variation comes from a stable process, then the system is always hunting for its equilibrium value. If a basic change takes place then the system adopts a new equilibrium value and continues to return to this new value after all random disturbances. An attempt by management to maintain total orders at 15 per week by controlling the number of letters mailed or by providing incentives to increase the repeat order rate can result in far greater fluctuation than would occur if the system were left alone. Only when management fully understands the nature of the system with which it is dealing can it provide rational decisions that might improve the performance of the system.

From examples such as the one given above, we learn that it is not necessarily the case that all objectives can be, or should be, achieved by rational selection of means to a given end. If we cannot identify rational behavior by observing the means that are chosen to achieve a specific end, can we recognize rationality in terms of the objectives themselves?

Table 3.1 Generation of orders of a mail-order house.

Week Number	1	2	3	4	5	6	7	8	9	10	11	12	13	14	15	16
Number of new customers	8	8	8	8	8	8	8	20	20	8	8	8	8	8	8	8
First repeat order		4	4	4	4	4	4	4	10	10	4	4	4	4	4	4
Second repeat order			2	2	2	2	2	2	2	5	5	2	2	2	2	2
Third repeat order				1	1	1	1	1	1	1	2	2	1	1	1	1
Fourth repeat order				-	-	-	-	-	-	-	-	1	1	-	-	-
Total orders	8	12	14	15	15	15	15	27	33	24	19	17	16	15	15	15

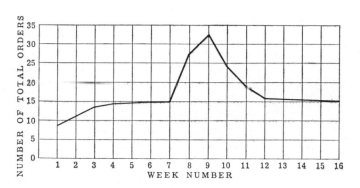

Figure 3.1 The system returns to equilibrium after disturbance.

27. GOALS OF THE INDIVIDUAL AND OPERATIONALISM

Organizational objectives coexist with the objectives of the individuals who compose the organization. They are not the same. Our intention is to analyze the way in which objectives at different levels in the organization interact with each other. Therefore, we must begin with the individual's role, which is the smallest entity in the organization.

The goals of individuals have been the subject of discussion and debate for many centuries. To say that happiness is the goal of the individual, which is a frequent suggestion, does not solve any problem. We cannot define happiness in operational terms. Operationalism is an important concept for the understanding of operations research. It implies concreteness, the ability to observe, measure, and analyze. Since an analysis of the operations that must be performed in order to be happy cannot be obtained, we cannot treat happiness as an operational term. Measurements cannot be made to distinguish degree of happiness. Although each of us can testify to the fact that happiness exists, we cannot reduce our awareness to concrete terms. Similar problems result from any other suggested choice for the fundamental objective of individuals. Since life is too short to follow the arguments of philosophers in a book which is intended to be operationally useful, we must consider other ways of examining the goals of individuals.

28. GOALS OF THE ROLE

People play many roles. Each role can be associated with its own objectives. Individuals simplify their decision problems by establishing for themselves these multiple objectives instead of just one basic objective. Most people, for example, will establish some kind of objective for themselves in the area of their professional activities. They will usually have other objectives relating to their interpersonal relationships; e.g., father, husband, son. They will also have objectives regarding their relationship to society as a whole, e.g., political activity or public-spirited work. They will often have some objectives regarding their leisure activities. And, of course, we can continue and obtain quite a catalogue of the different areas in which people are likely to set themselves some kind of objectives. It appears that most people handle their decision problems in a particular field of activity by ignoring the objectives of other fields of activity. Thus, a business executive will solve his decision problems in business—for example, what position he will accept—in terms of his professional objective.

Even within a single field of activity an individual has many different roles. An executive reports to his boss and in turn has people reporting to him. His position in the organization determines the extent of his responsibility and the importance of decisions he must make. The goal of the executive is strongly tied to the complex image he has of his role. Although no two executives have the same situations, the similarity of goals which they share as a group causes us to speak about executive goals.   However, similarity should not blind us to the differences.   In the same way, for convenience, we group employee goals, ownership goals, salesmen's goals, and so on.   There is a certain relevant pattern of goal-seeking within each of these groups.   It is hardly necessary to expand on what these might be.   On the other hand, it is an observable fact that sometimes there is a conflict between the objectives of several groups to which the individual belongs.

29. CONFLICT BETWEEN GOALS

The individual has various roles and each role has its objectives.   The groups and subgroups to which the individual belongs have organizational objectives.   Conflicts between goals can occur in a number of ways. There can be: (1) conflicts between roles, (2) conflicts between group objectives, and (3) conflicts between the individual's role and the group objective.   Looking at conflicts of the first type, the individual cannot confine his attention to the objective of one field of activities and ignore the other parts of his life.   Thus, a new position may entail relocation and possible stresses and strains on the individual's family relationships. In this event he must attempt to weigh his different objectives, one against the other.   Now, this is difficult to do because there is no under-lying single objective that suffices as a means of measuring the impor-tance of the different subobjectives.   Nevertheless, people do it many times in their lives.   Generally, they convert the decision problem into some estimates of the amounts of happiness involved—even though there are serious difficulties and even contradictions involved in this notion of happiness.

Considering the second kind of conflict, the individual who participates in two groups that have conflicting objectives may not even be aware of this fact.   The reason is that his roles may not come into conflict.   This point is intended to emphasize the fact that an individual cannot entirely identify with and share the objectives of an organization.   Furthermore, the individual does not weight the groups to which he belongs as being of equal importance.   For example, an employee who participates in a stock-purchasing plan is also a part owner of the company to which he belongs.   When this employee demands higher wages, he is, in effect, reducing the dividend which he could receive as a stockholder.   It is clear that the employee does not consider his role in the ownership group to be as important as his role as an employee.   Whenever the individual's role objectives strongly coincide with the objectives of the groups that are in conflict, the result is either conflict between roles or between the individual and at least one of the groups.   In the latter case, which is the third type of conflict, the individual withdraws from the organization that he feels he is in conflict with, or else he tries to change that group's objectives.

30. SUBOPTIMIZATION

Whenever there is no conflict between objectives, the individual can proceed to solve his decision problems separately. As long as the action taken to achieve either objective is independent of the other, he can do this. However, when objectives are dependent, the optimization of one can result in a lower degree of attainment for all the others. This condition is known as *suboptimization*. For example, an executive may decide to take a new position on the basis of his professional objectives. The new job, however, entails extremely long hours and much traveling. Assume that the new job is optimal in terms of the executive's professional objective. The fact that the time he can now spend with his family is sharply reduced may have such adverse effects that he will find that his optimization in terms of one objective has produced a result which is very much less than optimal in terms of all his objectives.

This same notion of suboptimization is involved in the effects on the decision problem of the fact that we lead our lives through time and that we have only very imperfect ability to foresee the future. This means that any decision problem can be solved only in terms of the knowledge and situation obtaining currently. But the action chosen may, and probably will, have effects on the decision-maker's situation for a considerable period in the future. An optimal action at one time may, therefore, turn out to have been a very inferior suboptimization in terms of a longer period of time.

Consider, for example, the decision problem of selection of courses as electives which faces an engineering student. In terms of his professional objective he wants to become as good an engineer as he possibly can so he decides to use all his electives to take additional engineering courses. This decision may appear to be an optimization in terms of his professional objectives at that time. But some years later this engineer may discover that the stultification which results from too narrow specialization has had serious consequences on his ability to achieve satisfactory interpersonal relationships or on his desire to have a well-rounded life or even on his objective of achieving professional advancement. His decision, in short, may have resulted in distinctly less than an optimal situation with regard to subsequent decision problems, even in the same field of activity.

It is quite clear that we can never really achieve optimization. Over time, unexpected events can change what had appeared to be an optimal decision into an inferior decision. There is almost no reversibility in decision systems. Generally speaking, by the time we find out that a decision was not a good one, we cannot return to the state which prevailed before the decision had been made. Consequently, decision systems should provide the best possible predictions of future expectations. And in addition, decision systems should not commit us to irrevocable action for very long periods of time. And so we reach the conclusion that a *sequential decision process* permits maximum flexibility with respect to both objectives and actions.

31. BOUNDED RATIONALITY

We have been using the word "optimum," and some other forms of the same word, rather loosely. In fact, it is important to note that people rarely make a prolonged effort to achieve the optimum action in any realistic decision problem facing them. To paraphrase John Maurice Clark, people simply don't have such an irrational passion for dispassionate rationality. Furthermore, there are good reasons why they shouldn't. All of the reasons have reference to the exorbitant complexity of any realistic decision problem. Three main aspects of this complexity should be noted.

First, consider the point just made, that an optimum decision made at one point in time is only suboptimum in terms of subsequent times. Since we are very limited in our ability to foresee the future it follows that it would be useless to go to extreme lengths in order to achieve an optimum solution to any decision problem.

Second, there are an enormous number of possible choices of action (strategies, as we have called them) and any attempt to obtain information on all of them would be self-defeating. Consider the decision problem of the executive looking for a new job. Should he attempt to catalogue every available position in the world in order to select the best one? Obviously, if he tried he would die of old age before he got the necessary information. People simply don't behave this way, and if they did it is unlikely that humanity would have survived this long.

Third, there are virtually innumerable factors outside the control of the decision-maker (we call them states of nature) which may affect the outcome of his decision. It would be simply impossible to list them all and determine the effects they might have in order to discover the optimum action. Often the necessary information isn't even available. The umbrella manufacturer does not attempt to determine the effect of war, nuclear holocausts, prolonged depression, or explosion of the sun on the outcome of his decision regarding the number of umbrellas to make. He simply assumes some reasonable kind of stability and acts accordingly.

The net effect of these limitations on human decision-making procedures has been observed and neatly summarized by Herbert Simon in his "principle of bounded rationality." Accordingly to this principle human beings seldom make any effort to find the optimum action in a decision problem. Instead, they select a number of possible outcomes of their available strategies which would be good enough. Then they select a strategy (choose an action) that is likely to achieve one of the good-enough outcomes. Thus, the executive looking for a new job makes no effort to discover all possible jobs from which he can then select the best (optimum) one. Instead, he decides what he wants from a job in terms of his various objectives. Then he searches for a job that will provide him with the things he wants, e.g., a certain income, satisfactory working conditions, chances for advancement. He does not try to find that one job somewhere in the world which might give him the optimum. The principle of bounded rationality is a neat way to describe the actual procedure of human beings involved in the decision problems of life, and it succinctly reminds us not to assume any irrational extremes of rationality.

32. PRINCIPLES AND MAXIMS

The difficulties involved in these everyday decision problems appear to be enormous. Yet introspection and observation would indicate that people do attempt to be rational in their selection of actions despite all the problems. In short, they do as well as they can. Fortunately, everyone has available an important source of help. No one of us is the first to have to face any specific decision problem. More usually, millions of people have been faced with the same problem in times past and society has accumulated an immense store of information concerning possible solutions and approaches to solutions. This wisdom is stored up in the form of a great number of ethical and other principles and maxims which warn us to consider certain factors or proceed at our own peril.

These principles are no guarantees of success. Often there are contradictory maxims: "Look before you leap" but "He who hesitates is lost." Yet both of these maxims serve to remind us that the speed with which we reach a decision may be an important factor. Kant's dictum that we should always treat other individuals as ends in themselves rather than as means to our own ends suggests that we consider whether any action on our part may not subsequently redound to our disadvantage, i.e., turn out to have been a suboptimization. The Golden Rule is another codification of considerations which should govern our choice of actions lest we end by suboptimizing in terms of our interpersonal objectives. Finally, these ethical maxims provide a necessary and powerful pressure on us to consider whether our objectives themselves are reasonable. The eight-year-old boy can have as his major objective the eating of a maximum number of chocolates. Indeed, if one speaks to him of the pleasures of marriage he may ask if it is like eating chocolates. It is fortunate that society offers us a great deal of advice to the effect that we should not commit ourselves too wholly to the pleasures of eating chocolates because we may subsequently find that it was not a satisfactory objective.

33. SUMMARY OF THE GOAL-SEEKING CHARACTERISTICS OF INDIVIDUALS

Let us examine what we have discovered by considering the decision procedures of people involved in the business of living.

1. Being unable to satisfactorily describe their goals in terms of any one objective, people customarily maintain a number of different objectives. Each objective is relevant to some phase of their life activities.

2. The existence of multiple objectives leads to the problem of possible conflict between objectives. We have called this a *suboptimization problem*.

3. A particularly important aspect of the suboptimization problem is that we can only optimize in terms of the time when the decision is made, and this may be a suboptimization in terms of subsequent times.

4. The typical decision problem is so complex that any attempt to discover the optimal action is useless. Instead, people find outcomes that are good enough and attempt to achieve them (Simon's principle of bounded rationality).

5. Granted all the difficulties, human beings do try to be rational in their decision problems. As help, they have a great store of past human experience codified for them in the form of ethical principles. These principles and maxims are not such that adhering to them is any guarantee of success but they do afford some guides to the avoidance of error.

34. ORGANIZATIONAL OBJECTIVES

When we turn to consider organizational objectives we find the same difficulties and similar resolutions of them. Certainly an organization differs from an individual with regard to rationality, suboptimization problems, and the principles that help in guiding it. Nevertheless, in essentials we will find that the organization's problems of formulation of objectives are just the same as those of the individual.

First, what is an organization? Most business organizations take the form of corporations, which are legally created persons. But these fictitious persons are markedly different from real persons in several major respects.   They have no appointed number of years and for all practical purposes they can be considered to be eternal.   Obviously, such qualities as happiness have no relationship to organizations.   Nonetheless, the usefulness of having a basic overriding objective remains, as well as the impossibility of formulating one that covers all cases.   Probably the best that can be done in this context is to affirm the fundamental assumption of accounting: that the business is a going, continuing concern.   Phrased in terms of objectives we can state that the fundamental objective of every business organization is to continue its existence.   If we return for a moment to the case of the individual we see that the analog to this corporate objective would be the individual's object of continuing his life.   Survival is not the all-important objective of most individuals, notwithstanding the fact that it is a singularly important subobjective.   This is demonstrated by the historical fact that literally millions of individuals have given up their lives, reluctantly or cheerfully, for the sake of values and objectives which they held more dear.   This fact should give us pause in the case of corporations.   Perhaps they, too, have more deeply held objectives than merely continuing their existence.

Fortunately we do not need to enter into any analysis of this question.   For corporations, as for individuals, the search for any single underlying objective is likely to prove a fruitless one.   Further, even if the above-stated objective were accepted it would provide little help in solving decision problems.   The question would still remain to be answered: What state of affairs ensures a continued existence?   The problem of suboptimization over time would be one of many which would arise to haunt us when we tried to deal with this question.   No, for corporations, as for individuals, we find that the maintenance of multiple objectives is an analytical, as well as a practical necessity.

35. MULTIPLE OBJECTIVES

Just as in the case of the individual, the organization is likely to maintain objectives in the different areas of its activities.   Peter Drucker lists eight areas in which objectives have to be maintained:

*Market standing, innovation, productivity, physical and financial resources, profitability, manager performance and development, worker performance and attitude, public responsibility.**

Now, the areas could be classified differently or arranged in a different way but it does appear that most businesses do, in fact, maintain these kinds of objectives.   A specific business entity can ignore any one of the

* Peter Drucker, *The Practice of Management* (New York: Harper & Brothers, 1954), p. 63.

areas only at the risk of its future performance in any of the others. And as soon as we recognize the existence of multiple objectives we are immediately faced with the problem of suboptimization. How does this work out in the case of the business organization? Let us follow Peter Drucker in his discussion of what may happen if a business devotes its attention exclusively to profit.

To obtain profit today they tend to undermine the future. They may push the most easily saleable product lines and slight those that are the market of tomorrow. They tend to short-change research, promotion, and the other postponable investments. Above all, they shy away from any capital expenditures that may increase the invested-capital base against which profits are measured; and the result is dangerous obsolescence of equipment. In other words, they are directed into the worst practices of management.*

Any one of the objectives, emphasized to the exclusion of the rest, can lead to equally unpleasant consequences.

36. ORGANIZATIONAL PROBLEMS OF SUBOPTIMIZATION

Under what conditions does suboptimization arise in business? Of course we can answer that it arises whenever an action has an effect on several different objectives simultaneously. But this is merely to state the same thing in different words. In fact, there is no general answer to this question. The best that can be done in any specific decision problem is to utilize intuition, experience, and all available methodology to endeavor to see whether actions intended for one purpose have any probable effects on other objectives. If they do then it follows that the problem is one that involves a possible conflict of objectives and it must be handled with this fact in mind.

It should be explicitly noted that no genuine problem of a conflict of objectives can be reconciled by expressing all the possible outcomes in terms of the utility measure for one of the objectives. Now, it is fortunate that many decision problems of business can be framed in terms such that the possible outcomes can be measured in dollars. But it is by no means the case that all business objectives can be expressed in dollars. If, to take an instance, workers' attitudes could be measured in dollars, then it would follow that all possible outcomes in the area of workers' attitudes could be expressed in dollars. The total objective need only be stated as the maximization of profit. We would not require a special description of workers' attitudes. No such easy solution to the problem of conflicting objectives is usually available. Fortunately, we do have

* Drucker, *op. cit.*, p. 62.

some resources and procedures with which to attempt to deal with this problem; they will be presented in a subsequent chapter.

Looking at the bright side, there are a great number of important decision problems that do not involve any conflict of objectives. For any one of these we can attempt to optimize with no fear of difficulties arising from suboptimization. In particular, we can state that, at the minimum, a business must attempt to optimize its situation with regard to each specific objective as long as it does not affect adversely its situation with regard to any other objective. This construction is a variant of an idea introduced in a different context by the Italian economist and sociologist, Vilfredo Pareto. Pareto was concerned with the problem of what should govern the actions of society if it is assumed that the utilities of the various individuals composing the society cannot be compared. By utility we mean the subjective value that each individual subscribes for the various goods and services available. Under these circumstances society cannot act to achieve the greatest total utility because this idea has no meaning for the stated conditions. Pareto suggested that society should then try to achieve at least an optimum such that each individual had the maximum utility possible without subtracting anything from anyone else's utility. In other words, if society can act so as to increase one individual's total utility without taking anything away from anyone else, then it should do so. A condition where this has been accomplished is known as *Paretian optimality*.

The problem with which Pareto was dealing arises because there is no common standard or measure of value between individuals. And this is precisely analogous to the problem of multiple objectives with which we are dealing. Our problem arises because there is no common measure of value for the various objectives. If there were one common measure we could formulate one objective rather than several. Therefore we can state, along with Pareto, that any business should always attempt to achieve a condition of Paretian optimality with regard to its various objectives.

As we saw above, the problem of suboptimization also arises for individuals with reference to time. This is obviously true of organizations and for precisely the same reason: the very limited ability of human beings to foretell the future. It must be emphasized that the ability is limited but nevertheless existent. The decision to build a new factory requires knowledge of sales trends, economic trends, costs of land, costs of building, and so on. The location chosen, the design of the building, the dates of construction, and many other factors represent opportunities to optimize if we could only predict the future. However, with imperfect predictions we must suboptimize. As another illustration, many companies manufacture products that must be on the drawing boards years

in advance. As much as possible, they would like to reserve judgment
on design commitments that would inexorably fix the nature of the product. As far as possible, decisions are made that permit a broad range
of eventualities. In this way, suboptimization can be improved over
time, permitting them to gradually approach an over-all optimization.
The same reasoning applies to short- and long-range company planning.
If a decision made in a short-range plan does not permit several eventualities in the long-range plan, then it creates a suboptimization that cannot be improved upon.

Business organizations are subject to still another kind of suboptimization problem. Whereas a real person is a unit that is more or less
indecomposable, the fictitious person of the business corporation is usually
made up of a number of different departments or divisions. The successful functioning of the business demands the integration of the efforts of
the various departments that compose it. The achievement of any of the
business objectives requires that the various departments should each
achieve some departmental objectives. But, by the very nature of things,
departments are likely to have considerable autonomy and it can happen
that the objectives they set are not in accord with the over-all business
objectives. It can also happen that the actions of one department have
an effect on the situation of other departments such that an optimal
strategy for one department in terms of its own objectives deleteriously
affects other departments and, hence, the entire business. Both of these
kinds of situations represent other variants of the suboptimization problem.

Examples of both kinds of problems are legion. Lack of accord of objectives is a major problem facing businesses. On the simplest level, an
executive, on his doctor's orders, may have a new-found objective of
peace, quiet, and avoiding stress which may be very much out of phase
with the business objectives. Or the salesman's objective of maximizing
his income may be in poor accord with a desired product mix or with
the need to devote time to prospective customers. At a different level,
a research department might devote 90 per cent of its time to short-range
projects so that its record of achievement is impressive. If the company's competition does not have a similarly short-range point of view,
the research department's objectives will cause extreme hardships for its
own company.

This kind of suboptimization problem is of particular importance and
it will be worthwhile to present a more lengthy example of it. This example, which follows, will illustrate a lack of accord in business objectives
in inventory policy.

A chemical manufacturer has ten plants located at different places in
the country. Four of the plants are quite large, four are of medium size,

and two are small. The production units use many thousands of different kinds of parts. A sufficient supply of parts is always kept stored at
a warehouse adjacent to each plant. Management decides that the capital investment in spare parts is high enough to warrant doing a methodological analysis of inventories. Their objective is to minimize the total
cost of inventory. In the course of the analysis each plant manager is
asked to determine the frequency with which each part could be allowed
to go out of stock, i.e., one time out of ten demands, one time in a hundred, one time in a thousand. This allowable rate of outage is known as
the *alpha-level*. The plant managers accordingly group all spare parts
into alpha-classes. Some parts have an alpha-level of 0.001, others 0.01,
and so on. The criterion the manager uses in assigning parts to classes
is the importance of the part to his operations as contrasted with the cost
of the part. In other words, a very costly part which is not crucial to
maintaining production might have an alpha-level of 0.5, or even 1.0
(the value of 1.0 would mean that the part was never kept in stock and
was always obtained on demand). If we assume that the plant managers
rate all of the parts that are in common use in the same way, then it will
fall upon central management to introduce differences in the alpha-levels
based on the relative importances of the various plants. The reason is
that the alpha-level shows the permissible frequency with which parts
can be out of stock. However, the loss of goodwill and/or production
resulting from an out of stock in a small plant will probably be less costly
to the company than would be the case for a large plant. For example,
central management might say, our large plants are four times as important to us as our small plants. We will multiply all small-plant alpha-
levels by 4, thereby increasing the permissible frequency with which the
small plant goes out of stock.

What does this mean to the small-plant manager? It means that he
will be out of stock four times more frequently than the large plants.
He is justified in asking: Will central management always remember why
I am out of stock more often than the large plants? Or will top management forget and use my repeated outages to illustrate the greater compe-
tence of the large-plant managers? Will this system spoil my chances
of becoming a large-plant manager? After considerable soul-searching
the small-plant manager finds an answer that satisfies his conscience
and his desire to look as good as the next fellow. He decides to inflate
his forecasts of demand. In other words, he protects himself from going
out of stock by ordering more than he expects to need. Now the alpha-
level is applied to this inflated figure with the result that the manager
may go out of stock less frequently than the large plant. Within his own
organization he is much more highly respected than he would be if he had
to explain to the sales department, the production men who work for him,

and others that they have to expect to go out of stock more often because they are less important in central management's eyes.

Let us consider further the question as to why the managers rated their alpha-levels the same while central management did not think that this was so. Was central management wrong? No. Central management was attempting to estimate the relative penalties for being out of stock at each location and to correct the managers' estimates for this factor. On the basis of company-wide information they were in a position to do this, whereas the managers were too localized to have the necessary perspective. The only way that the managers could have derived the same results as central management would have been if they knew the actual cost to the integrated company of being out of stock at their location. It is usually difficult, however, to estimate the cost of being out of stock. The alpha-level can be directly determined if the costs of carrying stock, C_1, and the costs of being out of stock, C_2, are known. The relationship is

$$\text{Alpha-level} = \frac{C_1}{C_1 + C_2}$$

where $C_1 =$ the cost of carrying a unit of stock for a unit time, and
$\quad\ C_2 =$ out-of-stock cost per unit for a unit time.

The cost of carrying stock will not be identical for each location. Generally, however, it will be nearly the same. On the other hand, the out-of-stock cost will differ markedly depending on the amount of goodwill sacrificed by not filling an order and the size of the production unit that might have to close down if a single part is missing. Thus, for one particular part, assume that both a large plant and a small plant have a C_1 equal to one dollar. The large plant has a C_2 of \$49 while the small plant has a C_2 of \$9. Then

$$\text{Large plant alpha-level} = \frac{1}{1 + 49} = 0.02$$

$$\text{Small plant alpha-level} = \frac{1}{1 + 9} = 0.10$$

Since neither plant manager knows the C_2 costs, central management adjusts the alpha-levels for them on the basis of its integrated information. Even when the C_2 costs are unknown central management can proceed as we suggested earlier, by weighting the alpha-levels according to the relative importance of each plant. Generally the individual plants would not be able to do this.

At the expense of a digression, we have gone into this inventory situation in some detail. It is a clear-cut case of a company that tries to optimize across all of its components. Optimization is achieved to the disadvantage of the small plant, and the small-plant manager conceives of a strategy which he hopes will offset the loss he would otherwise have to take. The small-plant manager's strategy is to attempt to optimize his position and his plant's position. The result of this conflict of objectives is suboptimization.

We have given a number of examples of suboptimization occurring between one part of a company and the over-all organizational objectives. We can now look at illustrations of suboptimization where two parts of the company are in conflict with each other. For example, a division's objective of achieving the best possible profitability record may lead it to purchase parts from competitors rather than from another division of the same company. This may lower the profitability of the division that normally supplies parts. As another aspect of the inventory problem, a sales manager's objective of getting the largest possible sales may lead him to want a large inventory so that all orders can be promptly filled. This might be in conflict with the controller's objective of tying up a minimum of capital in inventory. Which one is in the best interests of the business? As a final example, a production department uses less steel by cutting down on the upper limit of the tolerances to which it machines a part. This results in a higher number of rejects of the finished assembly and an eventual complete redesign of the product with no appreciable gain in quality.

All of these examples serve to demonstrate the crucial importance of the suboptimization problem. Once again we could raise the question: When does this kind of problem arise? And once again, there is no general answer. Being aware of the problem we must rely on common and uncommon sense to help us to discover which particular decision may exemplify it. Fortunately, the majority of the forms of this kind of suboptimization problem involve objectives that can be expressed in quantitative form, so many of these problems can be resolved by methods which we will be discussing at length below. Thus, for example, the problem of inventory size and the conflicting interests of the sales manager and the controller can generally be resolved by expressing all the costs in dollars and solving the decision problem in terms of the over-all business objective of minimizing costs. This simple statement may make it seem easy. It isn't, as we know from the problem of the small-plant manager. How can we express the loss of dignity which he experiences as a result of being out of stock more often than he would like? Similarly, how do we represent the loss of customer goodwill that results from being out of inventory on an item that the customer wants immediately? Nonetheless, despite some difficulties, these kinds of problems can often be satisfactorily resolved.

37. BOUNDED RATIONALITY OF THE ORGANIZATION

Simon's idea of bounded rationality holds for corporations just as much as and perhaps even more than it does for individuals. First, the sub-optimization difficulties force some boundaries on the various possibilities taken into account. For many decision problems it is necessary and reasonable to assume that the action taken in one department will have no significant effect on another department. Yet we know full well that a business entity is a functioning whole and that adjustments in one area will almost always have at least some slight effect on other areas of the business. In spite of this, the assumption of independence is usually made, and successfully. Not every factor can be considered in every problem precisely because of the limitations of human rationality.

Second, there are sharp limitations on the availability, at least at a reasonable cost, of information that is obviously needed in order to re-solve a decision problem. For example, many decision problems on sales promotion and advertising would have better solutions if detailed information were available about the sales of competitors by regions. Yet this information is rarely available with any degree of accuracy. So we do as well as we can without it.

Third, sometimes there are enormous excesses of information which simply cannot be sorted, classified, and processed. Consider the promotional problems of a large mail-order house. Such an organization typically will have huge masses of information in its files concerning the location of its past customers, what they bought, how they paid, and various other items of information. It is quite possible that accurate formulation of promotional decision problems would benefit from an analysis of all this information. Yet even the modern large-scale computers may well be insufficient for the task, assuming that someone was willing to take responsibility for the expense. And even so, who would have the time to study the many thousands of results? So, instead, we take bits and pieces of the information, using informed judgment, and more or less hope for the best.

Fourth, there are an incredibly huge number of possible states of nature, to say nothing of competitors' actions, and no decision problem could be even formulated if the attempt were made to include all these possibilities. Business is dependent on the national economy. Almost any change in the economy is reflected in the business and, hence, may affect the decision problem in question.

These and other difficulties mean that an optimum solution of any specific decision problem in terms of its formulation will probably be less than optimum in terms of the factors left out of account. Therefore, the realistic decision-maker is not likely to strive for any optimum in this sense.   Instead, he will select a group of situations that are good enough and he will be satisfied with a reasonable degree of suboptimization.

38. PRINCIPLES AND POLICIES

Fortunately, the business executive has, just like the individual in his life problems, a vast store of knowledge abstracted from the good and bad experiences of his innumerable predecessors.   These generalizations and rules of thumb function for the executive in the way ethical principles function for the individual.   And, similarly, they are not laws that can be disproved by a contrary instance.   Rather, they are means of calling the attention of the decision-maker to things he might overlook and to risks he might be running.

Consider, for example, the policy that the current liquid assets should be at least equal to the current liabilities.   This policy is not falsified by the case of a corporation that ignored it and went on to achieve success and affluence.   It simply codifies the fact that many businesses have run into difficulties when they have ignored this ratio.   As another example, consider the frequently stated policy of large department stores: "The customer is always right."   Do they really think that this is true?   Far from it.   Do they always act as if it were true?   Certainly not.   It serves only to call the attention of the clerks and department managers to the fact that the objectives of the store demand careful attention to customer relations.

In short, it is the exceptions that must be justified, not the principles or policies that traditionally guide the executive of a business organization.

39. SUMMARY OF THE GOAL-SEEKING CHARACTERISTICS OF ORGANIZATIONS

We can now attempt to summarize the important aspects of organizational objectives that we have considered.

1. Organizational goals cannot be described by one simple objective. Therefore organizations are credited with multiple objectives.

2. Multiple objectives are required to understand the organization's relationship with the outside world.   Conflicts between these objectives lead to one type of organizational suboptimization.

3. Multiple objectives also exist within the organization.   The fictitious entity which is the organization is built of many groups and subgroups which are in themselves entities.   The individual is the basic building block of the structure.   Conflicts of two basic kinds occur, but

it is quite clear that many variations can appear. Conflicts between the organization and any lesser group are one cause of suboptimization. Conflicts between components of the organization can also result in suboptimization.

4. As was the case for the individual, suboptimization occurs in time. The relationship of short-range to long-range planning requires that short-range planning should not destroy the possibilities contemplated by the long-range plan. Short-range planning is certainly suboptimization, but it is decision-making in a framework that is expected to include the opportunity for optimization. Moving in steps, the suboptimization approaches optimization in the long run.

5. Organizational decision problems are admittedly very complex. But organizational objectives do not have the entirely tenuous nature of many individual objectives. Frequently it is possible to find measurable quantities that represent utility to the organization. The discovery of "true" optimality is no more available to the organization than it is to the individual; nevertheless, it is frequently possible to determine a suitable or allowable degree of suboptimization.

6. The executives of organizations make every effort to be rational in their decisions. They are, of course, affected by bounded rationality as are all individuals. However, they have a vast body of past experience, part of which is codified in the form of policy to guide them.

Despite difficulties, we all know that executives strive valiantly to achieve rational decisions. No amount of emphasis on the difficulties should ever be permitted to obscure this fact. Creativity, intuition, know-how, experience—all these play their role in the decision process. But the creative burst of insight precedes, it doesn't replace the rational part of the decision-making process. To convince others, to evaluate between two different creative insights, to subject the creative insight to the cold light of reason—all these require the weighing and evaluating of alternative strategies in terms of the objectives, the possible states of nature, and the competitive strategies. In other words, the rational decision-making process is called into play. We must now turn, in the next chapter, to a consideration of how decision problems can be formulated in a manner that permits a rational approach to their solution.

PROBLEMS

1. What would be the teleological explanation of a severe drop in sales? What would be the positivistic explanation? How would an "open systems" analyst view the loss in sales?

2. Considering the example of the mail-order company, Table 3.1 and Figure 3.1, assume that new customers are obtained in an oscillating pattern as fol-

lows: 6, 8, 10, 8, 6, 4, 2, 4, 6, 8, 10, 8, 6, 4, 2, 4, 6, 8, ... Draw the graph of total orders when the repeat order rate is: First week, $\frac{1}{2}$; second week, $\frac{1}{4}$; third week, $\frac{1}{8}$; .... If management can control repeat-order rates, what values should they establish in order to smooth the curve of total orders? (Notice the effect of allowing no reorders in the first, second, and third weeks.)

3. A manager of a supermarket wants to set up a test to determine how to make each aisle section yield optimal profit. In what way is the manager suboptimizing? How serious is the mistake? How can suboptimization between aisle sections be avoided?

4. Two products are manufactured on the same equipment. A decision is to be made concerning the proportion of each product that will be manufactured. Why is this not a genuine suboptimization problem? It is then learned that the president's wife favors one product over another. Why has the problem now become a real suboptimization situation?

5. The cost of carrying a unit of stock, C_1, is frequently determined by applying the interest rate that can be obtained on capital to the cost of the item plus the cost of storage, insurance, and so on. For example, $\frac{1}{2}$ of 1 per cent, or 0.005 (a yearly interest of 6 per cent), is multiplied by the combined costs of the item, if C_1 is to be determined on a monthly basis. Therefore, an item with total costs of $100 has a C_1 of $0.50. Using the 6 per cent interest rate, and estimating the carrying costs and C_2 factor, determine the alpha-level for (a) a new-car salesman, (b) a used-car salesman, (c) an airplane manufacturer, (d) a kite manufacturer.

6. Assume that the ordering quantity specified by the inventory plan of the chemical manufacturer is given by the following formula:

$$Q = x + \frac{10(1 - 2\alpha)\sqrt{x}}{3}$$

where Q = reorder quantity,
$\quad x$ = forecasted demand for a specified period, and
$\quad \alpha$ = alpha-level.

For a particular part, the small-plant manager is given an alpha-level of 0.20. For the same part, the large-plant manager is given an alpha-level of 0.02. By how much will the small-plant manager increase his reorder quantity in order to have the same alpha-level as the large plant? (Give the answer in terms of x.)

Chapter four

The Decision-Theory Approach

We saw in Chapter 2 the necessity for some measure of the degree to which an objective is achieved. And in that chapter we noted that some objectives seem to permit only two possibilities: either they are achieved or they are not. Other objectives have a natural measure of the degree to which they are achieved—for example, the amount of profit. And there are still other objectives that seem to have degrees of achievement but for which there appears to be no straightforward way in which to measure this degree.

For rational decision-making, we require some kind of measurement. As much as possible, our decision theory will be based on numbers and not on words. Even when numbers seem to be available as a natural consequence of a process, it cannot be taken for granted that they are the right numbers. Therefore, we must investigate in detail the means at our disposal for measuring the degree of attainment of an objective.

40. DEVELOPMENT OF THE PAYOFF MEASURE

In our formulation of the decision problem we have suggested that the decision-maker has various possible *strategies* available to him, that he has one or more *objectives* which he is trying to achieve, and that a *state of nature* will occur which, together with the strategy he selected, will determine the degree to which he actually achieves his objective. Another way of saying the same thing is that his selection of a strategy and the occurrence of a specific state of nature will result in a certain state of affairs for the decision-maker. This state of affairs will yield him a certain utility in terms of his objectives. What we need is a measure of this utility, which is appropriately called the *payoff measure*.

The idea of utility, and a measure of it, as previously mentioned, is one with which economists have long concerned themselves. So we are by no means developing a brand-new concept. However, the interest in measuring utility which has resulted from its decision-theory applications has led to some new approaches to the problem. We don't need to discuss all the conclusions concerning the measurement of utility, but we will need some of them for our subsequent discussion.

The first important point is that utility is defined in subjective terms. It is utility for some specific individual or organization, and not utility in terms that are general and abstract. This immediately results in problems concerning the comparison of the utilities of different individuals. Various aspects of this problem have led to many new developments in economic theory, but for our purpose it is sufficient to note that the problem as stated is not solvable. There is no way to compare the utilities of different individuals. This creates no particular problems for decision theory as long as we are concerned only with the decision-maker against states of nature. But as soon as we become involved in decision problems where competitive actions are part of the situation we will find that the impossibility of comparing utilities of different individuals has some important consequences.

The second point we want to note is one that requires some development. The essence of the matter is that even for those objectives for which there seems to be a natural measure (profit, for example) it does not follow that the obvious measure is a measure of the utility to the decision-maker. In other words, the position of the decision-maker that finally results, when evaluated in terms of the objective, may have an entirely different measure of utility than the natural measure would indicate. This can be readily illustrated.

Suppose someone offers to gamble with you on the following terms: a coin will be tossed; if it comes up heads you will be paid $200, if it comes up tails you must pay only $100. Now, surely, this is an excellent arrangement for you. We might even suspect the sanity of the man who offered you such terms. However, the question is: Would you always accept the offer? It is clear that the amounts of money involved are distinctly in your favor. Half of the time you will win and receive $200 increments; whereas the other half of the time, you will lose, but only $100 increments. In terms of utility, the question can be phrased: Is the utility that I sacrifice when I lose less than, equal to, or more than the utility I gain when I win? And, as a little thought quickly discloses, this varies with your circumstances. If you have a sufficient sum of money so that the loss of $100 doesn't destroy your financial situation you will probably find that the gain in utility when you win is greater than the loss in utility when you lose.   (We will call this the first case.) Under these circumstances you would probably be happy to indulge in this gamble as often as your opponent would agree.   But suppose, to take an extreme, that the total amount you have is $100 and you need this in order to pay for transportation to the location of a new job which has been offered to you.   (We will call this the second case.)   Under these circumstances you might well feel that the loss of utility which might occur was far greater than the gain in utility which would occur if you won.

Now, this little example is a genuine decision problem.   To gamble or not to gamble are the two strategies that are available; to win or to lose are the two states of nature that can occur; and the objective is—what? Is it to maximize your total dollars?   It appears that we cannot say this because it wouldn't cover the second case.   Of course, we could say that this was the objective in the first case and something different was the objective in the second case, but it is certainly more convenient to formulate one objective that will cover either case.   And this is easy to do.   The objective in either case is to maximize utility.   Apart from being an elementary decision problem, this example shows that the utility of dollars is not necessarily the same as the number of dollars.

41. BERNOUILLIAN UTILITY

The question remains: What is the utility of a dollar and how can we measure it?   A famous early scientist, Daniel Bernouilli, had already treated this question in a paper he wrote about 1730.   But rather than concern himself with an empirical investigation of how the utility of money varied among individuals, Bernouilli hypothesized that the utility of money to an individual is inversely proportional to the amount of money he already has.   In other words, the more dollars he has, the less the utility of an additional dollar.   Actually, there are a great number of different mathematical relationships between utility and number of dollars that would represent this verbal description of Bernouilli's assumption or hypothesis.   In fact, however, he chose a specific one of these various possibilities.   He assumed that the utility of dollars could be measured to a sufficient approximation by using the logarithm of the number of dollars as the measure of utility.

There is nothing sacrosanct about the selection of the logarithm as the measure of utility.   As a matter of fact, although it possesses some uniquely important characteristics, which are developed later in this book, it isn't a particularly good representation of reality.   But it is convenient to use and it does reflect the decrease in utility of additional dollars as the number of dollars already owned increases. Therefore it will serve our present purpose to emphasize that even for objectives where the degree of achievement can be measured in dollars, the same decision problem presented to two different individuals may have two different solutions, both being completely rational. Why? Because the utility that the two individuals place on dollars is different.

To illustrate this fact we can use the same problem with which Bernouilli was concerned, viz., the problem of self-insurance. But before we can do this it will be necessary to introduce some of the more elementary concepts of probability theory. These concepts play a most important role in decision theory, operations research, statistics, and many other important areas, so we will be using them extensively in the material that follows. We need only some of the ideas of the probability theory, and it will be simplest to introduce them piecemeal, as they are required.

42. PROBABILITY THEORY

Probability theory deals with events of a special kind, called *random events*. These are events for which the outcome is determined by chance. Frequently this situation occurs when an enormous number of causes contribute to produce the final outcome which is the event in question. A typical example is tossing a coin. Whether it is heads or tails is a chance event because such a large number of causes contribute to the final outcome. Such factors as the force with which the coin is tossed, the amount of spin, air movements, position of the hand when the coin is caught, all act together to determine the outcome. Probability theory deals with the conclusions that can be drawn in reasoning about such events. The basic concept is that of the *probability of the outcome*. The probability of an outcome can be most simply understood as the percentage of the times in which this outcome would occur if the event were repeated a great many times. Thus, we say that the probability of the outcome of (the event) heads in tossing a coin is ½ because a great number of tosses will produce about 50 per cent heads. Similarly, the probability of rolling a 7 with two dice is ⅙ because a great many rolls will produce 7's about 16⅔ per cent of the time.*

---

* It is only fair to make mention of the fact that some probabilists would take exception to our last two sentences. They would maintain that one would get about 50 per cent heads because the probability of a head is ½, not vice versa, and similarly for the dice. This is one of the many controversies about the foundations of probability theory which continually shake that edifice. Fortunately, we do not need to concern ourselves with the direction of causality here. Either formulation will be quite good enough. But a different controversy will be important in the next chapter and will have to be discussed there.

Another way of putting the matter is to say that probabilities are measures of uncertainty. Exactly what do we mean when we say that the probability of heads is ½, that the probability of a 7 with two dice is ⅙, or the probability of being dealt a perfect bridge hand (13 cards of the same suit) is 1/158,753,389,900? In any of these cases the outcome in question will either happen or not—there is no intermediate possibility. What information, then, does the associated probability really give us? Only the percentage of times the outcome will occur if the event is repeated a great number of times. Note that the coin may show tails the first try, again on the second try, and perhaps for the first ten tries. But, in the long run, we can expect to find that we have gotten about 50 per cent heads. Similarly, one might deal 158,753,389,900 bridge hands and never get a perfect hand, or one might conceivably get one on the very first deal. Probability theory tells us, however, that if we dealt an enormous number of bridge hands—say one bridge hand for every electron and proton in the universe (2 times 15,747,724,- 136,275,002,577,605,653,961,181,555,468,044,717,914,527,116,709,366,231,- 425,076,185,631,031,296 according to Sir Arthur S. Eddington)—we would find that we had gotten pretty nearly one perfect hand for every 158,- 753,389,900 deals.

All of the probability examples we have used above have been of the sort that can be calculated in advance. But this is incidental for our present point of view. Suppose we are told that the probability is ⅒ that the average January temperature in New York City will be greater than 40°F. What does this mean? It means, first, that someone has gone over the New York City weather records and has discovered that in the past, 1 out of 10 Januaries had an average temperature of more than 40°F. It means, second, that barring a climatological change (i.e., the process is stable), we can expect approximately the same proportion in the future. At least this is the best information we have concerning the proportion to be expected in the future. The only difference between this case and the earlier ones above is in the method of determining the probabilities, not their interpretation. If we didn't know how to calculate the probability of getting a 7 with one roll of two dice we could roll the dice a great many times and observe how often we got the 7. As a matter of fact, this is exactly how it was done, and with considerable accuracy, by gamblers before probability theory was developed in the seventeenth century.

Now, the most important use of probabilities for our present purpose is in terms of the factors that govern rational behavior when money (or, more generally, utility) is involved in chance situations. The classical gambling situation is typical. What reasoning governs a wager on the toss of a coin? Suppose the same wager is going to be repeated a great number of times. Then we know that about 50 per cent of the time the coin will show heads. This means that the gambler who bets on heads will win about 50 per cent of the time and his opponent will win about 50 per cent of the time. So, if the game is not to produce an advantage for one or the other player it is necessary that the amounts bet should be equal for the two players. Thus, suppose the unit bet is $100 and the coin is tossed 1000 times. We would expect that either player would win about 500 bets and lose about 500 and so come out approximately even. Thus, in this case, the odds would be even—each player betting the same amount of money. It is this fact that gave so much advantage to one of the players in the coin-tossing example given before. If that game had been played 1000 times, the player who received $200 when he won and who lost only $100 when he lost could have expected to win 500 times and receive $100,000 while losing 500 times and paying out only $50,000, with a net gain of $50,000.

The same reasoning applies to any other probabilities. Suppose one is betting on a 7. If the dice are rolled 6000 times, we know that there should be about 1000 7's. Thus, the person betting on the 7 would win 1000 times and lose 5000 times. In order to have an even game it is clearly necessary that he should receive more when he wins than he pays when he loses. In fact, he must receive $5 when he wins for each $1 he pays when he loses in order for the game to be even. Thus, fair odds for this game would be 5 to 1. If the odds are larger than 5 to 1, then it is an advantage to bet on a 7. If the odds are smaller, then it is an advantage to bet against a 7.

43. EXPECTED VALUE

Much of this reasoning can be clarified by introducing one concept: *expected value*. This idea is not complex. Expected value is simply the old fashioned arithmetic average. It can be expressed in mathematical symbols by using W's (W_1, W_2, and so forth) to represent the possible numerical outcomes, and p's (p_1, p_2, and so forth) to represent the probability that each of the W's will occur. Thus, for two possible outcomes, we have

$$\text{Expected value} = W_1 p_1 + W_2 p_2$$

where $p_1 + p_2 = 1$, since either W_1 or W_2 necessarily has to occur.

The W's may be positive or negative, and occur in combinations, depending on the problem. For example, consider the executive who is certain to get one or the other of two possible bonuses, the first representable as W_1, the second as W_2. If we know for each the probability of his getting that bonus, our equation represents the executive's expected value of bonus. Both the W's are, in this case, positive. Now consider the situation of an importer awaiting a Customs' decision as to whether a shipment received from abroad shall be charged a 15 per cent duty or a 25 per cent duty. If both W's are allowed to be positive, our equation yields the expected value of the duty. If both W's are allowed to be negative, our equation yields the expected value of decrease of the importer's potential gain.

Frequently we will be using this equation where one of two W's is positive, the other negative. This is the situation of the possibility of either a gain or a loss—the gambler's predicament. For example, what is the expected value of a coin toss upon which two players each bet $100? Here we can let W_1 represent the gain of $100 ($W$ is positive), and W_2 the loss of $100 ($W$ is negative). Then we have $100(\frac{1}{2}) - $100(\frac{1}{2}) = 0$ as the expected value. What is your advantage if the other player puts $200 against your $100? Simply $200 $(\frac{1}{2}) - $100(\frac{1}{2}) = 50. Under these conditions you should average $50 gain on each play; if you play 1000 times you should have $50,000 to show for it.

Of course, we are not limited to expected values of return rates, gains, or wins, and losses. We can use expected values of any quantities whatsoever; in particular, we can directly take the expected value of total capital. For example, assume you have a total capital of $500 and you are offered the coin toss of $200 against your $100. Then we can identify the W's with total capital. If you win you will have $700, and if you lose you will have $400. Therefore we have $700(\frac{1}{2}) + $400(\frac{1}{2}) = 550, which is the expected value of your capital after one toss. Let us consider how one might more broadly use this concept of expected value.

Suppose you have the choice of making two investments of $1000 each. Presume that the return on investment A will be $4\frac{1}{2}$ per cent and the return on investment B will be 6 per cent. Granted the certainty of these statements and assuming that you are motivated by the objective of getting the greatest possible return you will undoubtedly invest in B. This conclusion follows because your return from B will be $60 compared to only $45 return from A. But now suppose that you are informed that both of the investments are risky and that the risk is greater on investment B. Suppose, to be precise, that you are told that the probability of a return on investment A is 0.90 (90 per cent) and the probability of a return on B is 0.65 (65 per cent). We will assume that either you will get the full stated percentage return or else no return at all. How would you choose between the investments?

We could calculate the expected values for the two investments in accordance with our equation. We will assume that the capital invested will remain secure in any event and the only question is whether there is a return or not. In this case the amounts won will be the return on the investment and the amounts lost will be 0—simply the fact of not receiving a return. In accordance with our equation, the expected value for investment A will be $\$45\,(0.9) - 0\,(0.1) = \$40.50$. The expected value of investment B will be $\$60\,(0.65) - 0\,(0.35) = \$39$. This means that if we made a number of different investments identical in every respect to investment A we would expect an average return of $\$40.50$ on each of them. For a number of investments similar to investment B we could expect an average return of only $\$39$. We could, therefore, conclude that we should invest in A because our expected return from A is larger than it is from B.

Note that we said "could conclude" rather than "must conclude." The reasoning we followed is perfectly logical and affords complete justification for choosing investment A. However, it is clear that one might prefer to play a hunch and invest in B and that he might be right and we might be wrong. This in no way changes the fact that our reasoning is impeccable, granting the probabilities as given and the objective as stated. The same question arises concerning gambling. One person may play the odds correctly and lose, while another ignores them completely and wins. Perhaps it may be the case that some individuals have a sixth sense. Those of us who don't have such a sixth sense can console ourselves with the fact that most individuals who do think they have one and who ignore the relevant probabilities eventually suffer the consequences.

In this reasoning concerning expected values we have ignored the very point with which we started—namely, that individuals do not have the same utility for money. We calculated above the considerable advantage accruing to the individual who receives $\$200$ in the coin-tossing game for each $\$100$ he wagers. Yet we have previously stated that under certain conditions (our so-called second case) we wouldn't accept this handsome offer. There is no contradiction. Instead of expected value we need only calculate the expected utility, using precisely the same procedure except that some measure of the utility of the amounts involved is used instead of the amounts themselves. This kind of calculation will be illustrated when we return finally to Bernouilli's problem of self-insurance.

44. SELF-INSURANCE

What is the problem of self-insurance? Individuals or organizations faced with the risk of loss of assets can either assume the risk themselves or pay an insurance company to assume the risk for them. The question is: When is it reasonable to do one or the other?

Let us take as an example a shipment of goods worth $\$10,000$ which has a probability of 0.10 (10 per cent) of being destroyed or lost in transit. What is the expected value of such a shipment? Using our equation we have $10,000(0.90) + 0(0.10) = $9000, reflecting the fact that out of 100 shipments only 90 will arrive. Put in another way, the shipper can expect that on the average he will sustain a $1000 loss in value for each shipment. It would follow on this basis that the shipper should be prepared to pay up to $1000 for each shipment as premium on insurance. In this way, he will suffer no loss on his merchandise value, but he will pay the same amount as his expected loss to the insurance company. If he paid $1000 for each shipment then he would pay a total of $10,000 in premiums for ten shipments and this would be repaid him for the one that was lost or destroyed. Thus, he would break even. The lower the premium, below $1000, the more advantageous it would be for the shipper to insure. But from the standpoint of the insurance company a premium of $1000 per shipment would only enable them to break even and they would demand a higher premium say $1500. Viewed in the same light as gambling games, if the shipper takes insurance at a $1500 premium, then he has a negative expected value. That is, he loses on each play (shipment). Yet, under exactly this kind of circumstance, people continually insure themselves against loss. Why? Are they all being irrational? Of course the answer is no. They are not.

The explanation resides in the fact that the parties to the insurance contract have different utilities for money. There is diminishing utility for money (the more one has, the less an additional amount will contribute to utility). That the diminishing utility should take precisely the form of the logarithm of the amount of money, as Bernouilli assumed, is unlikely but it will serve to illustrate the logic of the situation. Suppose the shipper has total assets of $15,000, including the shipment which must arrive safely that the shipper be paid. Then, according to Bernouilli's assumption of a logarithmic measure of utility, if he does not take insurance, the shipper will have a utility of the logarithm of $15,000 or 4.17609 with probability of 0.90 and a utility of the logarithm of $5000 or 3.69897 with probability of 0.10. His expected utility in this case is simply $4.17609(0.90) + 3.69897(0.10) = 4.12838$ (the utility of $13,439, since 4.12838 is the logarithm of $13,439). If he insures for a premium of $1500 he will always end up with $15,000 − $1500 = $13,500 and his utility will be the logarithm of $13,500 or 4.13033. Thus, the shipper's total expected utility is higher if he insures so this is the course of action he should take.

From the standpoint of the insurance company it is rational to offer the insurance because the company has so much money that its total utility is increased by accepting the insurance. Assume that the insurance company has assets of only $100,000. If it doesn't accept the insurance its utility will be measured by the logarithm of $100,000 or 5. If it does accept the insurance it will have the utility of $101,500 or 5.00647 with probability of 0.90 and the utility of $91,500 or 4.96142 with probability of 0.10. Its expected utility if it accepts the insurance will therefore be 5.00647(0.90) + 4.96142(0.10) = 5.00196, the utility of $100,454. The insurance company should, therefore, accept the insurance for a premium of $1500. Thus, both parties are acting with complete rationality—once account is taken of the differences in the utility of money.

What, then, is the answer to the problem of whether to insure or not? It clearly depends on the amount of assets the shipper has. From the equation for his expected utility it can be calculated that he has equal utility whether he insures or not if his total assets are about $16,000. If he has more than this it is to his advantage to bear the risk himself. If he has less he should insure. Perhaps the shipper would scoff at the idea that with only $16,000 he should carry this risk himself. If so, it should be realized that this only means that the logarithm is not a good representation of the diminishing utility of money, a fact which we have already noted. If we had, for a specific shipper, the correct representation of his utility for money, we could use precisely the same approach to determine exactly at what point it was to his advantage to self-insure. Our use of the logarithm, we repeat, was only to illustrate the idea that it is utility that is important—not the amount of money.

The point of all this discussion is that even for objectives with a natural measure of degree of achievement it is still necessary to recognize that the natural measure may not coincide with the utility the decision-maker receives from the degree of achievement of his objective. And, if it doesn't, it is the *utility* that governs the decision problem, not the natural measure.

But there are many decision problems for which the amount of money involved does satisfactorily measure the utility. This would tend to be true where the amount of money involved is small relative to total assets. Can this be made more precise? Only if the real relation of the utility of additional increments of money to the amount of money possessed is known. For example, if the true relationship between utility and money is expressed by the logarithm of the amount of money, as Bernouilli suggested, then decision problems involving changes in money of no more than 2 to 3 per cent of the total amount possessed can be approximated with sufficient accuracy by assuming that the utility is represented by the amount of money. In short, the amounts of money involved could be used directly without worrying about the utility of the money. For decision problems involving greater amounts of money than this it would be necessary to attempt to determine the utility of the sums involved.

It is important to note that problems arise at the other end of the scale, too. Even if the logarithm, as used, were a correct representation of the utility for money under most circumstances, difficulties arise as soon as a decision problem includes any risk of total loss, i.e., bankruptcy. The difficulty is indicated by the logarithm itself, since the logarithm of zero is negative infinity. For some people, negative infinity, which is an infinite loss, would properly represent the situation. Other individuals, with suitable temperaments, don't look upon bankruptcy as the end of the road. For these people, it wouldn't be accurate to suppose that a small chance of complete failure would deter them. Obviously, personality and temperament differ widely at the zero end of the log scale.* Under these circumstances it is necessary to give careful individual consideration to the measure of utility.

We have concerned ourselves so far only with objectives for which there exists a natural payoff measure of the degree of achievement. Even here we find difficulties, although they are not insuperable ones. Such natural measures exist for many business objectives because the business is involved in economic activities and one would expect to find that various economic indices would be relevant to many of the business objectives. Thus, we would expect that dollars would be a natural measure of payoff for objectives concerning profits and costs. A different kind of natural payoff measure is provided by brand share. In the same way, volume of sales, order size, number of customers, repeat order rate, and a large number of other payoff measures may be relevant to specific business objectives.

45. PAYOFFS WITHOUT A NATURAL MEASURE

But what happens when the objective is one of the many that obviously have different degrees of achievement—and, hence, demand a payoff measure—but for which there is no obvious measure of payoff? Of the eight areas listed by Peter Drucker † that require objectives (discussed in Chapter 3) there are four that are clearly of this type: innovation, manager performance and development, worker performance and atti-

---

* If there is a 0.01 probability of bankruptcy we could represent this as (0.01) log $1.00 which would then contribute zero utility, but subtract nothing from the utility which would result 99 per cent of the time. On the other hand, fractions of a dollar would subtract utility. One point of view is to take that fraction which subtracts as much utility as would be gained if bankruptcy did not result and apply the probabilities to these numbers. For example,

$$0.99 \log \$15,000 + 0.01 \log (1/\$15,000) = 0.99(4.17609) - 0.01(4.17609) = 4.09257$$

which is equivalent to $12,376.

† Drucker, *The Practice of Management*, p. 63.

tude, public responsibility. Some objectives in the other four areas may fall in this category also. To take an instance, an objective in the area of worker attitude might well be the achievement of satisfactory labor relations. Obviously, there are all manner of degrees of labor relations ranging from high turnover, stoppages, strikes, and poor performance to the case where everyone works until he reaches retirement, stoppages and strikes are unheard of, and performance is excellent. This example will serve to illustrate that it is possible to find some quantitative measures even for such an objective as this one. For instance, turnover rate, or average length of service, or some index of productivity may be suitable for a payoff measure in some cases. But the difficulty is usually that no one of these seems to correspond to what the decision-maker has in mind when he refers to satisfactory labor relations. If one of them is what he means, or some combination of several, then we need only try to discover whether there is a problem of determining the utility of various payoff measures. The more difficult case occurs when the decision-maker isn't really sure exactly what he means by satisfactory labor relations. He only knows that he will recognize them when he sees them.

This situation is not an unfamiliar one. Consider the problem of determining a quantitative measure of the state of health of an individual. There are an enormous number of quantitative measures involved in good health: blood sugar content, blood corpuscle count, weight, and the whole host of measures that doctors have occasion to use. For any one of them we can probably find limits such that it can be said that the individual won't be healthy unless this particular measurement lies between the limits. But the problem is that even if all the specific measures lie between their given limits the individual may still be unhealthy. It is precisely this fact that accounts for the need for the highly experienced diagnostician. If it were otherwise we could plug all of a particular individual's measurements into a computer and diagnose his condition from calculations. But it is important to note that wherever measurements are sufficient, doctors are quick to use them. Thus, since one of the major proofs of acute infectious mononucleosis is a change in the differential count of the white corpuscles, doctors are prone to use this as a major step in their diagnosis of this disease. And legitimately so, for such procedures give the doctor the opportunity to devote his experienced attention to other, more intangible evidence and to concern himself with the problem of the best treatment for the particular patient in question. The procedure is in accord with the usual development of knowledge. Some of the intangibles that one generation treats by experience are converted to measurable factors by the next generation. This process is a never-ending one because reality is too complex to be completely circumscribed by a finite set of measurements.

In economics the same kind of problem is known as the *index number problem*. How, for example, can one achieve a quantitative measure that will describe the state of the economy? This case is perhaps even more interesting because there are already available an extraordinarily large number of quantitative measures of different aspects of the economy. There is, quite literally, an embarrassment of riches. Part of the difficulty is due to the underlying notion that there must be a best state. But it is impossible to give a satisfactory definition of what constitutes the best state. Certainly the majority of economists would recognize it as a good state when they saw it. There are a great number of possible relationships between all the measurable factors which would constitute a good-enough state. Perhaps this is one of the areas in which the principle of bounded rationality is operating. The question isn't really whether the national economy is optimizing, only whether it is satisfactory.

So, recognizing that the problem we are dealing with is a general one, let us see what resources we have to deal with it. We can begin with a specific example. Suppose you are involved in contract negotiations with a union. You have, we will assume, the objective of achieving a satisfactory relationship with your workers. And, of course, you have a great number of possible strategies available to you in the form of specific offers and counteroffers to the union. Now, let us simplify the problem by assuming that there are only three possible relevant outcomes: strike, contract, or continuation of the doubtful situation where negotiations continue and the workers remain at work without a contract. First of all it should be noted that under some circumstances it might be feasible to express these three possibilities in terms of dollar cost to the company. If this were the case we could use the simpler methods discussed above, so we will assume that we cannot use dollar costs.

46. RANKING

Now, the first possibility available to the decision-maker is that he can rank the possible outcomes in order of their utility to him. Ranking the outcomes simply means that they are put in the order of their utility, the most utility first, the least utility last. Thus, in our example, the executive may rank a contract first, continued negotiations second, and strike third: 1, 2, 3, in that order. Of course, this plausible ranking is by no means a necessary one. It all depends on the utility of each outcome to the decision-maker. For example, under some circumstances the decision-maker might rank a continuation of negotiations first because he anticipates a change in the economic situation which would improve his bargaining position. In any case, we are suggesting that the decision-maker can rank the outcomes in order of their utility to him in terms of his objectives.

But can this always be done? Some things certainly can't be ranked. One cannot, for example, rank cities of the world in accordance with their distance from the equator and from the international date line. One could rank them in accordance with either one of these distances separately, but not simultaneously. Similarly, we cannot rank an airplane's position. That is, we cannot rank it unless our objective provides a criterion other than spatial position. In airport control, for example, planes are landed according to their altitude. The lowest plane in a stack is brought in first and all of the planes in the holding pattern are then lowered by one unit of altitude separation. The criterion is not to pass any plane through an altitude occupied by another plane. So we rank these airplanes by their order of arrival starting at one and counting up from the bottom. The position of a ship does not permit ranking; however, the rules of the road rank ships according to which ones have the right of way. We cannot rank color. But we can rank position of the dominant wave length in the visual spectrum. We can also rank purity and reflectance by wave length. Any given color can be defined in terms of three variables. By means of a suitable transformation, these can be reduced to two.

Nevertheless, the ranking problem remains. Mathematicians refer to this as a problem of *dimensionality*. A ranking implies only one dimension and cannot be used on factors that have more than one dimension, as our examples had. The sense of taste is a phenomenon that has been shown to have more than one dimension. As a result, psychologists have devised taste tests in which the individual must rank his preferences for various tastes and he cannot do it successfully. This shows up in the form of a breakdown of the transitivity of his preferences. *Transitivity* is a mathematical word signifying that if the individual prefers A to B, and prefers B to C, then he should prefer A to C. Transitivity holds as long as there is only one dimension. Examples of transitive relations are bigger, smaller, heavier, lighter, wealthier, healthier. Its breakdown in taste tests indicates the presence of more than one dimension of taste. Might this not happen when the business executive attempts to rank his outcomes? It is tempting to answer no, because the executive will reach a decision implying that he has ranked his outcomes. However, this would be circular reasoning with a vengeance! The modicum of truth that seems to be in this answer is that in order to make a decision the executive must *believe* that he has succeeded in ranking his outcomes. We leave open the possibility that he might not be able to do so on occasion.

If the outcomes can be ranked, the numerical ranks can be used as a measure of the utility of the outcome—the payoff. We shall find that rankings are sufficient for analyses of decision problems involving competitive actions in many cases, and that they can be useful in analyzing decision problems involving states of nature. But they are not sufficiently informative to support a very extensive analysis. The major limitations of rankings of outcomes as measures of payoff are obvious, since the majority of arithmetical manipulations have no meaning in terms of ranks. For example, in the case of our example, we cannot tell whether the difference in preferences between 1 and 2 is greater or less than the difference in preferences for 2 and 3. Averages of ranks, where several possible outcomes might occur with one strategy, have no meaning. In short, while rankings are helpful—and must serve if nothing better is available—we cannot expect to be able to use any very sophisticated methods of analysis based on ranks.

47. THE STANDARD GAMBLE

What else is available? John von Neumann and Oskar Morgenstern * developed a method for determining an individual's utility scale for outcomes which is known as the *standard-gamble* method. Their idea is an extremely ingenious one. We will devote the next several paragraphs to an attempt to present the essentials of the technique.

The idea of the standard gamble is to set the decision-maker a series of choices between which he must make a selection. But the choices are of a peculiar type. Take the executive faced with the decision problem in labor relations. Let us abbreviate the three alternatives by their initial letters: S for strike, C for contract, and N for negotiations. Our executive has ranked these three outcomes in order: C, N, and S. Therefore, we assign these outcomes the ranks 1, 2, and 3, respectively. But the lack of ability to arithmetically manipulate these ranks, mentioned above, is reflected by the fact that we could equally well summarize his preferences by any other three numbers in the same order: say, 1, 9, 28 or 7, 46, 259. What we would like would be three numbers that would reflect his preferences in such fashion that the ordinary arithmetical manipulations would have their usual meaning. This is what the standard-gamble approach attempts to accomplish.

Suppose we ask the executive to express his preference between: Choice 1, getting N certainly; and Choice 2, a lottery in which he will get C with probability p and S with probability $1 - p$. The reader should meditate for a moment on exactly what we are asking the execu-

* von Neumann, John and Oskar Morgenstern, *Theory of Games and Economic Behavior,* Princeton: Princeton University Press, 1947.

tive to tell us—his preference between having N for sure and taking a gamble on C or S. We propose to adjust p. Thus, suppose we set $p = 1$. This would mean that the executive was being asked to choose between N for sure and C for sure—and we already know he will select C. Suppose we put $p = 0$. This would mean that we are asking the executive to choose between N for sure and S for sure—and we know already that he would select N. But this would indicate that as p changes from 0 to 1, the executive's preference for N (Choice 1) instead of the lottery (Choice 2) must switch at some point to a preference for the lottery over N. It seems reasonable, then, to say that the preferences are equal at the value of p for which this switch occurs.

Suppose, for example, that our executive says that he has equal preferences when $p = 0.9$. Now, we know in advance that we can arbitrarily assign a 1 to the outcome with the greatest utility and a zero to the one with the least utility. The reason is that we could equally well assign any other two numbers to these two outcomes. If it were otherwise it would mean that the location and scale of an individual's utility measure could be absolutely determined. This would imply that the utilities of two individuals could be compared. And we know that this is impossible because utility is defined in purely subjective terms. Consequently, we have complete freedom of choice in assigning numbers to the outcomes with the greatest and the least utility. The other values are determined by the standard-gamble technique. It will be convenient to take advantage of this freedom of choice and always assign the outcome with the greatest utility the measure 1 and the outcome with the least utility the measure 0. In our example this means that C will be assigned the utility measure 1 and S will be assigned the utility measure 0. With this scale the utility measure of N will be 0.9—the probability we determined as the no-preference point. Now, what is the advantage of this particular measure of the utility of N, in conjunction with the assigned utilities of 1 and 0 to C and S, respectively? Simply that with these values the decision-maker can be guided in his thinking by the spread between the utilities of the outcomes, average utilities, expected values, and so on.

He can be consistent in his actions as long as he continues to accept the payoff measures he has determined. He can transfer this information in some operational form to subordinates. At the same time, we can erect a more suitable theoretical framework for the decision process.

It is an easy matter to extend this procedure to any desired number of outcomes. For each outcome with an intermediate rank we find the probability at which no preference exists between certainty of that outcome and the given lottery between the two extreme outcomes. The probability determined in this way is the measure of utility for that outcome.   Naturally, there are limitations to the validity of this procedure. The most important one which we should note is that transitivity should hold between preferences for outcomes.   This means, as we have seen, that the outcomes can be ranked—which is equivalent to saying that only a single dimension is involved.   However, the measures of utility that are obtained are a great deal more useful than are the ranks alone. For a more detailed account of the procedure, including various other restrictions, the interested reader should see Chapter 2 of Luce and Raiffa's *Games and Decisions.** Additional discussion from a special point of view will be found in Chapter 14 of this book.

It should be noted that attempts to use this technique in actual practice have not always been successful.   Sometimes there are inconsistencies in the stated preferences and no unique measure of utility can be constructed.   But, as L. J. Savage has pointed out,† often this means no more than that the individual in question is really inconsistent and, when it is pointed out to him, he will attempt to eliminate the inconsistency.   Certainly it is not always the case that inconsistencies can be blamed on multidimensionality.

Another difficulty arises if one of the outcomes is overwhelmingly bad —say bankruptcy.   The possible effect of this on the standard-gamble approach can be understood by the reader if he will envision himself using the method to evaluate his utilities for the following three outcomes: make $1000, lose $50, death.   Perhaps it is the case that no rational person should prefer any lottery involving death as one of the alternatives to losing $50.   One possible answer to this quandary is to note that even an entirely rational person might prefer the lottery between death and making $1000 to the certainty of losing $50 if the probability of death were so small as to make it virtually impossible—say 1 divided by the number of electrons and protons in the universe.   But the difficulty with this answer is that people are unable to distinguish realistically between small differences in probabilities that might make large differences in utilities.   It is probably more realistic to simply accept the fact that a special case arises when one or more of the outcomes are overwhelmingly bad.   We noted this difficulty when discussing the logarithmic representation of utility.

So we see that we are not completely helpless when faced with nonquantitative objectives in a decision problem.   On the contrary, there are several possible ways in which we can proceed to obtain a quantita-

---

* Luce, R. Duncan and Howard Raiffa, *Games and Decisions*, New York: John Wiley & Sons, Inc., 1958.

† Savage, L. J., *The Foundations of Statistics*, New York, John Wiley & Sons, 1954.

tive payoff. None of them is perfectly satisfactory and each is subject to limitations but, nonetheless, for many typical business objectives that are not obviously quantifiable, a payoff can be obtained.

Finally, the standard-gamble method sometimes can be used for those cases where several different objectives are involved simultaneously. The problem in such cases is to obtain a payoff measure that incorporates the utilities of all of the objectives—each achieved to a different degree. If the rankings are confused by multidimensionality there may not be too much that can be done. Often, however, the executive can approximate the utilities of the various outcomes by using the standard-gamble approach.

48. STRATEGIES AND STATES OF NATURE

So far we have considered the need and difficulty of formulating the objectives of the decision-maker as precisely as possible. We have also discussed the problems and possibilities of determining a quantitative measure of payoff. But our preliminary survey of the decision problem revealed the need for two additional components: strategies and states of nature. We must now consider these in more detail.

We have previously explained that strategies are based upon the resources under the control of the decision-maker. The decision-maker has alternative ways in which he can use his resources. The strategy which he selects is his decision as to what he will *do* with the resources under his control. The use of the word "resources" is justifiable since some kind of disposition of resources is usually involved in available business strategies. The executive's own time and effort can be included. But it may be misleading because some decisions use up only the executive's time and effort—and no resources, in the strict sense of the word, are affected. For example, the decision problem of pricing a new product does not require allocation of resources. Neither, for that matter, does the decision to wait and see involve the disposition of resources. Nevertheless, in its broadest sense, all of the talents, abilities, and experiences of the executive are resources of the organization. There is no particular need to emphasize this fact since most decision problems involve the allocation of physical resources and the decision-maker's strategy is the plan for their allocation.

At first thought it might appear that there are virtually an unlimited number of possible strategies in any realistic decision problem. In fact, there are often a great many, but various factors serve to limit the number of strategies that will be considered as genuine possibilities in a given decision problem. To begin with, strategies will be considered unacceptable if they violate any laws. In frontier days, one of the better strategies in some competitive decision problems was to shoot your opponent, but today, the laws of the land prohibit such sharp competitive practices. More seriously, a whole range of strategies is prohibited by the laws relevant to collusion between competitors. Another whole range of possible strategies is prohibited by the Pure Food and Drug Act. Certainly, we could go on listing restrictions to strategies that arise from legal agencies, statutes, and the common law.

Actually, even if there were no restrictions against bad practices, any company with its eye on its public-relations objectives would hesitate to indulge in them. This indicates that a more fundamental restriction on strategies exists—social mores and public opinion. The law, of course, is a reflection of these. Most companies attempt to limit their strategies to those which are consonant with the socially accepted practices of the time and place. Such self-imposed restrictions go under the name of *policy*. Policy is applied to situations that are not covered by the law, except for the primary policy: not to violate the law. In Chapter 3, we discussed policy in terms of conflict of objectives. At that time, we stated that policy was a collection of principles and rules whose purpose was to guide the executive to consider things which he might otherwise overlook. We can now extend this thinking to the present context. Policy relieves the executive from having to consider a great many possibilities and thereby saves his time for strategies that must be explored. If policy were stated in details instead of principles, it would not be an effective means of ruling out vast areas of possible strategies. To illustrate this point, it would be virtually impossible to play a good game of chess if every conceivable arrangement of pieces on the board had to be interpreted as a unique situation. For each situation there are so many possible strategies that a player who is not guided by policy would either play by memory or by chance. It is chess policy—the existence of principles stated in terms of general configurations—that permits the player to discard a great number of undesirable strategies. He discards them as classes of strategies and not one by one. In this same manner, the executive rejects classes of strategies.

Strategies that can be eliminated in lots rather than in units are generalized strategies. There are a number of methods for generalizing strategies so that they can be accepted or rejected in classes. We shall cover this in later chapters. But for the moment it is our purpose to show that law, social mores, and policy provide this same kind of discrimination. Usually, the strategies eliminated by these principles are those which would result in serious conflicts between the objectives of the organization and the important objectives of society. The type of conflict is such that the organization does not care to be placed in the situation where it must choose between its own objectives and those of society. Since the position of having to make a choice is a compromising one—even if the decision is always in favor of society—the principles are ingrained in the decision-maker. He does not even consciously reject the strategies that lead to these conflicts. He never even considers them.

There are other areas in which the decision-maker acts in the same way, but not with consistently desirable results. True, he succeeds in eliminating a great number of possibilities, but within those possibilities are optimum solutions that in no way conflict with social, legal, or policy goals. These additional restrictions on strategic possibilities appear in two forms: (1) unthinking acceptance of the conventions and customs of an industry, and (2) an individual's reluctance to consider certain kinds of change. In these cases, the *status quo* is taken for granted. There is hardly any awareness that there might be another way.

The fact that many strategies are never contemplated because of psychological deterrents is not, in anyone's terms, an advantage. For example, a dress manufacturer who has been identified for years with the $7.95 line of dresses may have so profound a revulsion to the perfectly reasonable strategy of shifting to the $3.95 line that he is unable to conceive of the possibility, or to listen to such suggestions. Similarly, the management of a firm that has been located for its entire existence in one particular area may have profound antipathy to the sound strategy of moving the company to a new location that has lower labor costs, lower transportation costs, or some other vital advantage. Psychological deterrents to the recognition of possible strategies cut down the size of the decision problem, but the saving is many times obtained at the expense of a simultaneous cut in the degree of achievement of the objective.

As far as trade customs are concerned, certainly many of them are beneficial. Many others, which serve as restrictions on the number of possible strategies, are neither beneficial nor harmful with respect to degree of attainment. Their consideration would add nothing to the sum total of possible strategies and subtract greatly from the executive's time. Therefore, in a sense, the inclusion of unusual or unthought-of strategies with high payoffs is reserved for a creative act on the part of the decision-maker. There is no way in which operations research, decision theory, mathematics, or the like can replace such creative acts. In some fortunate cases, the result of the analytic approach brings certain elements or relationships to the attention of the decision-maker, and he is led to break the barriers of bounded rationality. As a matter of fact, by introducing an external process of reasoning, these analytical methods do act as a catalyst for creative thinking.

States of nature have many characteristics in common with strategies.

Here, too, we want to be able to discover and recognize as many states of nature as we possibly can. But then, faced with overwhelming numbers of states of nature, we want to know how to classify them so that we do not have to consider each detail in every possible form. The discovery of states of nature is hardly limited by law, social mores, or policy. Neither is it affected by trade customs. Psychological deterrents, on the other hand, do play a part. There is no need to describe this further since the discussion in terms of strategies is relevant. As in the case of strategies, the methodological approach to restricting the number of states of nature will be developed in subsequent material. Discovery of all relevant states of nature requires systematic exploration, the full utilization of experience, and, if we are lucky, some creative insights which escape the confines of our bounded rationality.

Competitive strategies are a special class of states of nature. Now, it is quite clear that we should not be able to conceive of more strategic possibilities for our competitor than we can for ourselves. However, this may not always be the case. Sometimes, the competitor is in a different position than we are with respect to size, market share, product lines and so on. Many times, we lack sufficient information about the competitor and this seriously handicaps our efforts to predict his possible behaviors. The one thing we know is that his behavior will not be dictated by chance. The importance of this fact will become obvious in our later discussions of game theory. For the moment, it will be sufficient to say that sometimes it is a simple matter to list all relevant states of nature and all relevant competitive strategies. At the other extreme, however, we cannot hope to consider all possible shifts in the economy, calamities in nature, technological breakthroughs, fads in society—that is, all possible states of nature and competitive strategies.

PROBLEMS

1. Practice in calculating expected values helps to make the concept a familiar one. Here is an assortment of expected value problems:

   a. A particular stock has paid dividends of \$0.50 per share in 12 of the last 15 payments. The other three times it has paid \$0.25. What is the expected dividend?

   b. A company which sells two different models of one item finds that 65 per cent of its customers buy the cheaper model, for \$95. The remaining 35 per cent of its customers pay \$125 for the more expensive model. What is the expected purchase price?

   c. A magazine discovers that 40 per cent of the families which subscribe are ones in which there are two wage-earners. In the remaining 60 per cent of the families there is only one wage-earner. What is the expected number of wage-earners per subscribing family?

d. A salesman makes 35 calls without a sale, and 15 calls with an average sale of $60. What is his expected sales per call?

e. The same salesman has a particular trip of 48 miles which he often makes. Four times it takes him one hour and six times it takes him 1½ hours. What is the expected time for the trip? (Convert the data to miles per hour and calculate his expected speed. Compare the two answers. One must be careful in calculating expected values of rates!)

f. A small-loan company finds that 12 per cent of its borrowers default on an average 20 per cent of their loans. What is the expected percentage default?

g. A mail-order company finds that 18 per cent of the purchases of a particular item are returned. The company estimates that each return costs $0.70 in transportation and extra handling. What is the expected extra cost due to returns per unit of this item?

h. A second-hand car lot has a mark-up of $250 on 65 per cent of its cars and a mark-up of $400 on the rest. What is the expected mark-up?

i. A department store discovers that twice as many customers buy two units at $3.95 (for both) as buy one unit for $2.15. What is the expected purchase price per unit?

j. A magazine states that the average number of cars per family subscriber is 1.2. If 20 per cent of the family subscribers have no car what is the average number of cars per family of the families which do have one or more cars?

2. Suppose you have total capital of $5000. You have the opportunity to make a speculative investment of $2500 which will either be totally lost or will be worth $7500 in six months.

a. Using expected values directly, what is the maximum probability of total loss for which this would be a profitable investment?

b. Using the logarithmic measure of utility, what is the maximum probability of total loss for which this would be a profitable investment?

c. Use the standard gamble method to determine your own utilities for the three outcomes: $2500, $5000, $10,000. What is the maximum probability of a total loss which would be acceptable?

d. Another mathematical form which can be used to represent utility is:

$$\text{Utility of } x \text{ dollars} = \log \frac{1 + \dfrac{x}{c}}{1 - \dfrac{x}{c}}$$

where c is some constant larger than any of the x's involved. Try this form with several values of c and determine the maximum probability of a total loss which would be acceptable. How does this probability change with c?

3. A company with assets of $50,000 is considering the possibility of redesigning its product. Including new tools and dies, the total cost of the redesign

job will be $12,000. The company estimates the profitability of the product for three alternatives, No Change, Design 1 and Design 2. The new designs, 1 and 2 have the same cost.

No Change		Design 1		Design 2	
Profit (per year)	Probability	Profit (per year)	Probability	Profit (per year)	Probability
$4000	0.2	$8000	0.2	$6000	0.4
5000	0.5	9000	0.5	9000	0.2
6000	0.3	10000	0.3	12000	0.4

a. Compare the dollar expected values of total assets at the end of one year for each alternative strategy.

b. Compare the dollar expected values of total assets at the end of two years for each alternative stategy.

c. How long a period is required before the total assets obtained from Design 1 are equal to the assets if no change is made? How long for Design 2?

d. Instead of dollar expected values use the logarithmic measure of utility to answer questions a. and b. Comment on the differences resulting from the use of each method.

4. A reports to B, B reports to C, C reports to D, D reports to A, A reports to C, and D reports to B. Which relationships are transitive and which are not?

5. Determine the expected value of the executive's bonus if, for the past 15 years, he has received $200 5 times and $300 10 times and the system can be considered stable. If the executive has $10,000 in the bank, what per cent increase does each possible bonus make? Using the log utility assumption, what per cent increase in utility will each possible bonus contribute? What can we say about these results?

6. Rank-order your preferences for the following business conditions (H = high, L = low):

Price	Sales volume	Cost of manufacturing	Cost of selling
L	L	H	H
H	H	L	H
L	L	L	H
H	H	H	L
H	L	H	L
L	L	H	L
L	H	L	L

How many possible rankings are there? Does it seem possible that an executive could consider all of these? What happens if we describe the condition of each of the variables with high, low, and medium? What happens if we describe each variable with any number between 0 and 100? Check each column after ranking for transitivity. What does this tell us about an executive's decision problem? What consequences are there if an executive is not transitive in his decision-making?

7. Use the standard gamble on the outcomes you have ranked in problem 6, above. First obtain p values for ranking numbers $1-2-7$, $1-3-7$, $1-4-7$, $1-5-7$, and $1-6-7$. Then, repeat the procedure for $1-2-3$, $1-3-5$, $1-4-6$, and $3-5-7$. Check your results against the first five p values which you derived.

8. For the self-insurance problem discussed in this chapter, the insurance company asked a $1500 premium to insure a $10,000 shipment with a 0.10 probability of loss. The company had assets of $100,000. How much could it afford to pay the shipper above $10,000 so that it would have no gain in utility?

Chapter five

Analysis of the Payoff Matrix

Mathematics suggests a convenient way to present our breakdown of the decision problem. This is to put it in the form of a matrix—called the *payoff matrix*. A matrix is simply a two-dimensional array of figures arranged in rows and columns. A matrix representation of the decision problem is particularly convenient because we can let the rows be the available strategies (one row for each strategy) and the columns be the states of nature including competitive actions (one column for each state of nature). As might be expected, the entry at the intersection of each row and column is the payoff—the measure of the utility of that specific outcome which occurs for a given strategy and a particular state of nature. Thus, the payoff matrix summarizes all of the characteristics of the decision problem which we have been discussing. Symbolically, the payoff matrix looks like Table 5.1—using N's to designate states of nature, S's to designate strategies, and P's to designate payoffs.

Table 5.1

	$N1$	$N2$	$N3$	$N4$	...	N_j
$S1$:	P_{11}	P_{12}	P_{13}	P_{14}	...	...
$S2$:	P_{21}	P_{22}	P_{23}	P_{24}	...	...
...	...	...	...	...	...	...
S_i:	...	...	...	...	...	P_{ij}

What is the decision problem? The same as always—to select a specific strategy. The payoff matrix merely provides a means of presenting the relevant information easily.

49. CERTAINTY, RISK, AND UNCERTAINTY

We have already noted that the columns can be either states of nature or competitive actions, depending on the decision problem. But confining our attention for the moment to states of nature, there are three important forms in which they can appear. Depending on how much we know about the states of nature, we refer to decision-making under *certainty, risk,* and *uncertainty.* Since these three types of decision-making result in important distinctions in the decision process it is necessary that we should clearly distinguish between them.

Decision-making under certainty occurs when we have a decision problem in which we know with certainty which state of nature will occur. This means, in other words, that there is only one column in our payoff matrix. At first sight this may seem like a trivial case. How can there be any difficulty in reaching the best decision if there is only one column? Simply read down the column to find the largest payoff and that will be the optimum strategy. But it isn't quite that simple. The idea behind the suggestion is absolutely correct, but the difficulty is that there may be such an enormous number of rows that it would be quite impossible to list them.

Of what use then, it may be asked, is the payoff matrix—if it can't even be written down? The answer is that in some cases, when the payoff matrix can't be written down at all, it still remains a means of conceptualizing the problem. As we shall see, one of the contributions of operations research to decision-making is in this sort of problem. For the present, it suffices to indicate that real and important decision problems exist that are of this type.

Suppose, for example, that you run a machine shop and have 20 contracts for machined parts. You also have 20 machines, any one of which could do any one of the contracts. But since the machines are of different designs and for different purposes it is the case that each machine would require differing amounts of time for each contract—and, hence, would be more or less expensive. You would, quite naturally, like to assign the jobs to the machines so as to minimize the total cost. The first job could be assigned to any one of the 20 machines, the second job to any one of the remaining 19, the third job to any one of the remaining 18, and so forth. So the total number of ways in which you could assign the jobs is given by $20 \times 19 \times 18 \times 17 \times 16 \times 15 \ldots \times 3 \times 2 \times 1$ and if one takes the trouble to do the arithmetic he will find that the total number of ways to assign the jobs to the machines is 2.4329×10^{18} where we have rounded off the number. Now, each way of assigning these jobs to machines is another possible strategy, so this decision problem's payoff matrix would have only one column (because the costs of the various machines are assumed known), but it would have almost 2½ quintillion rows. That such a modest problem could produce so many rows in the payoff matrix may be surprising but it does serve to show that decision-making under certainty can be a genuine problem. And the same sort of problem is by no means confined to machine shops. On the contrary, a great number of different kinds of business decision problems fall into the category of decision-making under certainty.

The second kind of decision problem occurs where there are a number of states of nature but where the decision-maker knows the probability of occurrence of each of the states of nature. This kind of situation is called *decision-making under risk*. For the purpose of illustration, a simple example would be the decision problem facing a gambler—where the possible states of nature are the various chance events, the probability of which can be calculated by probability theory. More typically in business problems, if the probabilities of the various states of nature are known it is by virtue of determining how frequently they occurred in the past. Thus, the decision problem of a manufacturer of antifreeze might well involve various possible weather conditions, and the probabilities of occurrence of these different states of nature might be determined from past experience. Similarly, inventory decision problems involving parts for factory equipment would include various states of nature representing the various rates of failure of the parts, and these probabilities might be known from past experience. This kind of decision problem occurs frequently in business.

The third kind of decision problem is *decision-making under uncertainty*, where the probabilities of occurrence of the various states of nature are not known. Such problems arise wherever there is no basis in past experience for estimating the probabilities of occurrence of the relevant states of nature. The decision problems involved in marketing a new product would include various levels of demand as states of nature. Yet there is no past experience on which to base estimates of the relevant probabilities as there is in the case of established products. Decision problems concerning expansion of facilities may have states of nature including such things as war, depression, recession. How can probabilities be estimated for these states of nature? Many of the major decision problems of business are of this kind.

50. DECISION CRITERION UNDER CERTAINTY

Now that we have briefly outlined the three kinds of decision problems involving states of nature, we can turn to the basic question: How should a specific strategy be selected? In other words, how should the decision be made? What we want to investigate is the reasonable procedure or procedures by which a decision can be reached if we have the payoff matrix. We would like to find a criterion by which the decision-maker, given his payoff matrix, can select his strategy.

Certainly there is no difficulty, in theory, in determining the decision criterion under certainty. In theory, all we need do is find the strategy which has the largest payoff and that is the strategy which should be selected. There is no possible reason for doing otherwise. Each strategy has only a single payoff, since there is only a single column in the payoff matrix when the state of nature is certainly known. Since the payoff represents the degree of achievement of the objective, the largest payoff is the best that can be done in terms of the objective. The decision criterion, then, is: Select that strategy which has the largest payoff. The practical difficulty which arises when the number of strategies is enormous will be dealt with by the methods of operations research.

51. DECISION CRITERION UNDER RISK

What happens in the case of decision-making under risk? Here we no longer have just one payoff for each strategy. Instead, we have a number of payoffs, one for each possible state of nature. So a decision criterion will either have to be based on all the possible payoffs for each strategy, or on one or more payoffs selected according to some rule.

Let us take an extremely simple decision problem under risk as an example. Assume that a processor of frozen vegetables has to decide what crop to plant in a particular area. Suppose that the strategies are only two: to plant peas, or asparagus. Suppose, further, that the states of nature can be summarized in three possibilities—perfect weather, variable weather, and bad weather. On the basis of weather records it is determined that the probability of perfect weather is 0.25, the probability of variable weather is 0.50, and the probability of bad weather is 0.25. The dollar yields of the two crops under these different conditions are known and the utility of the company can be assumed to be measured by the dollar amounts. All of this information can be summarized in a payoff matrix:

	$N1$	$N2$	$N3$
PROBABILITY:	0.25	0.50	0.25
	PERFECT WEATHER	VARIABLE WEATHER	BAD WEATHER
$S1$: Plant peas	$40,000	$30,000	$20,000
$S2$: Plant asparagus	$70,000	$20,000	$ 0

What strategy should the decision-maker select? It is our thesis that the rational decision-maker, under these circumstances, will govern his selection of strategies by the expected utility of the strategies—he will select that strategy which has the largest expected utility.

We introduced the idea of an expected value at an earlier point but we confined our discussion at that time to the case where there were only two possible outcomes. The extension to the case of any number of outcomes is straightforward. For two outcomes we had the equation:

$$EV = W_1 p_1 + W_2 p_2$$

For more than two outcomes we can write:

$$EV = W_1 p_1 + W_2 p_2 + W_3 p_3 + \ldots$$

where $p_1 + p_2 + p_3 + \ldots = 1$.

In our present terms the equivalent of the outcomes are the payoffs. Therefore, substituting the P_{ij}'s for the W's, the general expression for the expected payoffs of the strategies, ES_i, may be written:

$$ES_1 = P_{11} p_1 + P_{12} p_2 + \ldots + P_{1j} p_j$$
$$ES_2 = P_{21} p_1 + P_{22} p_2 + \ldots + P_{2j} p_j$$
$$\ldots \quad \ldots \quad \ldots \quad \ldots$$
$$ES_i = P_{i1} p_1 + P_{i2} p_2 + \ldots + P_{ij} p_j$$

This idea of expected value perhaps seems stranger than it really is. It amounts to a particularly convenient way of calculating the old-fashioned arithmetical average when probabilities are given rather than frequencies. Using this equation we can calculate the expected payoff (ES) for each of the strategies ($i = 1, 2$).

$$ES_1 = \$40,000 (\tfrac{1}{4}) + \$30,000 (\tfrac{1}{2}) + \$20,000 (\tfrac{1}{4}) = \$30,000$$

$$ES_2 = \$70,000 (\tfrac{1}{4}) + \$20,000 (\tfrac{1}{2}) + 0 (\tfrac{1}{4}) = \$27,500$$

The expected payoff for strategy 1 is larger; this is the strategy that should be selected. The decision-maker should choose the alternative: plant peas. Why? Because if the same decision situation were presented to him a great number of times he would average $2,500 more from strategy 1 than he would from strategy 2.

But, one may think, aren't there other factors to consider besides the expected value? For example, let us suppose that the probabilities were different. Suppose the probabilities were $\tfrac{1}{2}$, $\tfrac{3}{8}$, and $\tfrac{1}{8}$, respectively, for the three states of nature. Then the expected payoffs for the two strategies would be:

$$ES_1 = \$40,000 (\tfrac{1}{2}) + \$30,000 (\tfrac{3}{8}) + \$20,000 (\tfrac{1}{8}) = \$33,750$$

$$ES_2 = \$70,000 (\tfrac{1}{2}) + \$20,000 (\tfrac{3}{8}) + 0 (\tfrac{1}{8}) = \$42,500$$

And, since the expected payoff for strategy 2 is larger, this should be the choice of the decision-maker. But at this point one may say: Why should it be? Look at the difference between the payoffs. If he chooses to plant asparagus (S_2), the expected payoff is higher because of the much higher return on asparagus with perfect weather. But if he plants asparagus and has bad weather he doesn't make anything at all. Whereas, if he plants peas he may not make as much when the weather is perfect but he never risks having no return at all. So why couldn't a perfectly rational decision-maker prefer to forego a little expected pay-off in order to avoid the possibility of no return at all? We could just say that he was paying the difference in expected payoffs as a premium on insurance against having no return.

This appears to be a valid objection to the rule that the strategy with the highest expected payoff should be chosen. However, the objection is misplaced. A completely rational decision-maker might well reject strategy 2 (plant asparagus), but it is because his utility for dollars can-not be measured by the dollar amounts. In short, for this case, the pay-offs are wrong.

This is an important point and will bear emphasis. Suppose we sus-pected that dollars might not adequately represent the utility for dollars. In order to get a measure of the decision-maker's utility for the various dollar amounts we would try to use the standard-gamble technique. There are five possible outcomes: $70,000, $40,000, $30,000, $20,000, and 0. To determine his utilities for the intermediate amounts we would present him with the usual choices. First, would he prefer $40,000 cer-tainly to a lottery between $70,000 with probability $4/7$ and 0 dollars with probability of $3/7$? In the case we are considering he would prefer the certainty of $40,000. So, we would adjust the probability upward until he indicated no preference. This might occur at a probability of $6/7$ of getting the $70,000. We would proceed similarly with the other two outcomes and might find the no-preference probability for $30,000 at $p = 9/14$ and the no-preference probability for $20,000 at $p = 3/7$. This would then give us the utilities for the five possible outcomes as follows:

Outcome	Utility
$70,000	1
$40,000	$6/7 = 0.857$
$30,000	$9/14 = 0.643$
$20,000	$3/7 = 0.429$
0	0

Our payoff matrix would then be

$$
\begin{array}{ccc}
0.857 & 0.643 & 0.429 \\
1.000 & 0.429 & 0.000
\end{array}
$$

We would now proceed to calculate the expected payoffs as before, using the second set of probabilities:

$$ES_1 = 0.857\,(\tfrac{1}{2}) + 0.643\,(\tfrac{3}{8}) + 0.429\,(\tfrac{1}{8}) = 0.723$$
$$ES_2 = 1.000\,(\tfrac{1}{2}) + 0.429\,(\tfrac{3}{8}) + 0\,(\tfrac{1}{8}) = 0.661$$

And the decision-maker should select strategy 1, which has the larger expected payoff. So the objection we raised is reasonable, rational, and in accord with the actual behavior of many decision-makers. But it is misplaced. If payoffs are measured in terms of the decision-maker's utility he has no other rational decision criterion than the selection of that strategy with the largest expected payoff.

52. DECISION CRITERIA UNDER UNCERTAINTY

The case of decision-making under uncertainty is more complicated. For an example we will take the decision problem of an investor who has the objective of achieving the maximum possible rate of return. We will assume that he has only three possible investments (his strategies): speculative stocks, high-grade stocks, or bonds. We will further assume that only three possible states of nature can occur: war, peace, depression. We will ignore all the nuances of capital gains, taxes, and so on, and assume that the investor has determined his payoffs for each of the nine possible combinations of a strategy and a state of nature. This example is very much oversimplified but it will serve our purpose. The investor has expressed his payoffs as rates of return on his investment and his payoff matrix looks like this:

	N1 WAR	N2 PEACE	N3 DEPRESSION
S1: Speculative stocks	20	1	−6
S2: High-grade stocks	9	8	0
S3: Bonds	4	4	4

Now, of course, the distinctive difference between this case and the preceding one is that the decision-maker has no knowledge of the probabilities of the various states of nature. He has, therefore, no way to calculate an expected payoff for his strategies. What criterion should he use in selecting a strategy?

One of the most interesting results of decision theory has been the discovery that there is no one best criterion for selecting a strategy. Instead, there are a number of different criteria each of which has a perfectly good rationale to justify it. The choice among these criteria is determined by company policy and/or the attitude of the decision-maker. And, as we shall see, the use of different criteria can result in the selection of different strategies. We will discuss some of the various criteria which have been suggested.

53. CRITERION OF PESSIMISM

The first one was suggested by Abraham Wald and is called the *maximin* criterion. The reason for the name will become clear as we go through the necessary steps. Wald suggested that the decision-maker should always be completely pessimistic. He should act as if Nature would be malevolent once he had selected his strategy and as if she would choose a state of nature that would always minimize his payoff. Wald suggested that the decision-maker should select his strategy so that he would get as large a payoff as he could under the circumstances. Let us consider our example in these terms. If the investor selects $S1$, what is the worst that can happen? Clearly, the worst is that a depression should occur in which case his payoff would be —6. Suppose he selected $S2$. The worst that could happen would again be if a depression occurred, in which case he would have a payoff of 0. If he selected $S3$, however, he will always get a payoff of 4, no matter what state of nature occurred. In other words, the worst that could happen to him in this case would be a payoff of 4. We can arrange these conclusions thus:

STRATEGY	WORST, OR MINIMUM, PAYOFF
1	—6
2	0
3	4

Following Wald's suggestion the best that the investor can do, assuming that Nature will always be malevolent, is to select that strategy which has the largest such minimum payoff—the maximum minimum or maximin. The largest such payoff here, the maximin payoff, is 4, which the investor will get if he selects strategy 3 and invests his money in bonds. In this particular case the investor will always get 4 from strategy 3, but that just happens by chance in the example we are using. In the general case the use of the maximin criterion will guarantee the decision-maker at least as large a payoff as the maximin payoff—and sometimes a larger payoff will result. This, then, is the Wald maximin criterion and it dictates the selection of strategy 3—investing in bonds.

54. CRITERION OF OPTIMISM

Hurwicz * suggested a variant of this criterion. He asks, essentially, why always assume that Nature will be malevolent? After all, we sometimes get good breaks. Suppose an optimistic decision-maker felt "lucky"

---

* Hurwicz, Leonid, *Optimality Criteria for Decision Making under Ignorance,* Cowles Commission discussion paper, STATISTICS, No. 370, 1951 (mimeographed); cited in Luce, R. D. and Howard Raiffa, *Games and Decisions,* John Wiley & Sons, 1957.

about his chances of having a good state of nature. How might he be rational about it? Let us first assume that the decision-maker is a complete optimist—the exact opposite to the Wald decision-maker. This one always assumes that Nature will kindly select that state of nature which will yield him the highest possible payoff for the strategy which he has selected. How would he proceed? Obviously, he would look at the various payoffs for each strategy and select the largest payoff for each strategy. In our case he would find:

STRATEGY	BEST, OR MAXIMUM, PAYOFF
1	20
2	9
3	4

And, since he thinks Nature will give him the largest payoff, he will naturally select that strategy with the largest such maximum, the maximum maximum, or abbreviated, the *maximax*. In this case the maximax is the payoff of 20 which he will receive if he selects his first strategy and war occurs.

Now, Hurwicz didn't suggest that a rational decision-maker should be completely optimistic. But he did suggest that if a decision-maker felt "lucky" or optimistic he should be able to be rational about it. For this purpose he introduced the idea of a *coefficient of optimism*. As we have seen, the complete optimist takes account only of the largest payoff for each strategy. The coefficient of optimism is a means by which the decision-maker can take account of both the largest and the smallest payoffs—and weight their importance to his decision in accordance with his own feeling of optimism. The coefficient of optimism is defined in terms of a lottery between the largest and smallest payoffs. In other words, the decision-maker assigns to the maximum payoff a probability which he would be willing to accept in a lottery between that maximum payoff and the minimum payoff. This probability is his coefficient of optimism. Suppose, for example, that our decision-maker had a coefficient of optimism of $\frac{3}{5}$. This means that he would be satisfied to accept a lottery in which the maximum payoff had a probability of occurrence of $\frac{3}{5}$ and the minimum payoff had a probability of occurrence of $\frac{2}{5}$. Now, by Hurwicz' criterion we must determine the expected payoff of each strategy, assuming that either the maximum or the minimum will occur and with the indicated probabilities. The calculations are straightforward:

STRATEGY	MAXIMUM PAYOFF	MINIMUM PAYOFF	EXPECTED PAYOFF
1	20	−6	$20(0.6) + (-6)(0.4) = 9.6$
2	9	0	$9(0.6) + 0(0.4) = 5.4$
3	4	4	$4(0.6) + 4(0.4) = 4.0$

By the Hurwicz criterion the decision-maker should select his first strategy—he should invest in speculative stocks.

It may be noted that a coefficient of optimism of 1 leads to the procedure of the complete optimist which we described above. Similarly, a coefficient of optimism of 0 leads to the Wald criterion—that of the complete pessimist. Suppose the decision-maker doesn't know his coefficient of optimism. Is there any way to determine what it is? Luce and Raiffa suggest one way.* Consider the following simple decision payoff matrix which is obtained from the original one by converting the payoffs to the 0–1 utility scale:

	$N1$ War	$N3$ Depression
$S1$: Speculative stocks	1	0
$S4$:	x	x

It should be noted that the new strategy $S4$ has been chosen so that the payoff will be the same no matter which state of nature occurs. For example, in the present case it might be the strategy of leaving the money in the savings bank rather than investing. The other strategy contains only the maximum and minimum payoffs in the original payoff matrix. Suppose, now, that the decision-maker has a coefficient of optimism of k (an unknown which remains to be determined; we know only that, by definition, it must be between 0 and 1). With k as coefficient of optimism the decision-maker would calculate the expected values of the two strategies as before. In this case they are

Strategy	Expected payoff
1	k
2	x

Now, for what value of x in the original payoff matrix would the decision-maker be indifferent between the two strategies? Note that this is really the standard-gamble technique again. Suppose the decision-maker is indifferent between $S1$ and $S4$ if x has the value $\frac{1}{4}$. This means that the expected payoffs, in the Hurwicz sense, must be equal at $x = \frac{1}{4}$, or else the decision-maker wouldn't be indifferent. We conclude, then, that for the decision-maker the coefficient of optimism, k, must be $\frac{1}{4}$.

55. CRITERION OF REGRET

A completely different criterion was suggested by Savage.† Savage points out that after the decision has been made and the state of nature

---

* Luce and Raiffa, *Games and Decisions*, p. 283.

† Savage, L. J., *The Theory of Statistical Decision*, Journal of the American Statistical Association, 46, 55–67, 1951.

has occurred the decision-maker receives the given payoff. Savage argues that at this point the decision-maker may experience regret because, now that he knows what state of nature occurred, he wishes he had selected a different strategy. Savage maintains that the decision-maker should attempt to minimize the regret which he may experience. Exactly what is his regret? It appears to be the fact that he may not have selected the best strategy in terms of the particular state of nature that did, in fact, occur. Savage suggests that the amount of his regret might be measured by the difference between the payoff he actually received and the payoff he could have received if he had known the state of nature that was going to occur.

Thus, in our example, suppose war actually occurred. If the investor had selected his first strategy, he would experience no regret because he got the largest payoff possible. But if he had selected his second strategy he would have lost $20 - 9 = 11$ which he might have had. This measures his regret. If he had selected his third strategy he would experience regret of $20 - 4 = 16$. Now, suppose peace occurred. If the investor had selected his second strategy he would experience no regret because he would have obtained the largest possible payoff. But if he had selected his first strategy he would experience regret of $8 - 1 = 7$. And if he had chosen his third strategy he would experience regret of $8 - 4 = 4$. And if a depression actually occurred, the investor would experience no regret if he had selected his third strategy because it would have given him the largest possible payoff. If he had selected the first strategy, however, he would experience regret of $4 - (-6) = 10$. And the selection of the second strategy in this case would give him regret of $4 - 0 = 4$. All of these measures can be conveniently presented in a matrix called the *regret matrix:*

	$N1$	$N2$	$N3$
$S1$:	0	7	10
$S2$:	11	0	4
$S3$:	16	4	0

Savage proposes to use as the decision criterion a straightforward, minor variant of the Wald criterion—applied to this regret matrix. In other words, he, too, chooses to be completely pessimistic about the state of nature that will occur—it will always be against the decision-maker's best interests. The variant is required because the regret matrix measures regret, which we want to make as small as possible, whereas the original matrix represented payoffs, which we want to make as large as possible. But the difference is only minor. We ask the same first question: What is the worst that can happen to the decision-maker if he selects each strategy? When we discussed the Wald criterion the answer to this question was the minimum payoff in each strategy. Here it is the maximum regret in the regret-matrix row corresponding to the strategy. We quickly obtain:

Strategy	Worst, or maximum, regret
1	10
2	11
3	16

The decision-maker, according to Savage, should insure himself against experiencing extreme regrets by selecting the strategy that has the minimum such maximum, the *minimax*. In this case the minimax regret is 10, which is the maximum regret the decision-maker will experience if he selects his first strategy which is to invest in speculative stocks. Of course, he may well experience less regret than this, but this is the most regret he can possibly experience.

56. CRITERION OF RATIONALITY

All of these criteria have been of relatively recent suggestion. But the last one we shall discuss can be traced back in one form or another for about 2500 years. For many years it has been subject to impassioned debate which continues to the present day. This criterion is called the *Laplace criterion* and it is simple enough to state. Since we don't know the probabilities with which the various states of nature will occur we will assume that they are all equal. In other words, we assume that every state of nature is equally likely to occur. Then we calculate the expected payoff for each strategy and select that strategy which has the largest expected payoff. That is, where there are n states of nature:

$$ES = P_1\frac{1}{n} + P_2\frac{1}{n} + \ldots + P_n\frac{1}{n}$$

$$= \frac{1}{n}(P_1 + P_2 + \ldots P_n)$$

Now, this is straightforward enough. Why all the argument about it? One of the main reasons for argument is the fact that the assumption of equal probabilities involves a famous principle called the *principle of insufficient reason*. The gist of this principle is that if there is no reason for a thing to happen, then it won't happen. The relationship of the principle of insufficient reason to the problem at hand is direct. Since we know of no reason for one state of nature to occur rather than another, we assume that one is as likely to occur as another. The principle when used in this way in connection with probabilities is associated with the name of Bayes. He enunciated the famous Bayes' hypothesis to the effect that when we know of no reason for probabilities to be different we should assume them equal. But the principle has other uses in probability theory as well, and all of them violently debated. For example, how do we know that a fair coin has a probability of ½ of showing heads when it is tossed? One answer is that we know it because of the principle of insufficient reason. There is no conceivable reason why the coin should come up one way rather than another so the probabilities must be equal, hence ½, since there are only two possibilities. Many probabilists reject this argument completely and state that the only reason we think the probability of a head is ½ is the fact that we observe it come up about half the time.

One of the best-known arguments of the Middle Ages had to do with this principle of insufficient reason. Jean Buridan, in the first half of the fourteenth century, invented an imaginary ass—known ever since as Buridan's Ass. This ass was supposed to be placed exactly in the middle between two identical bales of hay. Buridan maintained that the ass must starve to death because it would have no reason to go to one bale of hay rather than another—an interesting application of the principle. Another famous ancient use of the principle was with regard to the position of the earth in space. This argument ran to the effect that the earth couldn't be just any place in space because, if this were the case, God would have had no reason to put it one place rather than another. Therefore, He would never have put it anywhere. Starting from here they proceeded to prove that the earth must be at the center of the universe. Such uses of the principle as this sufficed to bring it into considerable disrepute. Nonetheless, the principle, if used with caution, appears to be as legitimate as many other basic principles which underlie our efforts to understand the nature of reality.

In any event, the application of this criterion is simple. Since there are three states of nature in our example we assume that the probability of occurrence of each of them is ⅓. On this basis we can easily calculate the expected payoff for each strategy:

Strategy	Expected payoff
1	$\frac{1}{3}[20 + 1 + (-6)] = 5$
2	$\frac{1}{3}(9 + 8 + 0) = 5.67$
3	$\frac{1}{3}(4 + 4 + 4) = 4$

Since the largest expected payoff is that of strategy 2, this is the strategy which should be selected according to the Laplace criterion.

Other decision criteria have been suggested but these four are the best-known ones. It is interesting to note that every strategy in our example has been selected by one of the criteria. Strategy 1 (speculative stocks) was selected by the Savage criterion and by the Hurwicz criterion with coefficient of optimism of $3/5$. Strategy 2 (high-grade stocks) was selected by the Laplace criterion. And strategy 3 was selected by the Wald criterion. The selection of the decision criterion is obviously of crucial importance. So it must be emphasized that there is no best criterion. The choice of criterion must be left to the decision-maker and is determined by his own attitude or by company policy.

A question might be raised at this point: If decision theory is so good, why can't the problem of the decision criterion to be used be formulated as a decision problem and solved using decision theory? In other words, why not assume that the decision-maker has four available strategies (the four criteria discussed above), determine the possible states of nature, the objective, the payoff, and establish the payoff matrix. Then the use of decision theory should lead to a selection of a strategy— which would be the decision criterion to be used for decision problems.

This question involves us with the mirror problem of how to decide how to decide which was previously discussed in Chapter 2. Although we cannot completely unravel this knotty problem, there are several important aspects which will be worthwhile considering. To begin with, how can we formulate this objective which is one step removed from our previous objective, which was to maximize the rate of return on our investment? Of course, we still want to maximize the return but we want something else in addition. In the investment example, all three strategies, under different criteria, held promise of maximizing our return. This seems like nonsense until we recognize the fact that uncertainty cannot be compromised. Our problem in rendering decisions under uncertainty is to do it in such a way that our attitudes and state of mind are not jeopardized. Consequently, the formulation of our new objective must include consideration of personality, attitudes, and way of life. Our strategies can be written down as the four decision criteria. The states of nature in this case become the range of values which the payoff measure (rate of return) could assume. For simplicity we can call them: win, lose, and draw. The new payoff measure must be some index of the change that will occur in our state of mind for any combination of strategy and state of nature. Let's see then what we have.

We must first characterize the individuals who would use the different decision criteria. We can call them: cautious, adventurous, bad loser, and rational. There are, of course, many other types of decision-makers and all shades between them. In this characterization we are taking some obvious liberties for the purpose of emphasizing the point. The four different kinds of decision-makers would now proceed to fill in the payoff measures for the matrix below.

	Win	Draw	Lose
Wald:			
Hurwicz:			
Savage:			
Laplace:			

Now, we can readily imagine that all four types of people will put different payoff measures into this matrix. For example, an adventurous person if he decides to act cautiously and he loses will be much more unhappy than if he had lost taking a sizable risk. The exact reverse will be true of the cautious person. The question now arises, assuming that we have such a payoff matrix filled in, how do we determine the probabilities of win, draw, and lose? Since they exist under uncertainty, we must choose a decision criterion (Wald, Hurwicz, Savage, or Laplace?), and we are back to the same problem with which we started. If we choose, we can pass on to the next mirror reflection. On the other hand, the adventurous person is likely to say: "I'm counting on luck," and he will rate win as more probable. The cautious person will say: "I can't count on luck," and he will lower the probability of win.

There is another way of looking at this problem. We will discard the possibility that there is such a thing as attitude. We shall use the Laplace criterion and introduce small changes into the assumption of equal probabilities. In other words, we are going to presume that we are not completely uncertain and that one of the states of nature is just a little more likely than any other state of nature. It will be recognized that if we make small changes in all of the probabilities of the states of nature we are no longer making decisions under uncertainty. We are now deciding under risk. Since the changes that we have made are small, the formulation is almost identical with the Laplace criterion. At some point, as we add little increments to the probability of one particular state of nature, while taking away an equivalent amount from the other probabilities, the strategy chosen by the Laplace criterion will be replaced by another strategy which has a larger expected value for the payoff.

For example, the Laplace selection of strategy 2 in the investment problem shifts to the selection of strategy 1 when the first state of nature (war) goes from 0.33 probability to 0.37. (The other two states of nature go from 0.33 to 0.31.) On the other hand, the probability of depression must increase from 0.33 to 0.53 for strategy 2 to shift to strategy 3 (while war and peace go from 0.33 to 0.23). Now, one possible way to interpret this is to say that if strategy 1 is chosen by a particular criterion—except the Laplace—that criterion was chosen because the decision-maker had more knowledge than he was aware he had. That is why he chose a criterion other than the Laplace. In fact, he believed that war was more likely than peace or depression by an amount of 0.04. Similarly, if the decision-maker's criterion selected strategy 3 then we infer that the decision-maker had reason to believe that a depression would occur and that he had as much as 0.20 additional belief in this outcome. This approach is based on the question: How unbalanced must the uncertainties be before we stop calling them uncertainties? Since if we knew the probabilities of the states of nature we would use expected values, the Laplace criterion is the only one that expresses no attitude except the desire to be rational. That is, if we say we don't know the probabilities then we must act as if we don't know the probabilities. That is why we characterize the Laplace criterion as rational. Therefore, the following observations about the attitude of the decision-maker seem relevant to the selection of the decision criterion.

1. States of nature may be equiprobable but it is unlikely that the individual has the chances of their occurring equally weighted in his mind.

2. It is possible that if you choose a criterion other than Laplace it is because you favor the probability that one or another state of nature will prevail. In any case, when it seems desirable, the Laplace criterion can permit the individual to think of the states of nature in equiprobable terms.

57. TYPES OF DECISION SITUATIONS AND GAMES

All of this discussion has been in terms of decisions (or games) against nature. What happens when rational opponents are involved? This part of decision theory is more usually known as *game theory* and is a complex, highly developed body of knowledge. The basic presupposition of decisions involving only states of nature (sometimes called *games against nature*) is that the state of nature which occurs will be independent of the specific strategy selected by the decision-maker. This is no longer true when the decision involves a rational opponent. On the contrary, it will usually be the case that the rational opponent will give careful thought to what he expects the decision-maker to do before he selects his own strategy. The essence of the game kind of decision theory is the conflict of interests between the opponents. Since they are all assumed to be rational it follows that they will be attempting to frustrate their opponents' wishes.

Games are customarily classified according to the number of opponents and according to the degree of conflict of interest. The theory of games with only two opponents, being the simplest (but not simple!), is the most thoroughly developed. We shall confine our attention to this kind of game. Games that have complete conflict of interest are ones in which what one opponent gains, the other loses. These are called zero-sum games. The nearest approximation to this kind of game in the business world would be a competitive battle for share of the market. It is certainly true that one competitor can only increase his *share* of the market at the expense of his competitors. Most of the games we play for recreation are of this completely competitive type. Games with less than complete conflict of interest are called nonzero-sum games. The majority of business-decision problems involving rational opponents are undoubtedly of this type. An example would be a competitive battle for sales. Here the *size* of the market is involved. An advertising campaign might result in an increased share of the market but it could also benefit the other competitors because of the tendency of advertising to stimulate sales for the product as well as for the brand. In other words, the gain of one competitor in terms of sales volume is not necessarily completely at the expense of the other competitors. The theory of these nonzero-sum games is a fascinating one but we will not discuss it here. Instead, we will simply see what effect a decision problem against a rational opponent in a zero-sum game has on the decision criterion.

Our concern is with competitive actions on the part of the opponent rather than with states of nature. So, instead of the N's we have been using we will use C's to represent the various possible competitive actions. Since what one competitor wins, another loses, in a zero-sum game, we can use one payoff matrix as before to represent the decision problem. (Note that we could not do this for a nonzero-sum game. In order to analyze nonzero-sum games we need a separate payoff matrix for each opponent.) Let us take as an example a decision problem involving a struggle for the share of the market against one opponent. Let us suppose that the decision-maker has available three strategies and his competitor has four (there is no need for them to have the same number of available strategies). Let the payoff matrix be given in terms of the percentage-points increase in market share accruing to the decision-maker:

	$C1$	$C2$	$C3$	$C4$
$S1$:	0.6	−0.3	1.5	−1.1
$S2$:	0.7	0.1	0.9	0.5
$S3$:	−0.3	0.0	−0.5	0.8

This payoff matrix is read in exactly the same way as the earlier ones. If the decision-maker selects his first strategy and his opponent selects his third strategy then the decision-maker will increase his share of the market by 1.5 percentage points. And, of course, since this is a zero-sum game, the competitor will lose 1.5 percentage points of the market. Negative entries represent losses to the decision-maker and gains to the competitor. Now, the question is: How should the decision-maker select his strategy? But the difference from the cases where there was no rational opponent is that now, in reaching our decision, we must take into account what the opponent is likely to do.

It might appear that this would greatly increase the complexity of our decision process and require some new kind of decision criterion. Actually, that isn't the case. In this kind of game it can be shown that the *only* rational decision criterion is the Wald criterion. Let us go through the reasoning to determine the strategy to be selected by using this criterion and then attempt to justify our statement that it is the only rational criterion. The decision-maker reasons, according to the Wald criterion, that if he selects $S1$ he might lose as much as 1.1 (if his opponent selects $C4$). If he selects $S2$ he cannot do worse than to gain 0.1 (if his opponent selects $C2$). If the decision-maker selects his $S3$ he may lose 0.5 (if his opponent chooses $C3$). Thus, for the decision-maker:

STRATEGY	MINIMUM PAYOFF
$S1$	−1.1
$S2$	0.1
$S3$	−0.5

Following the Wald criterion we now select the maximum of these minimum payoffs, the maximin. In this case it is 0.1, which results from selecting $S2$—which should therefore be the choice.

But, remember, the opponent is rational. What is he thinking? Suppose he, too, elects to use the Wald criterion. From his standpoint the worst that can happen if he selects $C1$ is that he will lose 0.7 (the maximum value in the column since the payoffs are in terms of his opponent). If he selects $C2$ the worst that can happen is that he should lose 0.1 (if his opponent selects $S2$). Proceeding similarly we obtain:

COMPETITOR'S ACTION	MAXIMUM LOSS
$C1$	0.7
$C2$	0.1
$C3$	1.5
$C4$	0.8

Following the Wald criterion, the competitor will want to minimize his maximum loss, the minimax value. This minimax value is 0.1, achieved by selecting $C2$. This, then, should be his choice. Thus, the best decisions on the part of the two competitors are that the decision-maker should select $S2$, his competitor should select $C2$, and the result will be an increase of 0.1 percentage points in market share to the decision-maker.

Why can we say that this is the only rational approach to such a competitive decision problem? Consider the situation from the standpoint of the decision-maker. He knows that his opponent could minimize his maximum loss by selecting $C2$. Suppose he did this. Then if the decision-maker selected any other strategy but his $S2$ he would do worse than he would by selecting $S2$. If he selected $S1$ he would lose 0.3 instead of winning 0.1. If he selected $S3$ he would gain nothing instead of gaining 0.1. Similarly, the competitor knows that the decision-maker can maximize his minimum gain by selecting $S2$. But if he does so the opponent does best by selecting his $C2$. If he does anything else he loses more. Thus, granted the complete conflict of interest, the opponents are driven to use the Wald criterion. Of course, if the decision-maker knows that his competitor will not use $C2$, or if he has any other pertinent information about what his competitor will do—other than what is expected of him—he will establish probabilities for the competitive strategies. From these, he can determine his own optimum strategy on the basis of decision-making under risk. In such an event, the information he has obtained has measurable utility. It will permit him to realize a greater payoff than he could otherwise expect. On the other hand, if he is unsure of his information he can continue to use his maximin strategy and gain the advantage which must come to him if his competitor does not act in an entirely rational manner.

It may be noted that in this payoff matrix the maximin value for the decision-maker equalled the minimax value for his opponent—both of them being 0.1. This is by no means always the case. When the two values are different it develops that the use of mixed strategies—where the specific strategy to be used is selected randomly with a determined probability—will make them equal. The proof of this fact is called the *fundamental theorem* of game theory. We shall not discuss this possibility here since it does not have any effect on the point that the introduction of a rational opponent can simplify the decision problem.

One remark about nonzero-sum games may be made. An example of how a nonzero-sum game could arise in business was given above. However, a far more common reason for competitive situations in business being nonzero-sum games is that the utilities of the competitors for the different outcomes are not the same. In this event, it is clear that the game cannot be zero-sum. Since utilities are, by definition, subjective, it may well be that the opponents do not know the utilities of their competitors for the various outcomes. As a matter of fact, one might expect that this would be the usual case. Of course, since businesses often have some degree of similarity in goals we would expect that the opponents would have some idea of the opposition's utility for the various outcomes. However, if a decision problem arose in which the decision-maker really had no idea about the utility his opponent ascribed to the outcomes, then the decision problem would be the same as decision under uncertainty. This results because, not knowing the utilities of his opponent for the outcomes, the decision-maker has no way of knowing anything about the probabilities of the different competitive actions—which is the definition of decision-making under uncertainty.

In terms of actual business conditions, which decision problems are most likely to arise? It is clear that a large number of decision problems of business are of one of the three kinds of decision-making against states of nature. So the usefulness of this part of our analysis is evident. But what about rational opponents? According to the classical conditions of free enterprise any decision problem is simply against nature because, by the definition of these conditions, no one business can have any effect on market conditions through any strategy which it might elect to follow. On the other hand, wherever free-enterprise conditions do not exist in a specific market we must include the competitive actions as part of the decision problem. In short, under oligopolistic conditions in a particular market it is necessary to include competitive actions in the payoff matrix. Many problems of a monopoly can be construed as games against a rational opponent. In this case, they are the suppliers and consumers. Generally, small organizations that deal in a large market place can ignore the effects of a rational opponent. This puts them in the position of deciding under conditions of risk or uncertainty. As the size of the company increases with respect to the market, the influence of rational opponents is felt. As a rule, a particular management can evaluate its situation with respect to the importance of competition.

PROBLEMS

1. A drugstore chain has six stores. A new company policy is established which, in effect, will reassign the present six store managers to the stores in such a way as to minimize the total traveling time of the managers from home to store. How many possible arrangements (strategies) are there? Why is this decision-making under certainty?

2. A department store has four different strategies for obtaining advance information about the line of merchandise which their chief competitor will carry in the next season. The amount of information that can be obtained will depend on whether or not the competitor is aware that the department store is trying to get this information. Assume the following payoff matrix:

	$N1$	$N2$
$S1$:	-4	10
$S2$:	2	2
$S3$:	3	0
$S4$:	-1	6

where $N1 =$ competitor is aware,

$N2 =$ competitor isn't aware,

payoff measures are the utility of information obtained, and
negative values represent misinformation.

a. If the competitor is aware (state of nature $N1$), what strategy should be chosen?

b. If the competitor is not aware (state of nature $N2$), what strategy should be chosen?

c. Assume that the probabilities are 0.90 for $N1$ and 0.10 for $N2$. What choice should be made?

d. What would be the maximin choice?

e. What would be the maximax choice?

f. Assume a coefficient of optimism of 0.70. Which strategy will be chosen? Now, assume a coefficient of pessimism of 0.70. Does the choice of strategy change?

g. What would be the result if we took the minimax of regret?

h. What would be the result if we use the principle of insufficient reason?

3. Assume that the boxes of a tic-tac-toe game are numbered 1–9. How many possible combinations of the numbers (strategies) are available to the player who begins the game? How many are available to the second player? How many boxes are there in the payoff matrix? Ignoring the numbers of the boxes, how many basically different opening moves are there? How many basically different second moves are there? How large would the payoff matrix be for the first two moves?

4. Instead of tic-tac-toe boxes, consider each number to represent a sales area. Assume that whichever company gets to an area first wins that area. Each company has only one salesman. The salesman must spend one day in each area in order to win it for his company. Say that every move of one box along a row or column takes one day traveling time. Every move of one box along a diagonal takes two days traveling time. Can you devise a game to fit these rules? What would be each player's objective?

5. You are working as a consultant in a foreign country where the exchange rate is 100 units of the foreign currency for $1. You will be there for five months and your expenses are fixed in units of the foreign currency at 50,000 units per month. A sky-rocketing inflation is temporarily in check while the government is attempting to negotiate a large loan. If the government gets the loan the effect will be to lower the exchange rate by 10 per cent. If the loan is refused the exchange rate will increase by 20 per cent. In addition, a gen-

eral strike has been called. If this strike is successful the government will be forced to take some economic measures which will increase the exchange rate by 15 per cent. If the strike fails the rate will decrease by 10 per cent. It can be assumed that the two events in question (loan and strike) are independent. Thus there are four states of nature:

N1: Loan, strike fails; rate drops to 81.0
N2: Loan, strike succeeds, rate increases to 103.5
N3: No loan, strike fails, rate increases to 108.0
N4: No loan, strike succeeds, rate increases to 138.0

For our purposes it will be sufficient to consider three strategies

S1: Immediately convert enough dollars into foreign units to meet all five months' expenses.
S2: Wait until the events above have occurred, meanwhile holding dollars.
S3: Hedge by converting half the amount now and holding half in dollars.

Your objective will be to minimize your dollar expenses.

a. Determine the payoff matrix in dollars of expense.

b. What is the minimax strategy?

c. What is the optimal strategy if the coefficient of optimism is 0.6?

d. What is the optimal strategy by the criterion of minimization of regret?

e. What is the optimal strategy by the Laplace criterion?

f. Suppose it is known that the probability that the government will receive the loan is 0.75 and the probability that the strike will succeed is 0.4. What is the optimal strategy?

g. Suppose the probability of receiving the loan is designated "p" and the probability that the strike will succeed is designated "r." What is the best way to hedge? In other words, can you find a different hedging strategy which is better?

PART 2

OPERATIONS RESEARCH AND DECISIONS

Chapter six

Applied Decision Theory

Let us presume that the executive has been convinced by the preceding five chapters and that he is now prepared to put decision theory to the test of practice. He is certainly aware that many problems will stand in his way. The total effect of these difficulties in applying decision theory would be sufficient to eliminate many, if not most, important applications if the executive were left to his own resources. Fortunately, however, he has available some means to help him cope with these difficulties. Operations research (O.R.) is the major tool that acts in the executive's behalf in this regard. And it is our thesis that when it is considered in this way—as an adjunct to the applications of decision theory—that operations research can best be understood.

58. DEFINITION OF OPERATIONS RESEARCH

What, then, is operations research? In common with many other fields, it is easy to point to but hard to define. That it originated during World War II in the form of attempts by various kinds of scientists to solve military problems, often totally unconnected in substance with the specialties of the scientists, is generally known. That it was extended to business applications after the war and has become a burgeoning field with consultants, professional societies, journals, courses and departments in colleges and universities, and a steadily growing number of practitioners is also beyond question. But there is, as yet, no generally accepted definition of what operations research is.

There are three main categories of definitions. First, many definitions are variants or elaborations of the definition proposed by Morse and Kimball:*

Operations research is a scientific method of providing executive departments with a quantitative basis for decisions regarding the operations under their control.

Any practitioner will recognize that much of his work does fall within the compass of this description; nonetheless, it is still not a suitable definition. Replace operations research in the definition by cost accounting and it holds equally well. Or, replace O.R. by control charts and the definition still holds. In other words, the definition does not distinguish O.R. from a number of other approaches to business problems, some of which have been in use for a much longer time than O.R. A definition that does not distinguish one field from related or different fields cannot be considered to be satisfactory.

A second approach to the problem of defining O.R. is to list the various techniques that have come to be associated with it. So, many presentations of the subject proceed by discussing seriatim such things as queuing theory, inventory theory, linear programming, Monte Carlo, search theory, and so on. It is certainly true that operations research does often utilize these techniques, but to define O.R. in terms of them is a mistake. It would be like defining medicine in terms of the collection of drugs which doctors use to cure their patients. It is obviously ridiculous in the latter case, and equally so in the former. If there is no more unity to operations research than the latest hodge-podge of techniques that can be culled from the literature there is no particular merit in giving it a name.

A third approach was whimsically suggested by the same Morse who collaborated on the first definition, given above. This is to the effect that O.R. is what O.R. practitioners do. And this definition has the undoubted merit of being completely correct. But, of course, it suffers from the equally undoubted demerit of being completely uninformative. We cannot use it to meaningfully define O.R. for persons unfamiliar with the field.

The approach that this book takes is that *O.R. is applied decision theory.* Operations research uses any scientific, mathematical, or logical means to attempt to cope with the problems that confront the executive when he tries to achieve a thoroughgoing rationality in dealing with his decision problems. Therefore, let us now examine, in a general way, the contributions that O.R. can make to the resolution of decision problems.

* Philip M. Morse and George E. Kimball, *Methods of Operations Research* (New York: John Wiley & Sons, Inc., 1951), p. 1.

59. O.R. APPLICATIONS TO DECISION THEORY

To begin with, there is a problem in formulating objectives. Multiple objectives, conflicts between objectives, and suboptimization are some of the reasons for the difficulties that have been previously discussed. However, there are a considerable number of decision situations for which these complications are not crucial. Basically, the identification and choice of objectives is an executive function. Operations research can provide some stimulation and guidance, but there is no way of replacing the executive responsibility for objectives.

Given an objective, it is not always easy to discover the appropriate measure of utility. We have treated this matter at some length in Chapter 4. At that point, a number of possibilities were examined including logarithms as utility for payoffs with a natural measure, and ranking and the standard gamble for payoffs that lack a natural measure. Problems of measurement concern every field of scientific endeavor. Operations research is no exception. As needed, methods are developed or borrowed for the observation and measurement of meaningful payoffs. The discussion in Chapter 4 gives some idea of how this is done.

60. USING O.R. TO DISCOVER STRATEGIES AND STATES OF NATURE

The discovery and enumeration of strategies, states of nature, and competitive strategies requires experience and imagination on the part of both the decision-maker and the O.R. practitioner. In the section on maximization principles in Chapter 2, the second of nine points stated that all variables should be isolated that are pertinent to the attainment of the objective. These variables are the components that when taken together form strategies, states of nature, and competitive strategies. What happens, then, when the variables that determine the outcome are not known? What can operations research methods do? Actually, a great deal.

The O.R. contribution in this direction has been so considerable that for a long time this particular aspect of O.R. was often identified with O.R. itself. Though the identification is erroneous, it does indicate the success O.R. methods have achieved in this area. Simply put, the O.R. practitioner, faced with such a problem, endeavors to discover the relevant factors by analogy with problems in totally different areas—those of any one of the sciences, for example. This approach demands wide experience in different fields and the ability to think creatively. But one main point that underlies many successes in this area may be noted

—namely, these analogies often stem from a similarity of verbs. For example, consider "search." A personnel department searches for new employees, an advertising campaign searches for new customers, a plane searches for a submarine, a scientist searches for the true hypothesis. Success in determining the relevant variables and relationships in any one of these areas could be extended to the others, with suitable translation of terms. For that matter, the verb "decide" is another good example. We have been discussing "decide" in great depth without requiring the specific details of any one situation. Other examples are "allocate," "replace," and "store." It is by finding such key verbs as these that the practitioner may be led to a suitable, and already developed, analogy in another field. However, many times the methods of discovery combined with the knowledge derived from experience produce too many possibilities for the mind to comprehend.

61. USING O.R. TO HANDLE EXCESSIVE NUMBERS OF STRATEGIES AND STATES OF NATURE

A decision concerning inventory level might include all the possibilities between stockpiling several years' supply of some raw material down to operating on an order-as-you-go basis, with virtually no inventory on hand. Many thousands of possible strategies might be required to represent this situation. Again, the complex decision of allocation of company resources can easily require an astronomical number of strategies in order to include all of the possibilities. And we have noted earlier a machine-shop problem, apparently of no great complexity, which involved 2.5 quintillion strategies. It is evident that no sane executive is going to seriously consider writing out a payoff matrix involving hundreds of thousands of rows—no matter how enthusiastic he may be about decision theory.

In the same way, the decision-maker will often find that the number of possible states of nature is prohibitively enormous. For example, the states of nature relevant to a particular decision problem might include ten different levels of gross national product, ten kinds of weather conditions, ten different situations regarding the interest rate and the availability of credit, twenty different competitive strategies, five different international situations, and ten possible levels of demand. This is not unreasonably exorbitant but it already adds up to 1,000,000 ($10 \times 10 \times 10 \times 20 \times 5 \times 10$) different states of nature. It is certainly not feasible to write down a payoff matrix with 1,000,000 columns!

How does O.R. help when there are an incredibly huge number of possible strategies and states of nature? Whether the excessive number belongs to strategies or states of nature or both, these difficulties are susceptible to the same treatment—mathematical representation. By using mathematical formulations the enormous number of strategies and/or states of nature can often, but not always, be subsumed under a few equations. When this can be done the number of strategies and states of nature no longer represents a difficulty. The possibilities in this direction have been tremendously enhanced by the development and proliferation of large-scale computers in the past two decades. Such computers can turn out what would formerly have been years of analysis in a few days. Since these computers can solve huge systems of equations it is possible to represent many more decision problems in mathematical form. Before the advent of computers the decision problems could, sometimes, have been equally well represented by equations but they could not have been solved. The computers enable us to solve them.

Of course, a computer must be fed the information it uses. And it must have careful instructions (called a *program*) built into it so that it can perform the appropriate operations on the information. General-purpose computers can be programmed for a variety of problem-solving operations. If a program does not exist for the solution of a particular problem it must be developed, which frequently takes a great deal of time and money. However, as more and more standard programs have been created, it has been possible to modify them for use at much less cost.

The operations a computer can perform are basically quite simple. For example, a computer can search for information that is stored in its memory; it can compare two numbers and accept or reject the larger or the smaller number; it can combine two numbers and thus perform addition, and so on. Computer programs are combinations of these simple operations, but the combinations are ingeniously chosen so that the result can yield complex mathematical analysis. Computer programming is, therefore, a translation of the operations-research description of a problem. Thanks to these developments, excessive numbers of strategies and states of nature are no longer so serious a handicap in the resolution of complex decision situations.

62. USING O.R. TO DETERMINE OUTCOMES

The major problem facing the executive who endeavors to use decision theory is the difficulty of determining the outcome. In other words, at the intersection of every strategy (row) and state of nature (column) there is a box. Into this box we insert the appropriate payoff measure. But the payoff measure is not the outcome. It is the executive's utility for the outcome. We have deliberately glossed over this problem in our preceding discussion. We have repeatedly examined—on occasion at some length—the necessity of determining the payoff that will result from a given outcome. We have developed ways by which the executive might quantitatively express his *utility* for the various outcomes, which would be the payoffs for those outcomes. But there is a question which we have never raised: How is the outcome determined?

The word "determined" is slightly ambiguous, and purposely so. In one sense it means: How does the selected strategy interact with the state of nature that occurs to produce a specific outcome? In the other sense it means: How do we find out what that outcome is? The two aspects are, of course, related. Specifically, if we know the first, we can often determine the second. The reader might think we should have said, "We can *always* determine the second." It would appear that if we know the process by which the strategy and the state of nature interact to produce the outcome, then we should certainly be able to determine the outcome. But a difficulty sometimes arises. We do not have the ability to solve the equations that describe the interaction. That is why we must say often instead of always. But even if we don't know the way in which the outcome is produced we may be able to know something about the outcome. This, most typically, is done through analysis of past experience. An example outside the field of business might serve to illustrate these remarks. The meteorologist believes he knows the way various factors work to determine weather. But, unfortunately, he cannot solve the equations describing their interaction—even with modern computing equipment. Nonetheless, he can do a pretty good job of predicting the path of a hurricane, for example, through careful study of past events.

Where the factors that produce an outcome are evident, or are known to the executive, the O.R. practitioner has powerful mathematical tools with which to determine the outcome. In fact, the determination of outcome is an area in which operations research has made a major contribution. Let us look at some simple business decision problems in this context.

Consider an executive in charge of some customer service like toll booths at a bridge, operators at a switchboard, waiters in a restaurant, or anything similar. The executive has the decision problem of determining the number of personnel to have on duty to meet the demand. In decision-theory terms his available strategies will consist of the different numbers of personnel he could assign, and his states of nature will include the various possible levels of demand. Now, whatever the objective may be, how do the given number of personnel in a specific strategy interact with the given level of demand in that state of nature to produce an outcome? What outcome is produced? This problem can be solved but it turns out that the way these two interact is by no means obvious. Some rather surprising results—quite contrary to common sense—emerge. In other words, determining the outcome in this decision situation is the crucial problem. Or consider the example of an executive who must determine the price for a new product. To determine the outcome between a specific price and a given potential demand curve (one of the states of nature) is a question dealt with by economic theory, but it is by no means easy to do empirically. These two decision situations are typical of the large number in which the determination of the outcome is one of the major problems. And even if the relationship cannot be worked out formally, there is still the possibility of using statistical methods for estimating the outcome on the basis of past experience.

As another example, consider a decision problem involving inventory level where the objective is to minimize total cost. As the inventory level is increased, some costs will increase—carrying charges, depreciation costs, loss of interest on capital, and so on. Some costs, however, will decrease as the inventory level is increased—out of stock costs, expediting costs, loss of customer goodwill, and others. For a given level of inventory a higher demand implies a greater risk of loss owing to lost sales, and a lower level of demand implies a greater risk of loss owing to overstock. If the price falls in the future, a larger level of inventory is penalized. If the price rises in the future, then a larger level of inventory is advantageous. These are only some of the factors affecting the cost that is to be minimized. It is evident that it is not a simple and straightforward matter to disentangle all these aspects and their effect on the final cost. Fortunately, in this case O.R. makes use of rather elementary mathematical methods which succeed in determining outcomes with a reasonable expenditure of effort. Many of the decision problems that will be dealt with subsequently in this book will afford demonstration of this aspect of the O.R. contribution.

63. USING O.R. TO SELECT A STRATEGY

Finally, we can assume that the payoff matrix for a large problem has been completed. Of course, it probably would not exist in an expanded form on paper. Rather, it would be condensed by mathematical equations which would represent the payoff measures of all relevant strategies with all possible states of nature. The executive must now apply his selected decision criterion to the mathematical representation of the payoff matrix. The essence of the problem is to be able to search and manipulate—according to the decision criterion—billions, quintillions, decillions, or even more payoff measures. Operations research has methods available for accomplishing this feat under many different circumstances.

In summary, then, O.R. is a necessary adjunct for the executive who wants to utilize decision theory. There are basically four ways in which O.R. provides assistance:

1. By the use of mathematical representation, large numbers of strategic possibilities and states of nature can be handled. Without such representation the limitations imposed by bounded rationality apply.

2. When the executive does not know the important variables, operations-research methods can help him discover them.

3. When the executive does know the important variables but does not know how to relate them to each other, to the outcome, and to the payoff measure, O.R. can many times provide the necessary problem-solving analysis.

4. When the executive cannot possibly search the innumerable payoff measures in order to apply his decision criterion, mathematical methods can frequently be devised to do this for him.

Each of the above points represents model-building under various circumstances and for different purposes. Chapter 7 is devoted to a discussion of qualitative models and Chapter 8 to quantitative models.

PROBLEMS

1. The best way to gain an appreciation of the advantages and difficulties of the use of analogies from other fields in solving business problems is to try and think one's way through some of them. Here is an assortment—with no promise that they are actually useful:

   a. The number of possible relationships between pairs of people increases rapidly with the total number of people. Precisely, if there are N people then there are $N(N - 1)/2$ pairs. Thus, with three people (A, B and C) there are three pairs $(3 \times 2)/2 = 3$): AB, AC, and BC. Does this have any implications in terms of managing or supervising?

   b. As physical bodies grow larger the relationship of surface area to volume changes. As an approximation, volume changes as the 3/2 power of the surface area. For example, when surface area increases 4 times volume will increase $4^{3/2} = 8$ times. This simple fact serves to explain why there are no small warm-blooded animals in the Antarctic or in the ocean and why the largest insect is about as large as the smallest warm-blooded animal. Now, organizations differ widely in size. Does this relationship between surface area and volume tell us anything about organizations?

   c. A complex and interesting mathematical theory has been developed to describe the interaction between an animal predator species and its prey (one or more species) and the resultant fluctuations in numbers of the two or more species. It would appear possible to construct an analogy between this situation and that of customers (the predators) and the one or more brands of some product they wish to buy (the prey). Try to define the important factors in the first case and the corresponding factors, if any, in the second situation.

d. In the text we mentioned some analogies connected with the word "search." Try to define the important factors involved in an airplane searching for an enemy submarine. Find the analogical factors in a personnel department's search for a salesman.

e. Try to define the factors which would be important in analyzing an inventory problem. Are there corresponding factors involved in a problem concerning total plant capacity? Are there analogical factors involved in budgeting for long-range research?

f. A mathematical analysis of a combat between two forces leads to Lanchester's law (see : Lanchester, F. W., "Mathematics in Warfare," in J. R. Newman, *The World of Mathematics*, pp. 2138–2157, Vol. 4, New York: Simon & Schuster, 1956). Let:

N_1 = units of A's force
N_2 = units of B's force
a = hitting power per unit of A
β = hitting power per unit of B

Then by Lanchester's law the forces are equal when

$$aN_1{}^2 = \beta N_2{}^2$$

This means that the strength of a force is directly proportional to hitting power per unit and to the square of the number of units. What applicability does this result have to advertising?

g. A complex mathematical theory has been developed to describe the spread of contagious diseases or epidemics through a host population. The spread of the disease depends on such factors as the number of contacts with infected individuals, the probability of contagion through contact, the length of the period of contagion, immunity characteristics, etc. Can you find analogical characteristics in the spread of word of mouth advertising for a product? Might this mathematical theory be useful in advertising?

2. A toy manufacturer has pricing points as follows: $0.09, $0.19, $0.22, $0.29, $0.34, $0.39, $0.62, $0.74, $0.99, $1.19, $1.59. A product is being marketed for which the relationship of sales volume and sales price is known.

$$n = 2500 - 2000s \qquad (1.0)$$

where n = sales volume per month, and
s = sales price (in dollars) per unit.

The cost and profit functions are also known:

$$c = \frac{450}{n} \qquad (1.1)$$

$$p = n(s - c) \qquad (1.2)$$

where c = cost per unit, and
p = total profit per month.

If the manufacturer holds to his pricing points, how many of his price strategies are profitable? What is his optimum price strategy? Construct the payoff matrix and fill in the values. (Assume that profit is the appropriate measure of utility.)

Note: If Equation (1.0) and Equation (1.1) are solved simultaneously and s is set equal to c, the range of profitable sales prices can be determined. When $s = c$, profit must be zero.

Equation (1.2) can be written entirely in terms of s and p. By methods of calculus, the derivative of this equation when set equal to zero can be solved directly for the s value that yields optimum profit.

This example aims to illustrate how mathematical representation can include a great number of strategies with economy. At the same time, it derives the outcome for the gamut of possible strategies and states of nature. Lastly, the mathematical form provides a means for applying the decision criterion to the entire range of possible payoffs and discovering the optimum value. What decision criterion has been applied? Why is it correct for this case?

Chapter seven

Qualitative Models

A term often used to describe the approach of O.R. to the decision problem is model building. In its original sense, models were physical representations of structures. It was generally understood that the model was related in scale to the object that was being copied. Consequently, the analysis of a model was the analysis of dimensions. At first the dimensions were limited to the physical aspects of the object such as height, width, length, and weight. As time went on, more and more dynamic characteristics were included, such as velocity and acceleration. Newton's Law of Similarity required geometric and dynamic equivalencies between the model and the object. In a sense, models of this sort reached their apex with the development of fluid mechanics. How, then, has this term come to be applied to problems of business? For that matter, the entire range of physical and social sciences are using this phrase. What has happened?

It would appear that thinkers in various fields who are continuing the efforts of their predecessors have suddenly discovered that they are building models. Aside from the areas of study mentioned above, the predecessors had paid little or no attention at all to model building. Now, the discovery of models brings to mind Monsieur Jourdain in Moliere's *Bourgeois Gentilhomme* who found to his amazement that he had been talking prose for more than forty years without knowing it. It isn't that a totally new way of looking at problems, model building, has been discovered. Rather, this term emphasizes an aspect of our attempts to understand reality that has always been present. And since it is a particularly important aspect, the use of this term serves to make the effort explicit and to direct our attention to its relevance in our thinking. The model builders of today accept all dimensions, including such things as time, profit, satisfaction, and so on, as being part of the description of the subject that they are studying. Newton's Law of Similarity cannot serve under these circumstances. In order to understand the requirements of present day models we must attempt to untangle the meaning of model building. And in particular, we must show the connection between model building and decision problems.

What are we attempting to do when we think about, or try to understand, some part of reality? There are many motivations, but the result which is hoped for is that we may somehow be able to describe, explain, or perhaps predict that part of reality. The most evident fact about this process is that we cannot get that part of reality being studied into our heads. The best that we can do is to get a lot of thoughts about it crammed into our brains—the reality stays outside. In other words, our thoughts are abstractions from reality. But they are not abstractions from the totality of that part of reality we are concerned with. We don't have somewhere in our heads a neat little abstract representation of reality that differs from the reality only because it is somewhat ghost-like. We formulate our thoughts in terms of words and concepts that correspond, with considerable fuzziness, to various aspects of reality. From the unlimited complexity of that part of reality which we are trying to understand we select a few aspects, represented by a few concepts. These are the basis upon which we erect our thought structure. So our thinking process is abstractive in two ways: first, the thoughts are an abstraction from reality; and second, the thoughts deal with only a few aspects of the rich complexity of reality.

Before we condemn this thought process, let us note that it is the best we have and that we have done pretty well with it so far. But it does have its dangers. One must make continual efforts to avoid confusing the two: reality and the thoughts about it, or the concepts from which the thoughts are constructed. Philosophers would refer to such confusion as the fallacy of hypostatization—assuming our concepts to be the reality. This polysyllabic mistake is exemplified by the child who said, "It's a good thing they call pigs 'pigs' because they're such dirty animals"—which, besides being an injustice to pigs, is a confusion of concept with reality. A directly relevant form of this mistake arises when we assume that because a specific explanation of some aspect of reality seems to work it is right. This just isn't necessarily so. The explanation may not lie in the handful of concepts we have selected at all but in unconsidered aspects of the reality we are dealing with.

64. DEFINITION OF A MODEL

A model can be defined as a representation of reality that attempts to explain the behavior of some aspect of it. Since a model is an explicit representation of reality it is always less complex than the reality itself, but it has to be sufficiently complete to approximate those aspects of reality which are being investigated. We have just seen that the whole thought process corresponds to this definition—we are continually building models of reality. And this explains why model building is so ubiquitous. One can find it in any organized thought process simply because it is bound to be there owing to the very nature of the thought process. As a matter of fact, we have just been thinking about thinking and, in the process, have constructed a model of thinking. Just as in every other reduction of the complexity of the reality, we can only hope that we have not merely broken the fragile butterfly of thought on the wheel of our abstractions. Here, also, as in every other abstraction, we have drastically oversimplified the complex reality of thinking in the effort to understand some salient aspects of it.

The best definition of a model that we can offer in a simple statement is not satisfactory. There are so many different aspects of models that it is quite clear that no simple statement can expect to capture the essence of model building. At the one extreme, all human effort is based on model building; at the other, scientists and methodologists construct explanations of reality that require highly specialized understanding in order to comprehend their meaning. That is why we will now proceed to examine models from many different points of view. In the process, the full impact of this subject on decision-making should become apparent.

65. MODELS CATEGORIZED BY DEGREE OF ABSTRACTION OF THE REPRESENTATION

We have already pointed out that our abstract conceptualizations of our thinking about reality qualify as legitimate models. These abstract models are based on language, or on its sophisticated variant—mathematics. The language models are obviously the most familiar to all of us because language is our collective basic model of reality. It has many weaknesses which we are able to sense but we cannot express. If we could express them we could modify the language correspondingly. But these weaknesses are continually being corrected as society modifies its means of expression in the historical process of achieving a better correspondence to reality. At the same time, language is changing in the direction of more efficient communication, and the two objectives are not always compatible. This accounts for the specialization of language and the existence of scientific vocabularies. It also explains the development of logic and mathematics and the increased emphasis that progress seems to place upon them.

Now, an important question arises as to why mathematics should be called more abstract than our language of words. There are many possible avenues to follow in explaining this distinction. However, the most immediate reason is that words are chosen to denote a specific class of objects, actions, or qualities. If two things can be called by the same name they must be carefully modified by an adjective to distinguish them. The language of mathematics, on the other hand, treats large classes in an identical fashion. In other words, x can stand for apples, automobiles or automata. There is no reason why we couldn't have the word "x" in our language, but people would be hard pressed to employ it. Although mathematics is more abstract than language, nevertheless language is quite abstract in itself. The word "book" subsumes an enormous number of items. Furthermore, it in no way resembles the object.

At the other extreme there are concrete models. These are the models that gave birth to the term. Many times they look like the thing that they are representing. They are as close to reality as we can get and still enjoy the advantages of manipulation. For example, an engineer will use a small ship in a mercury tank as a model for the behavior of the full-size ship in the ocean. Model planes and wind tunnels serve in the same capacity. One step closer to abstraction are the Tinker-Toy type models used by a chemist to represent a protein molecule. Similarly, an engineer may use an electrical circuit as a model for a complicated hydraulic system.

Between the extreme abstract and the extreme concrete there are a large range of models. Industry uses models that run the full gamut. We can start with the highly abstract models that exist in the research laboratory and end with the very concrete characterization of a process that is used to determine the feasibility of a larger operation—the pilot plant. Business schools use case histories to serve as models for likely future encounters of the student when he has become an executive. Executives abstract the crucial elements of their company in the familiar profit-and-loss model and balance-sheet model.

Generally speaking—and it is not possible to be specific—concrete models have advantages over abstract models for purposes of communication and observation. Abstract models have greater flexibility for both analysis and manipulation. Concrete models are closer to facts while abstract models are nearer to laws and general principles which can be applied over and over again. It is quite clear that these thoughts tie in with the decision-maker's difficulty in handling great numbers of strategies and states of nature. Bounded rationality results from too many detailed, concrete models. They cannot all be put together without some larger abstract model that can contain them.

66. MODELS CAN BE CATEGORIZED BY THEIR DIMENSIONALITY

The abstract-concrete scale is only one of many ways of looking at models. But before we leave it, we must observe that we can differentiate models by the kind of representation that is used. Each of these kinds of representation can be associated with some degree of abstraction. Also, they can be identified by the number and kinds of dimensions from which the model is constructed. Spatial, temporal, and symbolic dimensions can be used to differentiate models from each other. On this basis, models can be grouped together according to the number of each kind of dimensions present.

For example, we have two-dimensional models such as maps, photographs, blueprints, and plant layouts. Maps and charts are constructed in a variety of ways depending upon the purpose for which they are intended. A touring road map shows highways, mileage between cities, points of interest, and so on. Other kinds of maps show elevation, average rainfall, population densities, average temperatures. In the same way, an organization chart is a kind of map which has to be read in a special way. Graphs of production, turnover, cost, and profit can also be viewed in this light. Basically, this class of models is intended to convey information. It is certainly evident that although these models are constructed in terms of two dimensions they contain information about a great many more.

Three-dimensional models include scale prototypes such as ships, planes, bridges, buildings, and automobiles. Generally, scale models are utilized to overcome the expense and difficulty of working with the actual size of the subject. The transformations of scale can be accomplished in both directions, increasing the size of atoms and molecules or decreasing size as in the case of ship or plane models. The results obtained from scale models must be reconvertible to terms that are commensurate with the full-scale subject. Models of planes and ships are seldom built for the sole purpose of looking at them. Usually models are intended to do something. Operating scale models involve an additional dimension —time. This brings us to four-dimensional models which include full spatial liberty and time. There are also three-dimensional models that are restricted in space to a plane surface and that include time, e.g., a motion picture and a radarscope. Furthermore, it is quite obvious that the classification of scale models as three- or four-dimensional overlooks the countless numbers of other dimensions which they are used to study. Some models have so many dimensions that it is not possible to categorize them. They are called n-dimensional models. When the decision-maker is dealing with vast numbers of strategies and states of nature, he is thinking in terms of an n-dimensional model.

As the correspondence between a physical model and the subject becomes more abstract, we stop calling it a scale model and refer to it, instead, as an analog. In fact, when one thing that is being used to represent another stops looking like it, we can be fairly confident of general agreement in calling it an analog model. At the same time, there must be strong correspondence between certain characteristics. Models of planes that are tested in wind tunnels and models of ships that are tested in towing tanks look like planes and ships and so they are on the border line. But certain transformations of either the model or the results must be understood in advance in order to permit a prediction to be made of the behavior of the full-scale subject. A towing-tank model does not have to be an exact replica of the intended ship. Neither does a wind-tunnel model have to include reclining seats or numerals on its wings. Models must correspond in terms of the variables that are relevant to the model criteria and the objectives that led to the construction of the model. For example, the righting angle of a ship (i.e., that angle of roll beyond which the ship will not return upright, but will capsize) is determined by the distribution and height of weights. Similarly, the lift and stalling speed of a plane are not affected by the color scheme of the interior. With respect to functional criteria, many rules and laws of correspondence exist, such as Reynold's number which relates velocity and length with fluid characteristics and Mach's number which applies to compressible flow. It is only in this way that test results derived from a scale model can be applied to the eventual scale of the program.

If scale models and analogs existed only for ships and planes we would have no reason to dwell on them. In fact, there are numerous examples of scale models being used in industry. The operation of a pilot plant is a clear utilization of a reduction in scale to avoid costly mistakes. Many pilot-plant operations have led to important changes in the design of the full-scale plant and sometimes a pilot plant has resulted in the cancellation of the entire program. Another scale model, which is generally not recognized as such, is the test market. Here, too, the model looks like the full-scale subject. The results of the test market must be able to be transformed so they predict the expected results of the over-all market effort. Statistical sampling is still another example. The less than 100 per cent inspection of parts, materials, machine downtime, and so on for certain qualities with respect to specified criteria is generalized by statistical laws to describe the composition of 100 per cent of the parts. The social sciences are replete with scale models and many of these are finding their way into the industrial world. Small experimental communication groups are generalized to production lines, executive decision systems, and research problem-solving in laboratories. Rats in a maze and chimpanzees with complex tasks yield experimental results which are transformed into learning curves and incentive systems.

At this point, we can see that by our definition the organization chart is a two-dimensional analog model. The laws of correspondence are the conventions for reading and interpreting it. However, these laws are vague. They are not defined as clearly as the laws of correspondence for fluid mechanics. Demand curves and frequency distributions are also two-dimensional analogs.

When a model no longer has physical form we call it a symbolic or mathematical model. Frequently, mathematical models are re-interpreted into physical form in order to solve the equations as rapidly as possible. The most striking example is the analog computer which performs the symbolic operations of add, subtract, multiply, and so on by means of physical components such as resistors, potentiometers, gears, levers, and heat conductors—depending on the design of the computer. In particular, there are well-known electronic analogs for hydrodynamic and thermodynamic systems. At the same time, mathematical models of various business situations have been constructed and programmed as analogs on computers. The computer receives information about a particular strategy in the form of an input. It processes this information in order to obtain payoffs for whatever state of nature exists. The choice of a state of nature is based upon the probabilities which can be assigned in some reasonable manner. Of course, the result is not expected to accurately describe the real world. It is more useful in a qualitative sense, since it is possible to try many different strategies and observe the results.

6 / . ANALOG MODELS THAT INCLUDE THE DIMENSION OF TIME

Analog models that contain time as an active dimension are worthy of special attention. Such devices produce an outcome that varies over time depending upon the inputs received. At other times, the output is fed back as a new input. That is, the next move depends upon the last outcome, and the model proceeds in a stepwise fashion to produce a sequence of outputs. These kinds of models belong to a general class which are called *simulation models*. Since time can be speeded up so that an hour of the simulation model represents a year of the company's existence, this class of model has particular significance to business. Fatigue testing, aging experiments, and the like have been used in research laboratories for many years and represent the same kind of contraction of time. However, there would be no need to use simulation models of this sort if mathematical equations that describe the situation could be written and solved. Many times the equations can be written but they cannot be solved. In such cases, the simulation model is built to represent the equations. We will have occasion to discuss simulation models again as we progress. A small part of our discussion will have to do with qualitative simulation models and after that, quantitative simulation models will be examined in more detail. We will now observe that the difference between these two basic types of models (qualitative and quantitative) results from differences in the form of the outcomes.

68. PAYOFF MEASURES AND OUTCOMES MUST BE DIMENSIONALLY SOUND

It is not absolutely necessary that outcomes should be stated in numerical terms. For example, a perfectly legitimate outcome would be that department BCD will improve its productivity when foreman X is transferred. Chapter 8 is distinguished from this present chapter by the fact that it deals with quantitative models, which must yield numerical outcomes. Qualitative models do not yield numerical outcomes. Therefore, the example given above represents a qualitative model. Sometimes quantitative observations cannot even be made, and this almost inevitably means that a qualitative model will result.

Frequently, qualitative outcomes can be translated into quasi-quantitative payoffs by such means as ranking and the standard gamble. In spite of this fact, the model is essentially of a qualitative nature. At other times, the outcomes result in quantitative values but the relationship between the payoff measures—which express the utility for the outcome—and the outcomes themselves cannot be formulated. Again, the methods of ranking and standard gamble can be used. This situation is basically a quantitative one, but the model that is required to transform outcomes to payoffs is more qualitative than quantitative.

Although operations research is, in essence, a quantitative approach, decision-making is frequently restricted to qualitative or quasi-quantitative results. In these situations, operations research plays an important part by deriving suitable models to represent that part of reality which is being investigated. A suitable model is one that uses all of the dimensions that are under study and that combines them so that the outcomes and the payoff measures are dimensionally sound. For example, a manufacturer who does not have numerical data to relate profit, sales volume, price, and cost is still able to benefit from the qualitative relationships that he knows must exist. As cost goes up he realizes that profit must go down. In dimensional terms, we can write the expression $p = n(s - c)$ as follows:

$$\text{Profit} = \text{sales volume (price per unit} - \text{cost per unit)}$$

$$\$ = \text{units} \left(\frac{\$}{\text{unit}} - \frac{\$}{\text{unit}} \right)$$

It can be seen that "units" cancel out leaving $'s on both sides of the equation. When the manufacturer thinks in terms of total costs and price per unit, his conception of the relationship must be different if he hopes to get the correct qualitative outcomes. In this case, he must be thinking

$$\$ = \text{units} \frac{\$}{\text{unit}} - \$$$

This discussion may seem ethereal; nevertheless, it is at the heart of a vitally important subject. Whether we formally write down a description of a system or just think about it, in either case we must use dimensions and the dimensions must be consistent. Precisely because of the difficulty of checking the consistency of qualitative models, the subject appears to be vague. We shall emphasize this point with another example. Let us assume that sales volume (n) has a linear relationship with price (s). The characterization of the relationship as linear is a qualitative description. Lacking data, the executive can only write (or think)

$$n = a + bs$$

where a and b are the unknown parameters that define the exact relationship. If we rewrite this expression in terms of the dimensions of n and s, we obtain

$$\text{Units} = a + b\frac{\$}{\text{unit}}$$

From an analytical point of view it is quite clear that the dimensions of a must be units and the dimensions of b must be units²/$. But what meaning do they have? In the first place, when the price is zero, only a units can be given away. In qualitative terms this represents an extreme value of a units which is total market potential. Furthermore, another qualitative feature of a has been found, namely that it has a positive sign. How about b? If b had a positive sign then as price went up sales volume would go up. Perhaps for a certain price range this does hold and the executive might be able to describe that price range in qualitative terms. However, in general, b would be negative, and the executive has discerned another qualitative characteristic. Lastly, what is b?   The answer to this question is more easily given in terms of the Figure 7.1.

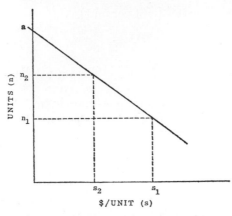

Figure 7.1 Dimensional interpretation of the lin-   Figure 7.2 There is a range of prices in which
          ear relationship between sales vol-   sales volume decreases as price
          ume and price.   decreases.

The slope of the line is b.   That means

$$b = \frac{n_2 - n_1}{s_2 - s_1}$$

In dimensional terms

$$b = \frac{\text{units} - \text{units}}{(\$/\text{unit}) - (\$/\text{unit})} = \frac{\text{units}}{\$/\text{unit}} = \frac{\text{units}^2}{\$}$$

Therefore, b is the ratio of the change in sales volume to the change in price.   There is no question but that this was a simple example.   Had it been more complex it would have required a great deal of explanation and interpretation.   Figure 7.2 depicts the situation when there is a range of prices for which sales volume increases as price increases.   When an executive intuits and considers the relationship of sales volume to price in some way he is mentally performing the operations which we have described above.   If his thinking is dimensionally inconsistent, then the model he is using is incorrect.   That is why explicit qualitative models can be very useful.   We will come back to dimensional analysis in Chapter 8 at which time it will involve quantitative measures.

69.   MODELS CAN BE CLASSIFIED ACCORDING TO THE DEGREE OF MODEL DEVELOPMENT

Undoubtedly, one of the most meaningful descriptions of models would sort them out according to their function or purpose.

1. One primary function of a model is to *convey information*. We have previously mentioned several different kinds of models that serve in this capacity. The criteria by which this kind of model is judged are the accuracy and efficiency of communication as well as the amount of information transmitted. It does not seem important, for our purposes, to distinguish between the kinds of information such models transmit— that is, whether it is qualitative or quantitative. In this regard, the road map, organization chart, matrix of numbers, profit-and-loss statement, photograph, TV screen, blueprint, or the printed book are all forms of information transmitters. Because communication models are important to all organizations it is necessary to consider the mathematical theory of information. This discussion will appear in Chapter 8.

2. *Observation and measurement models* are a second fundamental type. The purpose of such models is quite clear, but the underlying complexity of the theory of scaling and measuring is not widely known. Of course, observation must precede measurement. Purely observational models contain reality itself, but are reduced in complexity. This is necessary because of our limited powers of observation. In other words, we cannot perceive, understand, and measure the totality of any experience. Our senses are not broad enough nor are they sensitive enough. Further, we are unable to observe an environment without changing that environment in some way. That is, the observer and his subject are bound together in some mutual relationship which alters both of them. This effect, which is known as the *Heisenberg uncertainty principle* in physics, has something of a counterpart in the social sciences where it is generally called the *observer effect*. The principle has been the center of much discussion and disputation, but it remains an important factor which must be included in even the briefest treatment of measurement models. Man experiments with nature. He attempts to influence weather by cloud seeding, increase the yield of land by fertilization, utilize rivers for power. But no model is initially experimental. The model must begin in the mind. The choice of what to observe is the minimal link between reality and the model, and this is always an abstract thought model.

Measurement models can be defined in terms of order, distance, and origin.* Models having only order have a nominal system of measurement which is more aptly called a classification system. Objects and events can be sorted and separated on the basis of order alone. For example, A is equivalent to B, or A is the same as B; C is greater than D, or C is preferred to D; E is not as good as F, or E is not as smart as F. Measurements of this sort play an important role in the decision systems

---

* Warren S. Torgerson, *Theory and Methods of Scaling* (New York: John Wiley & Sons, Inc., 1958), pp. 15–21.

of executives. Models that start out in this strictly qualitative framework are destined to be qualitative models. Without question, there are more of these models in the business world than any other kind. Models for classification have been elaborately developed in a number of fields including logic and mathematics.

A good classification system is not something easily accomplished when the elements to be sorted and arranged require complex descriptions and can coexist in several places at the same time. These problems can be found in formulating almost any classification system. In the natural sciences the principles of taxonomy have been applied, in a painstaking manner, to animals and plants according to their natural relationships. Libraries must sort and arrange their books in a fashion that will permit rapid access and discovery. Questions such as whether a particular book should be put in the economics section or in the section devoted to business have dogged the librarian for years.

The filing system of every organization represents a qualitative classification system. Before a classification system can be created it is necessary to specify the variables by which the data can be sorted. The simplest classification system involves only one variable where that variable has only two subgroups. For example, some bills we file "paid" and others "unpaid." These subgroups are mutually exclusive since a bill cannot be "paid" and "unpaid" at the same time. However, there are always the bills that require special attention. This leads to additional classes which can be quite difficult to determine.

Problems of definition are extremely important in classification. For example, borrowing from a Census problem, when does a rural location become an urban location? Similarly, how can we classify things by shape? It is quite clear that the problem consists of defining the variable. Accountants are frequently involved with situations of this sort. For example, how should overhead be assigned to the various departments in a company? The difficulties of classification become more acute as additional variables are added. If we are classifying personnel records by age and skill, we will find that within any one age group there will be many different levels of skill. Similarly, within any one level of skill there will be many different ages. The degree of dependency between variables can frequently be recovered from properly classified data. If skill improves with age, then there should be a noticeable increase in the number of skilled workers that appear in the older age groups.

The methods of information theory can sometimes be quite useful in developing optimal classification systems. In any case, it is important to remember that a theory must underlie all classification. The appropriate classification model should provide outcomes with sufficient utility to warrant using them.

Information about *distance* represents a big step forward. That is, C is greater than D and D is greater than E, but the difference between C and D is greater than the difference between D and E. As an example, assume that we have three candidates for a particular job. The executive in charge of this decision is able to rank these men in the order which he believes describes their relative abilities to do the job. He finds it hard, however, to say how much better they are than each other. In other words, he is able to employ order but not distance.

Many times an executive cannot obtain information about distance. This situation is particularly acute when dealing with behavioral problems, with the outcomes of complex strategies, and with systems based on multiple objectives. Now, let us assume that the executive decides to make things easier for himself and therefore employs a test rating to differentiate the candidates. He can then say that one man is so many times better than another man. If the test score is a measure of intelligence then the model does not have a natural origin since it is hard to conceive of a man with zero intelligence. The use of a standard of "average intelligence" does provide an origin by means of which all three men can be rated against the general population. But an origin of this sort is subject to a good deal of question.

Problems that center around dollars usually have order, distance, and a natural origin. They form a basis for quantitative measurement models which can be found in abundance in the accounting department of any company. Many models, however, do not possess distance or a natural origin and cannot be expressed in numerical form.

Measurement models are far more developed in the physical sciences than in business. Their weaknesses in economic and behavioral applications are continually reflected in the attempts of executives to find superior methods of determining work standards, measures of corporate efficiency, true appraisals of costs, profits, market potential, effectiveness of advertising, creativity of research, and so forth. The development of improved measurement models requires a combined effort on the part of management and personnel with appropriate technical skills.

3. *Transformation models* are required to provide a basis for deriving the full-scale values of scale models. In this way, the distances shown on a map can be converted to actual distances. Similarly, the performance of the ship model in the towing tank is extended to the ocean liner. Fahrenheit values are transformed to Centigrade values by the symbolic transformation model: $°C = \frac{5}{9}(°F - 32)$. Inches are converted to feet by the symbolic transformation model: $x = 12y$, where x is given in inches and y is given in feet. Transformation models concern changes in scale but they leave the nature of the dimension intact. They are utilized when the form of the data obtained from the most efficient or convenient measurement model is not compatible with subsequent ana-

lytical operations, or when the analytical operations can be performed in a more meaningful manner as a result of the transformation.

One of the best-known transformations is the use of logarithms to add, multiply, raise to powers, and so on. In no way are the original data altered except by scale. The original form is recovered by use of the antilog. Another well-known transformation is from a sample to the full population. For example, we apply the results obtained from a test market to the entire country.

The importance of transformations to the business executive lies in the fact that seemingly inadequate measurement models can sometimes be transformed to provide valuable information. For example, consider the data in Table 7.1, which describes the number of trucks arriving at a company's loading dock.

Table 7.1

HOUR OF THE DAY

	MORNING HOURS						AFTERNOON HOURS						EVENING HOURS				
	7	8	9	10	11	12	1	2	3	4	5	6	7	8	9	10	11
:00–:14	4	1	4	5	1	2	2	1	3	0	3	1	2	3	1	0	1
:15–:29	1	2	1	1	0	1	2	0	2	0	2	0	0	1	1	0	0
:30–:44	1	0	2	2	0	1	1	0	3	2	3	0	2	2	1	0	1
:45–:59	1	0	1	1	1	3	1	2	1	2	3	0	1	2	2	0	0
TOTAL:	7	3	8	9	2	7	6	3	9	4	11	1	5	8	5	0	2

Number of trucks arriving within 15-minute periods of each hour.

If the data had been collected in hourly periods, which corresponds to the total (bottom row in Table 7.1), a frequency distribution would be obtained which would be of little help in predicting future arrivals. It is an irregular distribution which does not look like any of the well-known frequency distributions. The distribution is obtained in the following way:

NUMBER OF TRUCKS ARRIVING PER HOUR	FREQUENCY WITH WHICH THIS NUMBER OCCURS	FREQUENCY CONVERTED TO PROBABILITY
0	1	0.0588
1	1	0.0588
2	2	0.1176
3	2	0.1176
4	1	0.0588
5	2	0.1176
6	1	0.0588
7	2	0.1176
8	2	0.1176
9	2	0.1176
10	0	0.0000
11	1	0.0588
		0.9999

On the other hand, if the period is transformed from an hour into 15-minute units, the distribution closely approximates the Poisson distribution. Figure 7.3 compares the distribution that is obtained for periods of one hour with the theoretically derived Poisson distribution based on the same average number of truck arrivals. Figure 7.4 represents the same comparison for truck arrivals in 15-minute intervals. It is quite clear that based on a 15-minute period, truck arrivals exhibit regularity and predictability. We have used two kinds of transformations in this example. In the first place we have changed frequency into probability estimates. Secondly, we have transformed the period during which observations are taken in order to obtain this close approximation to a well-known distribution.

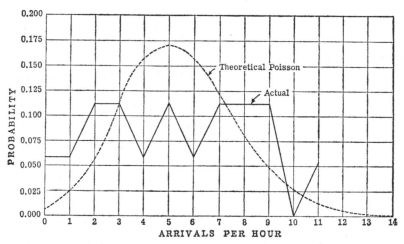

Figure 7.3 *Comparison of Poisson distribution with actual distribution derived from data based on hourly truck arrivals.*

In qualitative models we make use of the same kind of transformations, but we do it intuitively. It is, of course, very important that we don't distort dimensions when we utilize transformations. Operations research can provide important guidance for both qualitative and quantitative transformations.

4. Another important category of models consists of a wide variety of *test models*. The function of a test model is to confirm or reject those hypotheses which underlie the construction of the test model. We can test the water of bathing beaches for pollution. We agree to permit bathing if the count of harmful bacteria (such as coliform bacteria) is below specified levels. It is the measurement model that is responsible for the numerical or qualitative determination of how many bacteria of each type are present. The measurement, if qualitative, may be nothing more than a comparison with a standard to determine if there are more

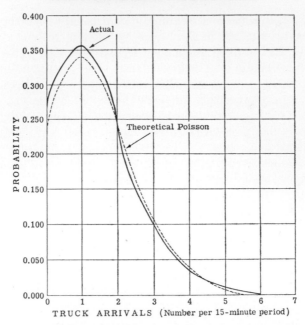

Figure 7.4 Comparison of Poisson distribution with actual distribution derived from data based on truck arrivals every 15 minutes.

or less bacteria present in the sample that in the standard. It is the standard, in this case, that functions as the test model.

Test models are frequently based on arbitrary standards—for example, the determination of piece-work rates, TV program ratings, personnel test scores, and so on. Although they are arbitrary, they are usually not haphazard, and are determined as carefully as possible in terms of fundamental objectives. There is no clear-cut line with respect to how many coliform bacteria can be permitted before they jeopardize health. Qualitative test models can frequently be backed up with quantitative test models which can determine the *degree of relationship* between two factors, such as the number of coliform bacteria and their effect on health.

Test models can also be used to accept or reject a sample as being derived from a specified population of elements. Assume, for example, that an executive wants to know how long it takes for two different brands of tires to wear out on fork-lift trucks. He gets a sample of ten of each kind and puts them on his trucks at the same time. As the tires wear out he gets reports on them. However, can he be sure that the tires are each representative of the two manufacturers' products? Perhaps one batch was older than the other. Were the trucks employed in the same way? These and many other questions must be answered if the executive is to come to a meaningful conclusion with respect to which kind of tires to purchase in the future.

In this regard, we have available various experimental designs which will assist the executive. There are t tests to determine whether a mean value observed in a sample set of data came from the hypothesized population. We have other tests for variation, tests for the shape of a distribution, and tests to detect change from a stable population. Statistical tests are necessary because no matter how refined and precise a measurement technique is, there will be chance cause elements at work which introduce random variation. Intuition and qualitative models cannot be relied upon to sort out nonchance factors, the occurrence of which must be detected.

Nevertheless, we cannot test everything with statistical methods. Judgement must continue to play an important part in the development of test models. Many executive decisions are based on such qualitative test results. Frequently, a negative test result produces no action whereas a positive test result triggers an executive decision. In a very real sense, every quarterly report is tested by executive judgment. The decision as to when sales have fallen off so much that something should be done about it is an example of a qualitative test model which is of major importance in every executive's life. Similarly, at what point have sales increased to warrant building a new plant, or when have costs grown too large, how much is too much absenteeism, when should something be done about pilferage, when should another salesman be hired? How many observations must be made for each of the above questions before we can be reasonably certain that a real change has taken place and that we are not just observing random variation? All such decision criteria are based on test models, and whether they be qualitative or quantitative, operations research can lend a hand.

5. One of the most fundamental purposes of models is to discover *which variables are the pertinent variables*. As we have previously explained, the choice of which variables to investigate is a complex conceptual process which is followed by a measurement model. In these cases, the basic notion is to explain the behavior of one variable in terms of other variables.

For example, if we are interested in determining the factors that influence the time required by an executive to make a decision, we can obtain from a group of executives a list of variables that they consider relevant. Such a list might include the number of employees working for the executive, dollars involved in the decision, degree of reversibility of the decision, number of years that the executive has spent with the company, and so on. Now this list is obviously just a list of suggestions. No one pretends to know the relationship between decision time and these other factors.   Data are then collected for each decision of a number of executives of the company, and a correlation analysis can be run to determine the relevance of each variable to the decision time.

Qualitative correlation goes on in our minds all of the time.   Quantitative correlation is a statistical means of determining the extent to which a change in one factor is accompanied by a change in another factor. Sometimes, the changes are linearly related—that is, equal changes in one of the controlled variables results in a nearly constant increase in the payoff every time.   Quadratic relationships exist where equal changes in one of the controlled variables produce an outcome that is proportional to the square of the value of the variable.   Higher-order correlation possibilities also exist.

There are many weaknesses in both qualitative and quantitative correlation.   Nevertheless, within the limitations of bounded rationality, the mind does seem to be able to correlate variables which when correlated quantitatively result in very complex equations.   Perhaps it is not that the mind just correlates on the basis of frequency patterns, but rather it is able to discern causality in a logical sense.   Correlation does not involve notions of causality.   If a causal relationship makes one variable appear more frequently in the presence of another, correlation cannot discern in which direction the causal relationship works.   Put another way, correlation is a means of isolating factors that have a tendency to appear together for whatever reasons.   Certainly, qualitative appraisal can be useful when there seems to be no other way to determine the outcomes that result from a given strategy and a given state of nature.   For example, there will be day-to-day fluctuations in sales although the company's strategy remains unchanged and the state of nature could not have shifted very much.   Since a company's strategy includes so many different elements, it is frequently impossible to tell which action brought which result when a basic change in the outcome is observed.   In the same way, it is hard to detect changes in the state of nature that could account for variability in the outcomes.

In this connection, we should mention that in the nineteenth century J. S. Mill formulated a number of rules which are the antecedents of present-day methods for identifying pertinent variables.   We shall discuss only two of these rules, and we shall illustrate them in terms of an example of how qualitative models pertain to the executive problem of qualitatively discerning the important variables.

The method of agreement can be stated:

if $X–ABCD$ is observed, and
   $X–ARST$ is observed, then X and A are related.

Let X be a foreman in department BCD.   Let A represent low production.   The executive in charge of production changes foreman X from department *BCD* to department *RST* because the production of department *BCD* is not high enough. After a time the executive learns that the production of the second department is dropping. Therefore, he concludes that the foreman is to blame.

The method of difference can be stated:

if *X–ABCD* is observed, and
  Y–MBCD is observed, then *X* and *A* are related.

M we will assume to be high production. The executive notices that after foreman *X* is replaced by foreman *Y* in the first department, *BCD*, the production of that department goes up. Therefore, he concludes that foreman *X* is to blame.

Now, let us see what can be wrong with this approach. One possibility is that the executive by removing the foreman from a department with a poor production record gave the workers cause for concern and so they improved their performance. The second department, on the other hand, had a good production record and when their foreman was removed it lowered their morale and their productivity. Or what if the productivity of the first department, *BCD*, had not improved but had been so strongly affected by foreman *X* that foreman *Y* could do nothing to raise the production level? Lastly, what if the executive, unknown to him, was said to favor *Y* over *X* and the departments were reacting accordingly? Complications of this sort can lead to erroneous conclusions. It is important to always bear them, and their like, in mind when applying qualitative models of this type.

6. The discovery of pertinent variables is intimately connected with the *investigation of the relationships that exist among variables*. The use of correlation techniques requires some hypothesis to be made about the relationship that connects the variables with the outcome. If the wrong relationship is hypothesized, then the variable will be rejected as not being pertinent. The reader might then ask, why didn't we include this class of model in the previous section? The answer is that sometimes logic tells us that certain variables are important factors in determining what outcome will result. Since we do not know the relationships, correlation cannot bear us out. We must look for other means to learn how the variables interact with each other to yield the outcomes. This is the class of models which we are considering here.

For example, an executive believes that patience, strength, and intelligence are the vital factors that determine how well a particular job can be done. We can assume that he has developed adequate measurement models to describe the patience, strength, and intelligence of each applicant for the job. Now, what he must find out is in what way these three variables are important to the outcome. Are they equally important, or does one count twice as much as another? How do they combine to yield the outcome? He must develop a method that will permit him to relate all possible outcomes to the values of the variables. The outcomes themselves he might list as speed of doing the job, quality of the workmanship, endurance, and so on.

One of the first approaches he can use is to examine the data that are available. To these data, he can attempt to fit curves. He will hold patience and intelligence constant while he varies the value of strength and observes what effect that has on each of the outcomes. He will follow the same procedure for the other variables. If this approach does not yield any results he can then attempt to derive a model by deduction. Deductive reasoning starts out with generalizations and moves toward particulars. Perhaps one of the best examples of this process is the discovery of analog models which can be taken from one situation and fitted to another. We have already mentioned how verbs sometimes help us to find appropriate analogs. At other times, something we read or something we hear strikes us as incorporating elements that exist in our own problem. Once such a model has been created, be it in physical or symbolic form, it is necessary to test the hypotheses that are the foundation of the model. Testing these models is not always a simple process. The fact that outcomes occur that go contrary to reason is not sufficient evidence to reject the model. However, empirical methods must be explored to determine on an experimental basis whether certain values of the variables do produce the predicted outcomes.

There are times when the relationship between variables and outcomes is known over a short range. The problem is to determine the outcomes that result outside of the range. This is the problem of *extrapolation*. If two outcomes are known but the values in between are not known, we use methods of *interpolation* to find them. Extrapolation is the more important case, especially when the relationship that must be extrapolated is in statistical form. This is the case in most prediction models. Qualitative extrapolation of a very complex sort is being done all of the time by executives in order to project trends, anticipate cycles, and forecast in general.

Another type of model falls into this same class of outcome-seeking models. We have referred to it before as a simulation model. Actually, there are a number of types of simulation models. They can be categorized by degree of abstraction. Qualitative forms of simulation models are the operating scale models. The plane in the wind tunnel simulates flight conditions. The pilot plant is intended to simulate the full-scale production plant. Fatigue tests and wear tests are attempts to compress time; the dimension that is scaled down is time—such that perhaps one minute is the equivalent of one day. These kinds of simulation models have been with us for a long time. They have been studied as problems of similitude. It can be recognized that many of the variables that take part in producing the outcomes cannot be specified. Most of the relationships and interrelationships are unknown. But as long as the rules for similitude can be formulated, outcomes derived from the model can be transformed to their full-scale equivalents.

When O.R. and systems people speak about simulation models they usually have reference to the next level of abstraction—that is, analog models. Frequently, these analog models incorporate probability terms. In other words, they deal with problems that have a number of different states of nature, each of which can occur with some probability. Such models provide simulation by allowing the states of nature to appear randomly in proportion to the assigned probabilities.

Simulation of military problems has a long history which includes war games and board games. Complex military problems have been simulated involving both competitive strategies and states of nature (such as the weather) that might affect the outcome of the military operation. Executive business games are of this same type, involving both competitive strategies and states of nature.

Generally speaking, analog simulation models are based on known variables and known relationships. However, in most cases, the relationships are too complex to solve. Many times the mathematical equations can be written. Since they cannot be solved in their symbolic form, they are transformed into some kind of physical equivalent. Computers are one type of device favored for this purpose because of high speed. If the simulation model is not excessively time-consuming, pencil and paper can be used.

A number of simulation models operate on a problem-solving sequence where the outcome of one stage serves as the input to the next stage. There is also the application of simulation to situations characterized by statistical distributions that are not of well-known forms. Many times, several probability distributions interact with each other in special ways and it is not possible to solve for their combined effect in a mathematical equation. For example, the executive in charge of production for an oil refinery obtains information about the frequency with which certain components need remedial attention. When any one of these components fails and requires maintenance, the entire section of the refinery composed of them is forced to close down. The executive wants to know what the probabilities are of the entire section's being down. This same sort of problem applies to the use of any multicomponent equipment where various parts can fail and each has its own particular failure characteristics. The method of solving such problems is based on a quantitative model called the *Monte Carlo method*, which appears in the next chapter.

7. There still remains one major problem. Assuming that we have all

of the outcomes and that the outcomes have been transformed into payoffs, how do we pick the strategy that yields the "best" payoff? There
are both qualitative and quantitative models that accomplish this end.
To begin with, we can enumerate some general rules to be followed in
searching for an optimum payoff.

(a) In order to discover the best payoff, we must know the objectives.

(b) We must know the strategies that are available, the states of
nature that can occur, and the various possibilities for competitive strategies. The decision-maker's strategies, in particular, should be conceived
of as variables whose possible values lie along a continuum.

(c) All possible outcomes cannot be examined if there are too many
of them. Therefore, on the basis of logic and intuition we can choose one
or more strategies that should, in our opinion, lead to "reasonably good"
payoffs.

(d) The payoff measures derived above can then be compared with
the payoffs that would result from rather extreme conditions for the
variables. The extreme conditions should be selected so that they represent strategies that are feasible, although not necessarily reasonable from
our starting point of view. If possible, the extremes should include between them the reasonable strategies that were chosen. Payoffs derived in this manner can sometimes detect that logic and common sense
have failed us. They can also indicate that one direction in which a
variable is changed is superior to the opposite direction.

Figure 7.5 illustrates these remarks. Assume that the curved line,
$f(x)$ is known, but that it cannot be seen. That is, for any value of x
we can derive the appropriate value of y from the expression $y = f(x)$.
However, we do not know how to solve the problem of obtaining the
maximum value of y which is indicated by y^*. We must assume that
there are too many possible values of y for us to attempt to compute all
of them and draw the curve. In this simple two-dimensional case that
may seem like an unreasonable request. However, when it is pointed
out that a realistic problem would involve a surface in multidimensional

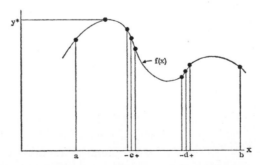

Figure 7.5 Locating an optimum payoff by qualitative means.

space, the assumption makes sense. Now, y is the payoff and x is the variable under our control. We are trying to locate the optimum value of y which is the maximum value of y, denoted y^*. We choose $x = c$ and $x = d$ as our reasonable strategies. We select $x = a$ and $x = b$ as our feasible, extreme values. For the case that we have shown, the problem is particularly difficult since the curve does not continuously increase or decrease. However, we find that the extreme value a produces a y value that is about equal to the payoff of our reasonable strategy c. This would lead us to investigate some more points falling between a and c. Both the y values produced by b and by d are lower than the y values produced by a and by c. This would indicate that the payoff tends to decrease as the x value increases above a certain point.

(e) The conditions that produced the "reasonable" payoffs should then be altered gradually in both directions to see whether an improvement occurs. The results that were obtained at the extremes should be kept in mind. If improvement is observed, another change should be made, and this process should be continued until no more improvement can be achieved. In terms of Figure 7.5, we have altered c and d by small amounts, $+$ and $-$. We observe an important improvement when we try $c-$ which will lead us to continue in this direction. Hopefully we will eventually reach y^*.

(f) The advantages and disadvantages of qualitative searching procedures should be more evident now. It is a simple matter to overlook important peaks even on a two-dimensional plane. With complex surfaces in n-dimensional space, the problem is enormously difficult. Nevertheless, with systematic procedures it is possible to make significant improvements in the payoffs with strictly cut-and-try methods. The job of searching for optimal payoffs can be time-consuming. It is essential that all results be recorded so that directions that result in improvement can be observed. Also, we avoid having to go back over the same ground.

Operations research can frequently provide the executive with better means for determining optimums. As an example, we shall consider the following problem. A lock manufacturer makes replacement parts for items which the company no longer produces. In addition, it manufactures a new line of locks which must carry the cost of the replacement business. It has always been this company's policy to carry stock on obsolete models because of its belief that it creates goodwill. However, if the company charged the proper amount in order to make a profit or just break even on replacement parts, the cost of these parts would be so exorbitant that it would defeat the purpose of improving goodwill. The company learns that a competitor is considering the possibility of manufacturing the entire line of replacement parts. As a result, the appropriate decision problem is formulated. There are three possible strategies and two states of nature.   The sales manager of the company determines the outcomes as below:

	$N1$	$N2$
$S1:$	O_{11}	O_{12}
$S2:$	O_{21}	O_{22}
$S3:$	O_{31}	O_{32}

$S1:$ continue making replacements.

$S2:$ announce suspension of the policy to make replacements to become effective at some date in the far future.

$S3:$ stop making replacements.

$N1:$ competitor decides to make replacement parts.

$N2:$ competitor decides not to make replacement parts.

$O_{11}:$ we lose some replacement customers—but gain some new customers since the competitor's prices on his new line must go up to absorb the cost of replacement parts.

$O_{12}:$ we lose no replacement customers—but we gain fewer new customers (present policy).

$O_{21}:$ we lose more replacement customers than in O_{11}—but we gain about the same number of new customers as in O_{11}.

$O_{22}:$ we lose fewer replacement customers than in O_{11}—and we gain fewer new customers as in O_{12}.

$O_{31}:$ we lose all our replacement customers—and we gain more new customers than in O_{11}.

$O_{32}:$ we lose more replacement customers than in O_{21}—and we gain fewer new customers than in O_{31}.

These outcomes can be further simplified by a logical analysis of the statements.   This produces the following:

$O_{11}:$ lose x	gain y
$O_{12}:$ lose 0	gain $y - a$
$O_{21}:$ lose $x + b$	gain y
$O_{22}:$ lose $x - c$	gain $y - a$
$O_{31}:$ lose all	gain $y + c$
$O_{32}:$ lose $x + b + d$	gain $y + c - e$

If the sales manager can put in values appropriate to the gains and losses, he can then quantitatively solve this decision problem.   However, if he cannot supply numbers, he can rank the outcomes according to his best judgement.   Let us assume that he has ranked the outcomes with the numbers that appear in the payoff matrix below.   (1 represents the poorest payoff—6 represents the best payoff.)

	$N1$	$N2$	MINIMUM PAYOFF
$S1:$	4	6	4**
$S2:$	3	5	3
$S3:$	1	2	1
MAXIMUM PAYOFF:	4*	6	

If we now apply the maximin (**) and the minimax (*) criteria, we find that the company will do best to continue on its present policy. We can also observe that if the competitor has the same approximate utility as the sales manager, and derives approximately the same estimates for the payoffs, he will begin to manufacture replacement parts.

This example illustrates the way in which a qualitative decision model can be used to determine an optimum payoff measure. It is quite clear that models intended to search for payoffs are, in fact, combinations of many kinds of models—the data are derived from information models or by observation and measurement; outcomes are transformed into payoffs; strategies and states of nature (or competitive strategies) require knowledge of the variables; outcomes are dependent upon an understanding of the relationships among the variables; and the choice of one particular payoff is made by searching all possible payoffs with specific decision criteria.

It is not possible to treat all of the different kinds of decision problems that can arise. There are too many variations. We have attempted to give the reader a fairly broad perspective of the range of problems and some methods to cope with these situations. There are ingenious ways of putting the component models together so that an optimum payoff can be found, but it is considerably easier to do this when quantitative conditions prevail.

70. MODELS CAN BE CLASSIFIED BY SUBJECT

There is no one theory that will explain all phenomena. Not even within the highly developed field of physics is a unified theory available. Therefore, it is not surprising that there is no unified theory of models. Many classifications of models afford some insight. We will consider one more: by the subjects to which the models are applied.

For example, economists are particularly concerned with certain variables. The relationships that underlie the behavior of the economic system have many characteristics in common with relationships that can be found in other fields. Nevertheless, it is clear that the strategic possibilities available to the economist and the states of nature that are likely to prevail are somewhat unique. In other words, the dimensions of the economist's problems are a particular set. What can we say is characteristic of the economist's set? He wishes to be able to predict economic developments and, ultimately, to be able to control economic conditions. However, he is confronted with the fact that, as yet, there is uncertainty as to the relevant variables. That is why there is a great deal of interest in the kind of model that will help to indicate and point out relevant variables. Of course, it is possible that the variables that are being considered are correct, and that their relationships have not been properly specified.

Psychologists' models also suffer from uncertainty as to the relevant variables. That is why psychologists have been designing models aimed at locating pertinent variables. Whereas the economists' models utilize variables of supply, demand, price, and the like, the psychologists' models are involved with such variables as motivation, reinforcement, conditioning, gestalt. Although the models in each field seem quite different, a development in one area can profoundly affect the other.

Medicine is another field that is particularly suitable to the subject of this chapter. Physicians primarily use qualitative models. They have many forms of quantitative data, such as temperature, pulse, blood counts, but they have no models that can combine these data to yield quantitative payoffs. Similar discussions can be used to describe the decision-making situations of meteorologists who have a model that cannot be solved, biologists and biochemists who cannot formalize the relationships that describe physical patterns and arrangements in mathematical terms. Chemists, physicists, electrical engineers, and architects, to name just a few more fields, all have their own characteristic problems within the decision-making framework. But we are particularly interested in the problems of business.

Business has many different ways of looking at itself. Each point of view represents a qualitative model and is intended to accomplish different things. However, all these models have one aspect in common: they all provide frameworks to use in thinking about the problem area.

The executive breaks down the decision problems that appear within his area on the basis of classification by subject. He recognizes the limitations of this approach. Areas relate to other areas, and boundaries are frequently illusory. Nevertheless, there is a convenience in separating areas so that fundamentally different decision situations are represented by each class. Let us examine these classes and see to what extent this objective is achieved.

1. *By product type.* There are a variety of ways in which the characteristics of a product are classified. For example, we talk about "consumer goods" as opposed to "industrial goods." The strategies connected with selling consumer goods contain many variables that never appear in the strategies used in the industrial area. As a rule, we have many consumers to reach, convince, and supply, whereas there are relatively few industrial users. Problems of inventory, distribution, and so on are different in each area. It is worth noting that the states of nature of the economy seem to produce different effects in the sales of soft and hard goods. Another classification contrasts durable goods, which do

not spoil, with nondurable goods requiring basically different inventory management, selling procedures, and distribution policies. Fashion items require special strategies for the same reason.

2. *By integrated function.* We have reference to manufacturers, retailers, wholesalers, salesmen and sales agents, factors, and so on. Of course, it is apparent that strategic variables will not be the same in each of these areas. But more important, the objectives of each group will not concur completely. When one organization includes a number of these functions it is easy to see how suboptimization can be a serious problem. If the functions exist in separate organizations any one of these organizations must consider the others in terms of states of nature and/or competitive strategies.

3. *By commodity class.* Is it reasonable to classify decision problems by commodity class? The answer appears to be yes. As a matter of fact, perhaps not enough accent is placed on this classification. The usual consideration of competition includes only those companies which make very similar products and are clearly directly competitive. Yet real competition exists at a more general level. For example, milk, beer, soft drinks, fruit juices, and the like compete not only within each subgroup but also between themselves. We would call this commodity class "beverages." Other commodity classes could be textiles, transportation, coal, electronic devices, and so forth. The size of the commodity class can be enlarged or diminished depending upon the extent to which relevant competitive strategies influence the decision-makers' outcomes.

4. *By economic situation.* Here we mean pure competition, oligopoly, monopoly, monopsony, and the rest. When do competitive strategies have to be taken into consideration? The economic situation that prevails will determine the extent to which a rational competitor can affect the decision-maker's outcome. We have discussed this point at the end of Chapter 5, and we indicated that as we approach monopolistic conditions, the supplier and the consumer become "competitors" of the enterprise. Similarly, under conditions of monopsony—where there is one buyer and many suppliers, e.g., government contracts—there is complete competition between the bidders, and special problems must be considered. Economic models of these sorts are an important classification for business.

5. *By operations.* In this case, we are referring to assembly, inspection, machining, casting, storing, transporting, and the like. Since the organization can be viewed as a communication network in which the parts and materials flowing through the factory or warehouse are legitimate units of information (Chapter 2), it is useful to have this classification. Each step provides a transformation of information. Controllable variables can be isolated by this procedure. Important input-output

relationships can be detected. Although this method of classification may not be the most advantageous from a systems-analysis point of view, it serves the function of segmentation of operations to allow managerial control.

6. *By types of problems.* The most familiar classification is the breakdown that is generally used by management: production, marketing, personnel, and so on. Business schools take a magnifying glass to this classification and arrive at a basis for their curriculums: accounting, advertising, banking, business law, economics, finance, industrial relations, insurance, real estate, statistics, transportation, and so on.

What are the reasons behind this breakdown? Many of the classes coincide with employment positions. That makes hiring and training easier. To a large extent, these categories exist as separate file drawers in which a great many facts can be stored. These are the facts of tradition and custom; the classification is a convenient way to file and store them.

There are obviously many explanations—like the one above—to account for the existence of this kind of classification. But from the point of view of decision-making, how useful are these categories? The answer is that they are useful insofar as different strategies and states of nature apply to the different areas. They also emphasize the separate nature of certain functions which leads to conflicts of objectives and suboptimization. But while they emphasize differences between areas, they do not stress similarities.

Certainly, there is nothing wrong with this classification. There is just something missing. That something is a way of integrating areas and of tracing lines that uncover dependent relationships between the areas. Now, the classification of operations research by types of methods —allocation, search, replacement, inventory, queuing, and so on—cuts across the boundaries of the conventional business classifications. The O.R. breakdown is not necessarily the most useful from the point of view of the executive. He may, at best, find it informative. In this respect, O.R. provides just another classification system. It is *decision theory* that totally integrates all areas and that can explain the existence of any logical classification system employed by business.

71. QUALITATIVE TO QUANTITATIVE MODELS

As we have seen, a great many models are not quantitative. It is generally true that we can get more information from quantitative models and, hence, can say that we understand reality a little better than we can when we have qualitative models. But this does not gainsay the importance of qualitative models. Most thinking about reality starts with qualitative models and subsequently develops to a point where quantitative models can be used. The earlier qualitative model must reach a certain degree of correspondence to reality before the quantitative step can be taken. Many sciences that deal with particularly complex kinds of reality are still at the stage of developing suitable qualitative models. And these qualitative models can afford a great deal of insight into the complexities of their subject matter.

Operations research is the executive's source of assistance in systematizing qualitative models and developing them to the point where they can be quantified. This isn't meant to imply that operations-research methodology can quantify any qualitative situation. There are too many serious problems which must be overcome—problems such as the following:

(a) Inadequate measurement techniques.
(b) Too many variables required.
(c) The variables are unknown.
(d) The relationships are unknown.
(e) The relationships are too complex to be formally stated.

However, by the use of logical analysis, classification systems, dimensional analysis, and the decision-theory framework, O.R. can bring some useful formal concepts into play.

PROBLEMS

1. A suburban retailer asks his customers where they come from so that he can find out how distance affects his potential market. He knows that there is almost equal population density for 50 miles in any direction and that most people come to his store by car. He obtains the following information:

NUMBER OF CUSTOMERS	DISTANCE TRAVELED
640	0–2 miles
680	2–5 miles
520	5–10 miles
40	10–20 miles

The retailer concludes that up to 10 miles, distance has no effect on his business. What dimensional error is he making? What relationship actually holds? (Remember: area of a circle $= \pi r^2$.)

2. Three machine-tool companies (A, B, and C) supply a special part which is used by only four aircraft manufacturers (D, E, F, and G). Company A has received 5 orders in the year—4 came from D and 1 from E. The manage-

ment of company A would like to know how well they are faring in comparison with their competitors. They collect the following information: D has placed a total of 6 orders; E has placed a total of 4 orders; and G has placed only 1 order. F has placed more orders than E but less than D. How many different possibilities are there for the number of orders received by B? If it is then learned that C received more than 2 orders but less than one-half of the number received by B, how many possibilities remain? With this information can you tell how D, E, F, and G placed their orders?

3. The lock manufacturer in this chapter (p. 135) decided, on a qualitative basis, to continue manufacturing replacement parts. His competitor, on the other hand, went through the same reasoning process but obtained numerical estimates, as follows: $x = y/2 = 2a = 4b = 6c = 8d = 10e$. The total replacement market $= 100x$.

What conclusions did the competitor reach?

4. A secretary has five items to be filed. There are two filing cabinets with four drawers in each. Assume that the items to be filed arrive randomly and that all file drawers have equal probability of being used. What would you estimate is the probability that no two items will be filed in the same drawer? After you have tried your intuition and qualitative sense, solve the following equation to check your answer:

$$P = \frac{x(x - 1)(x - 2) \ldots (x - y + 1)}{x^y}$$

where $P = $ the probability that no two items will be filed in the same drawer,
$x = 8$, and
$y = 5$.

5. Using the data of Table 7.1 (p. 126), show how the distribution of truck arrivals per 15-minute period is derived. What do you think the distribution of truck arrivals per 10-minute period would look like? Explain the change in shape of the curve in qualitative terms. What would the .00005-minute distribution look like?

6. The superintendent of an oil refinery is installing four new units on which he has no data. However, the units are made up of components with which he is familiar. Three types of components, A, B, and C, are combined in different ways: unit 1 consists of one A, one B, and one C—(ABC); unit 2 consists of one A and one B—(AB); unit 3 consists of one A and one C—(AC); and unit 4 consists of one B and one C—(BC). When any one of the components fails to operate properly, the entire unit is shut down. At that time, maintenance crews work on all the components in the unit, in addition to the one which has caused the shutdown. Data are available for each of the components as follows:

$x = $ number of weeks that elapse between maintenance and failure, and
$P(x) = $ the probability that x weeks will elapse between maintenance and failure.

Component A		Component B		Component C	
x	$P(x)$	x	$P(x)$	x	$P(x)$
0	00	0	00	0	00
5	05	5	15	5	30
10	10	10	35	10	10
15	15	15	30	15	10
20	20	20	10	20	05
25	20	25	05	25	04
30	15	30	03	30	06
35	10	35	02	35	15
40	05	40	00	40	10
45	00	45	00	45	05
50	00	50	00	50	05
55	00	55	00	55	00

What is the expected value of x for A, for B, and for C? Using these data, see how well you can estimate the expected values of x for ABC, AB, AC, and BC. (The method for solution of this problem is included in the material of Chapter 8.) If the average down-time is 5 hours what is the expected loss in production hours per year for each unit?

Chapter eight

Quantitative Models

We have reached the stage where it may be helpful to consider the arrangement of this book. The material that preceded Chapter 8 was aimed at showing that decision-making is the fundamental model upon which the practices of management are based. Our treatment, in Chapter 7, of qualitative models was brief but it attempted to depict, in an inclusive manner, the nature of qualitative models. We were obliged to spend time on qualitative models for two reasons. In the first place, all quantitative models start out as qualitative models. Secondly, a great number of business problems are still at the qualitative level. However, the real *tour de force* of scientific decision-making emerges at the point where quantification becomes possible.

This chapter develops only the broadest aspects of quantification. It does not consider the classification of quantitative models which is familiarly associated with operations research. That discussion appears in Chapter 13 after the problem section which follows this chapter. The problem section demonstrates repeatedly the application of quantitative decision-making models. Most of the techniques used are operations-research methods. We have refrained from the explicit discussion of operations-research techniques until Chapter 13 in order to avoid the impression that the problem section is designed to illustrate O.R. techniques. It is our desire to show that decision-making raises certain characteristic problems for which operations research has found solutions. It is not our intention to parade a battery of techniques before the reader.

72. QUANTITATIVE MODELS OF TWO KINDS

We have ample evidence of the numerous ways in which models can be classified. We do not propose to go over this ground again. However, we want to distinguish between two important classes of quantitative models; (1) problem-solving models, and (2) optimum-value models.

Problem-solving models are the most familiar model form. They are quantitative models for discovering relationships, for uncovering pertinent variables, and for finding outcomes. The accountant must enumerate all of the variables that contribute to the cost of making a particular product. The industrial statistician in conjunction with the industrial psychologist designs experiments to determine whether one package is preferred to another. The quality-control engineer maintains close observation of a process in order to discern if and when the process changes. In none of these situations is the objective an optimal value. Let's look back at them.

The accountant observes the strategy that was followed and the state of nature that prevailed. They are past and recorded history. He must determine the outcome, which is a cost figure. He has no problem of risk or uncertainty. However, when the accountant is asked to estimate on the basis of a quarterly report what the annual business will be, he cannot be certain what state of nature will prevail. His prediction is necessary in order to determine an outcome. But his problem is not that of optimizing the outcome. Similarly, the statistician and psychologist who prepare questionnaires or interviews are attempting to discover the outcome that will result from a variety of strategies—different packages which are shown to groups of people with different demographic and psychological characteristics. Generally, such experiments assume that the state of nature is constant and will not undergo change in the foreseeable future. The quality-control engineer knows what outcome to expect from a stable process. As the states of nature shift they produce the random variation which he anticipates. However, what he is looking for is a change in strategy that is unintended. He spots this occurrence when a number of observed values all fall on one side of the mean value of a process—called a *run*—or when a point goes outside of the limits drawn on his statistical quality-control chart. The control engineer is not trying to optimize anything. He is devoted to maintaining the company's strategy.

Of course, all of these activities fit into the decision-making framework. Problem-solving consists of finding certain decision elements which are unknown when other decision elements are given. For example, the elements of the strategies are given—what are the outcomes?

An outcome is given—what strategy will produce it? A strategy and an outcome are given—what state of nature prevailed? Operations-research methods are useful when the state of nature is not certain and must be predicted, as the accountant had to do in order to estimate his company's annual business. There are, however, some special problems connected with the discovery of outcomes that can be handled by quantitative methods. We will now consider these.

73. TRANSITIONAL OUTCOMES

When a strategy and a state of nature produce an outcome that then modifies the state of nature in such a way as to produce a new outcome, the determination of only the first outcome does not suffice as a basis for decision-making. We can recognize that this is the description of a feedback model. The input, which is the strategy, in conjunction with

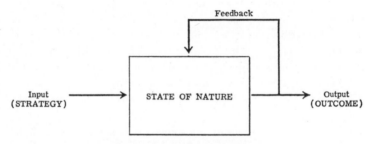

Figure 8.1 Decision feedback model.

the state of nature produces an output. All, or part, of the output is fed back as a new input. This input modifies the state of nature and a new output results which is then fed back, and so forth. Consequently, no one outcome describes the effect of the strategy. A whole sequence of outcomes is required. In terms of the elements of our decision matrix, we can represent this process in the following way:

STRATEGY	TIME SEQUENCE	N1	N2	N3	N4	...
			STATES OF NATURE			
S1	t_0		02			
S1 + (02)	t_1				04	
S1 + (04)	t_2	01				
S1 + (01)	t_3					08
S1 + (08)	t_4			03		
S1 + (03)	t_5		02			
S1 + (02)	t_6	01				
.	.	.	.	.	.	.
.	.	.	.	.	.	.
.	.	.	.	.	.	.

The state of nature that results from a given feedback might be known with certainty—as in the case of decision-making under certainty. It could just as well be subject to random variation and require a probability description—as in the case of decision-making under risk or uncertainty. Usually, it is quite difficult to observe the state of nature and so all that we are left with is a sequence of outcomes. In the above case, that sequence would be: 02 ... 04 ... 01 ... 08 ... 03 ... 02 ... 01. This is important; our total information consists only of a sequence of outcomes.

One thing is immediately apparent—we have very little information and we must collect more if we hope to be able to make predictions about future outcomes. That is the problem we wish to solve. But there is one thing we can observe. The outcome 02 led to the outcome 04 the first time that it appeared. The second time 02 appeared it was followed by 01. This means that at least two possibilities exist for outcomes that follow 02. Since outcome 02 can be followed by several outcomes—presumably with different probabilities—it is not possible to know with certainty what is going to happen. We describe this situation as a *stochastic process*. "Stochastic" is a Greek word meaning to aim or guess. In its present-day nontechnical usage it means "skillful in conjecturing." And so we can see that the name of the process implies some ability—but not absolute certainty—in knowing what will take place.

74. INFORMATION SYSTEMS

Observations made of a stochastic process constitute information. It is true that we would prefer to know what strategies are being utilized and what states of nature are occurring. If we knew all of the pertinent variables and the relationships that connect them we would not be studying outcome data. However, since we do not know the other important elements of the decision matrix we carefully analyze our outcome data in order to detect arrangements, patterns, and regularities. The mathematical theory of information enables us to measure the degree of order that exists in a sequence of outcomes. At the one extreme, we can find the situation where there is no order at all. This condition of complete disorder occurs only when all outcomes are equally likely. At the opposite end of the scale, we find complete order. This is the situation when only one possible outcome can occur. Between these extremes exist the countless variety of patterns that a sequence of outcomes can produce.

What kinds of patterns can there be in a sequence of outcome data? Secondly, how do we use information theory to detect them? The first pattern we look for is one with which we are already familiar—the relative frequencies of the outcomes. We have previously developed frequency distributions to describe various states of nature. In this case, we are applying the same procedure to outcomes. Many times we can view states of nature as outcomes and vice versa. So, nothing new has been added to this point. Our second step is to note the way in which one outcome follows another. We observe the frequencies of all possible transitions. From this, we determine the probabilities with which one particular outcome follows another. We shall illustrate these remarks as soon as we have explained the measures of information which are represented by H and R. H is a measure of the inherent order of a sequence of outcomes. H is called *entropy*, which is a thermodynamic term. It is used to describe the change of available energy in a system. In our sense, it measures the amount of information that is available in a sequence of outcomes. If it is to be an adequate measure, then it must reach its extreme values when the data are completely ordered and disordered.

When completely ordered, we have decision-making under certainty—complete predictability. When completely disordered, we have decision-making under uncertainty, with the Laplace criterion—all events are equally likely. In between, we have decision-making under risk. The following relationship accomplishes this end:

$$H = -p_1 \log p_1 - p_2 \log p_2 - p_3 \log p_3 \ldots -p_j \log p_j \ldots - p_n \log p_n$$
$$p_j = \text{probability of the } j\text{th outcome occurring}$$

$$p_1 + p_2 + p_3 + \ldots + p_j + \ldots + p_n = 1$$

The equation is written for n outcomes. If only one outcome can occur, then

$$H = -(1) \log (1) = 0$$

This is the situation of complete order. On the other hand, the maximum value of H occurs when each of n outcomes can appear with equal likelihood.

$$H_{\max} = -\log \frac{1}{n}$$

This is the situation of complete disorder. To determine the relative degree of ordering of a set of data, we can always use the ratio of the observed H value to the maximum H value that can occur. When we subtract this fraction from 1, we obtain an information measure called *redundancy*. Redundancy is the relative degree of structure in a sequence of outcomes.

$$R = 1 - \frac{H}{H_{\max}}$$

If H is observed as equal to zero, then the redundancy is equal to 1. This occurs when only one outcome is possible. On the other hand, $R = 0$ when $H = H_{max}$. Since $H = H_{max}$ when all states are equally likely, it is reasonable to obtain 0 redundancy. The redundancy measure ranges from 0 to 1, no matter how many outcomes are involved.

$R = 1$ (Decision-making under certainty)
$R = 0$ (Decision-making under uncertainty—Laplace)
$0 < R < 1$ (Decision-making under risk)

Now, let us consider the following situation. It has been purposefully designed to present a simple example with the characteristics we want to illustrate. A construction company bids on many contracts each year. If they win a contract, they record this outcome as 1. If they don't get the contract, they record the failure as 0. Over a long period of time, they produce the following sequence of outcomes:

0110110010101010101001101011010101011010.

If we count up the number of zeros and ones, we will find an almost equal number of each. When we apply the H measure to the relative frequencies of the outcomes, we observe that H and H_{max} are practically equal and so redundancy is almost zero. In other words, the prediction of outcomes on this basis will be hardly better than the prediction of heads or tails in a game of chance with a coin. Redundancy for the outcomes obtained from a true coin is zero. The calculation of H is shown below.

Outcome	Frequency	$p =$ Probability	Log p	$-p$ Log p
0	19	0.475	9.67669 − 10	0.1536
1	21	0.525	9.72016 − 10	0.1469
		1.000		0.3005

$$H_1 = (3.32)(0.3005) = 0.9976 \text{ bits *}$$

And what is H_{max}?

$$H_{max} = -\log_2(\tfrac{1}{2}) = 1 \text{ bit}$$

Therefore

$$R = 1 - \frac{0.9976}{1.000} = 0.0024$$

It is quite clear that analysis of the frequency distribution does not uncover the kinds of regularities for which we are looking. And so, we now analyze the sequence of one-step transitions in order to see whether, by looking at the system in this way, we can observe regularities, de-

---

* Information statistics are generally written in terms of the logarithm with the base 2. In order to convert from log with the base 10, we multiply by 3.32. We call the value derived in this form, bits.

pendencies, and greater structuring. We note that the first 0 is followed by 1. This 1, in turn, is followed by another 1. The second 1 is followed by a 0, and so forth. We continue in this way until we have counted the frequency of each kind of transition that can occur—in this case, four. The transition matrix below shows the number of times that each kind of transition took place.

	by 0	by 1
0 is followed	2	16
1 is followed	16	5

The matrix can be converted to probability form where the row probabilities sum to one.

	0	1	
0	0.111	0.889	1.000
1	0.762	0.238	1.000

Apparently, we have uncovered certain strong dependencies that exist in the sequence. These transition probabilities can now be used to determine the distribution of outcomes that could be expected to hold in the far future, if the process came to equilibrium. The method of determining the limiting distribution will not be shown here since it is explained in the chapter devoted to marketing in Part III. However, the probabilities of the outcomes in the limit are

$$p(0) = 0.461$$
$$p(1) = 0.539$$
$$\overline{1.000}$$

In this example, the limiting probabilities are not very different from the probabilities derived from the original frequency count. However, in many cases, the limiting distribution is substantially different from the initial distribution. In any event, we now have a means for predicting the next contract outcome with far better than a 50–50 chance. Our improved knowledge represents a gain of information. The H measure for the transition matrix is obtained by getting the expected value for H which is composed of the individual H values of each row—weighted by the limiting probabilities.

OUTCOME	p	Log p	$-p$ Log p
Row 0: Column 0	0.111	9.04532 — 10	0.1060
Row 0: Column 1	0.889	9.94890 — 10	0.0454
	$\overline{1.000}$		$\overline{0.1514}$
Row 1: Column 0	0.762	9.88195 — 10	0.0900
Row 1: Column 1	0.238	9.37658 — 10	0.1484
	$\overline{1.000}$		$\overline{0.2384}$

$$EV(H_2) = 0.1514(0.461) + 0.2384(0.539) = 0.1983$$

Again, we convert to values expressed by log with base 2.

$$EV(H_2) = 3.32(0.1983) = 0.6584 \text{ bits}$$

This H value is equivalent to the situation where one outcome has an observed probability of about 0.16 and the other 0.84. We can see how much we have improved our ability to predict outcomes. The maximum H value that could be obtained for the transition matrix would be 1. Therefore, the redundancy has also increased markedly.

$$R = 1 - \frac{0.6584}{1.000} = 0.3416$$

What kind of dependencies could account for this improvement in our ability to predict outcomes? One possible interpretation would be that having obtained a contract, the construction company feels less pressure to get another one. On the other hand, when their previous bid has failed to get them the contract, the executives work harder at getting the next one.

Our analysis has only examined dependencies on the previous outcome. Such one-step dependencies are characteristic of stochastic processes which are called *Markov chains*. Many times, dependencies go back further than one step. In such cases, we can include two, three, or more previous outcomes in our analysis. (That is, 01 is followed by 1, 11 is followed by 0, and so on, or 011 is followed by 0, 110 is followed by 1, and so on.) There are also other methods for analyzing dependencies in a sequence of outcomes, but in essence, they amount to the same thing—the attempt to gain information. The analysis of cybernetic systems utilizes the measures of information to determine the characteristics of a process and the effects of changing strategies. Figure 8.1 includes most of the elements that are generally considered in the cybernetic analysis of a system. To whatever extent information flow can be traced through the system, we improve our ability to control outcomes.* We have assumed throughout this discussion that the transition probabilities remain constant. If we were to change our strategy, or if our competitor changed his strategy, or if the state of nature changed by chance, the transition probabilities in the sequence of outcomes might also change. For this reason, we can observe and analyze the transitions of transition probabilities.

The analysis of sequential data can yield a great deal of information that might otherwise escape us. We have tried to present a short explanation of the nature of such analysis so that the reader will be familiar with the concepts and terms of this kind of problem-solving. At the

* W. Ross Ashby, *An Introduction to Cybernetics* (New York: John Wiley & Sons, Inc., 1956).

same time, he will be able to recognize situations in which quantitative techniques will be of value.

75. GENERATION OF OUTCOMES

Many times, the outcomes that interest us cannot be observed. We can only observe related phenomena. Sometimes the reason is that it would be too expensive, or too destructive, or too time-consuming to collect the necessary data. We may know the probabilities of many factors that underlie the outcome, and we can use this information to produce a sequence of outcomes. How do we go about generating such a sequence?

Let us consider the problem of the executive in charge of production for an oil refinery, which was mentioned in the previous chapter. For convenience, we will repeat the data given in the problem section of Chapter 7. Three components, A, B, and C, are combined to form different operating units, ABC, AB, AC, and BC. We know the probabilities with which A, B, and C, fail after x weeks of operation. What will be the probability distributions for the combinations? If the executive wants to have this information so that he can hire an adequate maintenance crew, he can hardly afford to wait several years until each of the units has failed enough times to provide the necessary data. Consequently, in this case, we will transform the information that is available into the information which is required. The method used to achieve this transformation is the Monte Carlo. To begin with, we list the probabilities for the known outcomes in the same way that we have done previously. However, this time we have an additional column for each component. This extra column is for the Monte Carlo identification.

If we take a bowl and put into this bowl 5 red chips, 10 blue chips, 15 yellow chips, 20 white chips, 20 black chips, 15 green chips, 10 orange chips, and 5 purple chips, we have then created a quantitative model of the failure characteristics of component A. We mix the contents of the bowl thoroughly. Then, we reach into it, without looking, and pull out one chip. We record the color and put the chip back in the bowl. Continuing, we mix, draw, record, and replace until we have obtained a large enough sample of colors. Of course, this sample will approximate the failure distribution of component A. If the drawings are properly done, very many times, it will almost exactly duplicate the distribution.

If we didn't have colored chips, we could use 100 chips of one color. We would number these chips from 00 to 99. There would then be 5 chips in the first category at the top of the table. They would be numbered 00, 01, 02, 03, 04, and they would be the equivalent of the red chips. Similarly, in the second category we would find numbers 05 to

COMPONENT A

x	p	COLOR	MONTE CARLO NUMBER
5	0.05	red	00–04
10	0.10	blue	05–14
15	0.15	yellow	15–29
20	0.20	white	30–49
25	0.20	black	50–69
30	0.15	green	70–84
35	0.10	orange	85–94
40	0.05	purple	95–99

14 which have the same meaning as the 10 blue chips, and so forth. Each Monte Carlo number category corresponds to a given color and hence to a given x. Every row in the table presents the set of Monte Carlo numbers that corresponds to the appropriate x value. Then, if we drew a chip numbered 86, we would know that this number was equivalent to an orange chip—and that an orange chip is equivalent to $x = 35$. Each of the numbers has an equal chance of being drawn. Since there are twice as many numbers in the category $x = 10$ as there are in $x = 5$, the probability that $x = 10$ will occur is twice the probability that $x = 5$ will occur. Using chips is an awkward and unnecessary procedure. Tables of random numbers are available in which any number is as likely to appear as any other. Therefore, we can put the bowl back on the shelf and use in its place the tables of random numbers. (A Table of Random Numbers will be found at the end of Chapter 11.)

The Monte Carlo numbers assigned to component A are given above. We now give the Monte Carlo numbers for components B and C.

COMPONENT B			COMPONENT C		
x	p	M.C. NUMBER	x	p	M.C. NUMBER
5	0.15	00–14	5	0.30	00–29
10	0.35	15–49	10	0.10	30–39
15	0.30	50–79	15	0.10	40–49
20	0.10	80–89	20	0.05	50–54
25	0.05	90–94	25	0.04	55–58
30	0.03	95–97	30	0.06	59–64
35	0.02	98–99	35	0.15	65–79
40	—	—	40	0.10	80–89
45	—	—	45	0.05	90–94
50	—	—	50	0.05	95–99

How do we combine these distributions to obtain the distribution for ABC? First, we take a random number. We see which value of x corresponds to that number for component A. We then do the same thing for component B. We take the next random number from the table and we mark down the appropriate x value for B. We do the same for C. Then, we start over again with A, and repeat the process over and over. The result is shown in Table 8.1.

Table 8.1　Using random numbers to generate outcomes.

Component A		Component B		Component C		Unit ABC
Random number	x	Random number	x	Random number	x	x
87	35	50	15	10	5	5
98	40	42	10	44	15	10
03	5	60	15	65	35	5
27	15	88	20	83	40	15
84	30	10	5	12	5	5
44	20	41	10	51	20	10
55	25	62	15	29	5	5
10	10	92	25	74	35	10
68	25	81	20	34	10	10
70	30	86	20	18	5	5
04	5	35	10	43	15	5
02	5	53	15	62	30	5
53	25	54	15	21	5	5
74	30	40	10	04	5	5
23	15	36	10	73	35	10
60	25	24	10	01	5	5
39	20	93	25	32	10	10
60	25	72	15	96	50	15
50	25	61	15	50	20	15
93	35	53	15	85	40	15
15	15	10	5	75	35	5
46	20	57	15	17	5	5
23	15	49	10	12	5	5
54	25	24	10	43	15	10
36	20	83	20	31	10	10

Let us look at the first line and see what it means. The random numbers 87, 50, and 10 appeared. They correspond to x values as follows: $x_A = 35$, $x_B = 15$, and $x_C = 5$. In line with the probabilities of failure, we have simulated the event that A fails at 35 weeks, B fails at 15 weeks, and C fails at 5 weeks. Since the first component to fail causes the entire unit to be shut down and repaired, the failure of ABC would occur, in this case, at 5 weeks. However, if the unit were only composed of AB, the first failure would occur at 15 weeks. For units AC and BC, the failure takes place after 5 weeks. The last column of Table 8.1 lists the x values for unit ABC. The others can be derived directly from the table by the reader. The more x values that are obtained in the sample, the more accurate is our description of the distribution of failures. The distributions that are derived from Table 8.1 are shown in Figure 8.2. Figure 8.3, which illustrates the distributions of the individual components, can be used for purposes of comparison.

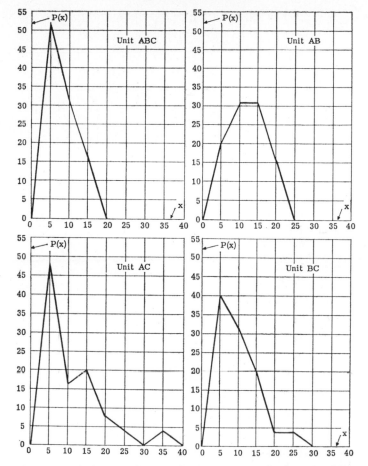

Figure 8.2 Probability that x weeks elapse between shutdowns for units.

Monte Carlo techniques can be applied in a great variety of situations where complex probability relationships hold. Their use does not require advanced mathematical knowledge, but it is very important to relate the probabilities to each other so that the final outcome is dimensionally sound.

76. OPTIMAL OUTCOMES

The methods of operations research are more frequently utilized for the solution of optimal-value models than they are for problem-solving models. In our example of the building contractor, in the section on information systems (p. 147), we did not permit the company's strategy to vary. If we had considered alternative strategies, we could have at-

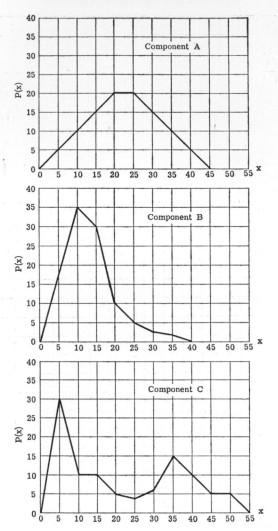

Figure 8.3 Probability that x weeks elapse between shutdowns for components.

tempted to simulate the sequence of outcomes. In this way, by compressing time, we would have obtained many years of outcomes for each strategy within a short period. We could then inspect the outcomes resulting from each strategy and pick the strategy that appeared to produce the "best" outcomes. Of course, this is a method of solution by brute force alone. But we cannot scoff at such methods because, at least, they give us some choice in attempting to achieve an optimal value.

On the other hand, there are some fairly refined methods available for searching through a great number of outcomes in order to find that outcome which maximizes the degree of attainment of the objective. One of the oldest and most useful techniques is the application of the derivative of a mathematical equation in which the derivative is set equal to zero. In the problem section of Chapter 6, we mentioned the use of the derivative to find the optimal sales-price strategy. The equation was

$$p = 2500s - 2000s^2 - 450$$

where p = profit, and

where s = sales price.

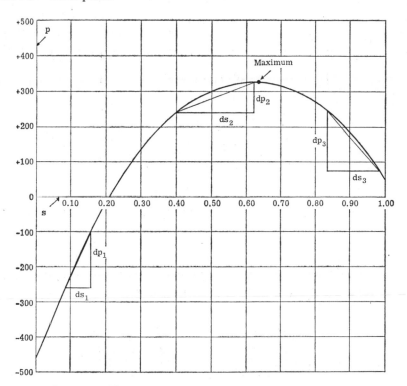

Figure 8.4   The use of the derivative to derive an optimal value.

Every point along the curve is a profit outcome that results from a different price strategy. The derivative of the equation is a measure of the slope of the curve at any point. In other words, it measures the rate of change of profit as compared to the rate of change of price. At three places on the curve in Figure 8.4, an exaggerated derivative relationship is shown. dp_1/ds_1 is a positive slope. dp_3/ds_3 is a negative slope.

Somewhere in between, the slope changes sign from plus to minus. That occurs when the slope is zero. dp_2/ds_2 is approaching a zero slope.

$$\frac{dp}{ds} = 2500 - 4000s$$

Since the slope of the curve is zero at its maximum * point, we can set the derivative equal to zero and solve for the value of s that satisfies this condition.

$$0 = 2500 - 4000s$$
$$0.625 = s$$

In this way, the derivative can frequently be employed to find the "best possible" outcome and strategy from among countless possibilities.

A great number of optimal-value models are based on the solution of inequations instead of equations. An equation always has an equals sign.

$$ax + by = c$$

An inequation can have

Greater than:	$ax + by > c$
Equal to or greater than:	$ax + by \geqslant c$
Less than:	$ax + by < c$
Equal to or less than:	$ax + by \leqslant c$

The ability to use inequations is extremely important to the decision-maker. Let us first examine why this is so, and then show how optimal values can be found by methodological means. For this example, we will assume that a candy manufacturer is attempting to find the optimal mixture for a box of chocolates. There are two kinds of candy that he wants in the box, C_1 and C_2. He lists the important characteristics of each kind of candy, and the characteristics of the box.

	C_1	C_2	Box
Number of pieces	x	y	35
Weight per piece (oz)	1.6	0.8	32
Space per piece (sq in.)	2.0	1.0	65
Cost per piece (dollar)	0.02	0.01	0.60

In other words, the manufacturer wants the box to weigh 32 ounces or 2 pounds. He wants 35 pieces of chocolate in each box. He wants the cost of the chocolates to be $0.60. Can he get everything that he wants?

---

* Setting the derivative of a function equal to zero will produce that value of the variable for which the function is either a maximum or a minimum. It is usually obvious from the form of the function whether it is a maximum or a minimum that is obtained. When there is doubt the question can be resolved by drawing a graph of the function that is being studied.

There will be x of the C_1 type and y of the C_2 type, so the total number must be 35.

$$x + y = 35$$

Similarly, the total space used must be

$$2x + y = 65$$

These two equations have only one solution:

$$x = 30, \qquad y = 5$$

If we now put these values into the cost equation

$$0.02x + 0.01y = \text{cost}$$

we find that the resulting cost is \$0.65, which is more than the manufacturer wanted to spend. It is impossible for him to obtain all of his objectives if he insists on having the exact requirements that he has listed. However, if we ask the manufacturer to restate the requirements in terms of inequalities, he will probably recognize that the inequalities are what he really meant to say in the first place. That is, the number of pieces of chocolate must be 35 or greater.

$$x + y \geqslant 35$$

As a matter of fact, the greater the better—as long as the cost per box does not exceed \$0.60. And if the cost can be less than \$0.60, this manufacturer will be delighted.

$$0.02x + 0.01y \leqslant 0.60$$

As far as the weight is concerned, it must be at least 32 ounces so that the box will compete in the 2-pound market. It can weigh more—as long as the cost restrictions are met. Therefore

$$1.6x + 0.8y \geqslant 32$$

Lastly, by means of fillers, the total space in the box can range from 40 square inches to 65 square inches. Let us see what the use of these inequations means by studying Figure 8.5. Each of the equations has been drawn on this graph. We should notice that the equation for the space requirement of 40 square inches is exactly the same as the equation for the weight restriction. Consequently, it is only necessary and possible to draw one line on the graph to represent both requirements. If we now transform the equations to inequations, each line drawn on the chart becomes a boundary. All values described by the inequation $x + y \geqslant 35$ lie on the line $x + y = 35$, or above that line. In the same way, all values of $1.6x + 0.8y \geqslant 32$ lie on the line $1.6x + 0.8y = 32$ or above that line. That is why the shaded area is only filled in above these two lines. No values can lie below them. Similarly, $0.02x +$ $0.01y \leqslant 0.60$ describes all points on the line $0.02x + 0.01y = 0.60$ and all points below that line. This constitutes the entire shaded area. It also constitutes the only area in which a solution can lie. The space requirements for the candy box must fall between the two lines $2x + y = 65$ and $2x + y = 40$. We see that this statement is irrelevant since the previous restrictions have already formed the permissible region for a solution. In other words, solutions to equations must lie somewhere on the lines; solutions to inequations must fall within the areas bounded by the lines. In this way, we are presented with a much larger number of alternative solutions. Every set of points within the shaded area is a solution to our problem.

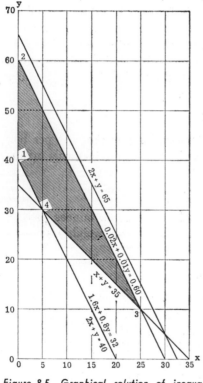

Figure 8.5   Graphical solution of inequations.

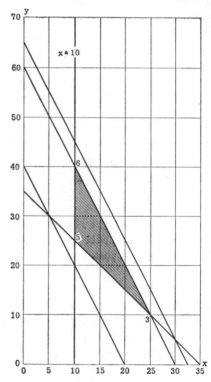

Figure 8.6   Graphical solution of inequations with an additional restriction.

We have increased the number of possible strategies that can be employed and have seemingly made the decision-maker's job much more complicated. Fortunately, the optimal solutions must lie on one of the corners of the convex polygon which we have constructed with our inequalities. Sometimes, the optimal solutions will also fall along the lines that form the perimeter of the polygon, but then the same optimal solution will occur at the corner point. Let us look at the four corner points that exist in Figure 8.5.

CORNER	x VALUE	y VALUE	WEIGHT	COST	SPACE
1	0	40	32	$0.40	40
2	0	60	48	0.60	60
3	25	10	48	0.60	60
4	5	30	32	0.40	40

There will be no solution with a cost lower than $0.40. Our manufacturer is a reasonable man and when he sees the solution, he is pleased to observe how low the cost can be made. However, he decides that $x = 0$ or $x = 5$ represents too few pieces of C_1. He then states that he wants at least 10 such pieces in the mixture. We use the same polygon, but we add the additional line $x \geq 10$. This is shown in Figure 8.6. The values of the two new corner points of the polygon are:

CORNER	x VALUE	y VALUE	WEIGHT	COST	SPACE
5	10	25	36	$0.45	45
6	10	40	48	0.60	60

So, he will probably choose the strategy of $x = 10$ C_1 and $y = 25$ C_2. Even for very complex sets of linear equations there are methods available for locating the corners of such convex polygons. When many dimensions are involved in the strategy, the polygons are formed in n-dimensional space so that they can never be adequately represented for visual inspection. The methods exist, however, for moving from one corner to another in such a way as to always improve the outcome. This procedure is continued until the optimal value is discovered.

77. MULTIPLE OUTCOMES

In the previous problem of the candy manufacturer, we obtained outcomes for weight, space, and cost. To simplify things, we assumed that cost was the factor to be optimized. Accordingly, we developed the solution of minimum cost, subject to the restriction that x should be equal to or greater than 10. If our objective had also included weight, and we had wanted to maximize weight in addition to minimizing cost, the problem could not have been solved. The data for the corner points show that maximum weight never occurs with minimum cost. In fact, weight and cost are related to each other as weight = (80) cost.

Therefore, it is apparent that as weight increases, cost will increase. In such a case, what should we do? Should we settle for a little of each, and choose that strategy which brings us neither minimum cost nor maximum weight? There is only one way in which we can decide what to do, and that is to determine how important each objective is to the decision-maker.

It will be recognized that our quandary stems from multiple objectives that occupy different dimensions. We cannot quantitatively combine these multiple outcomes in any simple fashion. Both methods of ranking and the standard gamble are inadequate to deal with complex, multi-dimensional outcomes. Certainly, we cannot add weight and cost together and choose the sum we like the best. We cannot do this even if we first weight each outcome in terms of its importance to us.

Let us consider the problem of the decision-maker who has to decide between two possible locations for a new plant which the company is planning to build. In order to determine the "best" location, he lists six different outcomes that result for each strategy. The decision-maker considers these six outcomes as the relevant dimensions of the company's objectives. He then rates these outcomes in terms of his considered judgement of their relative importance to the final outcome or payoff measure. (*Note:* This can be accomplished by ranking or standard gamble. Problems 4 and 5 suggest another possible approach.)

	OUTCOME	DIMENSION	IMPORTANCE
$X1$:	cost of land and cost of building a plant.	dollar investment	A
$X2$:	desirability of site.	preference rating (10 poorest—1 best)	B
$X3$:	cost of labor.	dollar expense	C
$X4$:	community relations.	cooperation rating (10 poorest—1 best)	D
$X5$:	raw-material supply.	quality and cost (10 poorest—1 best)	E
$X6$:	transportation facilities.	convenience and cost (10 poorest—1 best)	F

Data are collected for the alternative strategies and the resulting payoff matrix will have six outcome values in each box. For simplicity, we shall consider only one state of nature. If more than one state of nature exists, the methods previously developed for decision-making under risk and uncertainty can be applied—after the problem of combining the multiple outcomes has been resolved.

	$S1$:	$S2$:	IMPORTANCE
$X1$:	$1,000,000	$1,500,000	3
$X2$:	6	10	4
$X3$:	$1.70/hr.	$1.50/hr.	5
$X4$:	7	4	1
$X5$:	2	8	3
$X6$:	9	6	2

Importance increases with larger numbers.

An incorrect method of comparing strategies $S1$ and $S2$, but one that is frequently used, is to sum the weighted products of the outcomes from each strategy. That is,

$$O(S1) = 3(1,000,000) + 4(6) + 5(1.70) + 1(7) + 3(2) + 2(9)$$
$$= 3,000,063.50$$

$$O(S2) = 3(1,500,000) + 4(10) + 5(1.50) + 1(4) + 3(8) + 2(6)$$
$$= 4,500,087.50$$

By this method, $O(S1)$ is the better selection. The following ratio provides a comparison:

$$\frac{O(S2)}{O(S1)} = \frac{4,500,087.50}{3,000,063.50} = 1.50$$

Now, let us see what happens if we change the scale of $X1$ so that it is read in million-dollar units instead of single-dollar units. We know that if the method of comparison that we are using is dimensionally sound, the exact same ratio should result.

$$O(S1) = 3(1) + 4(6) + 5(1.70) + 1(7) + 3(2) + 2(9) \quad = 66.5$$
$$O(S2) = 3(1.5) + 4(10) + 5(1.50) + 1(4) + 3(8) + 2(6) = 92.0$$

Then, the ratio is

$$\frac{O(S2)}{O(S1)} = \frac{92.0}{66.5} = 1.38$$

The ratio is not the same, which shows that the change in scale introduced dimensional distortion in the ratio. The proper method for comparing multiple outcomes has been developed by P. W. Bridgeman.[*] This method uses the product of the powers, that is:

$$O = (X1)^A (X2)^B (X3)^C \ldots (X6)^F$$

We will now apply the unit-dollar scale and the million-dollar scale to this method.

($X1$ expressed in unit dollars)

$$O(S1) = (1,000,000)^3 (6)^4 (1.70)^5 (7)^1 (2)^3 (9)^2 \quad = 8.34 \times 10^{25}$$
$$O(S2) = (1,500,000)^3 (10)^4 (1.50)^5 (4)^1 (8)^3 (6)^2 = 1.89 \times 10^{28}$$

$$\frac{O(S2)}{O(S1)} = \frac{1.89 \times 10^{28}}{8.34 \times 10^{25}} = 226$$

($X1$ expressed in million dollars)

$$O(S1) = (1)^3 (6)^4 (1.70)^5 (7)^1 (2)^3 (9)^2 \quad = 8.34 \times 10^7$$
$$O(S2) = (1.5)^3 (10)^4 (1.50)^5 (4)^1 (8)^3 (6)^2 = 1.89 \times 10^{10}$$

$$\frac{O(S2)}{O(S1)} = \frac{1.89 \times 10^{10}}{8.34 \times 10^7} = 226$$

[*] P. W. Bridgeman, *Dimensional Analysis* (New Haven: Yale University Press, 1922), pp. 21–22.

We see that the ratio is invariant and not affected by the transformation of scale when the second method is used. That is because the second method produced a pure number—a number without dimensions.

To illustrate, if we add a certain amount of cooperation to a certain amount of convenience, we derive the ratio of the combined outcomes

$$\frac{\text{cooperation} + \text{convenience}}{\text{cooperation} + \text{convenience}}$$

which is equal to

$$\frac{\text{cooperation}}{\text{cooperation} + \text{convenience}} + \frac{\text{convenience}}{\text{cooperation} + \text{convenience}}$$

There is nothing more that we can do with these dimensions. Whereas, by multiplication, they all cancel.

$$\frac{(\text{cooperation})(\text{convenience})}{(\text{cooperation})(\text{convenience})} = \text{pure number}$$

Dimensional integrity is a requirement of any sound analysis. When we combine a number of outcomes that occupy various dimensions in an attempt to optimize the over-all outcome, the ratio of the outcomes should be a pure number. If some of the components are to be maximized while others are to be minimized, we can use positive powers for the outcomes to be maximized and negative powers for the outcomes to be minimized. For example, let us now compare the first two strategies of the candy manufacturer. He wishes to maximize weight and minimize cost. He lists their relative importance as follows:

	$S1$	$S2$	IMPORTANCE
Weight	32	48	2
Cost	40	60	3

$$O(S1) = (32)^2(40)^{-3} = \frac{4}{250}$$

$$O(S2) = (48)^2(60)^{-3} = \frac{4}{375}$$

$$\frac{O(S1)}{O(S2)} = 1.5$$

Therefore, the candy manufacturer will choose his first strategy. Since it is the best that he can do in terms of his stated preferences, it is the optimal strategy.

When dimensions are combined in this manner, the ratios will always produce a pure number. This follows from the fact that multiplication generates an area, volume, and so on, which has the property of being common space for the participating outcomes. This common space is proportional to the importance of the values. Addition creates no such common territory and is not properly used when it attempts to combine basically different dimensions as though they were the same. We can see that addition is satisfactory when we are adding along the same dimensional axis, or when we are adding spaces that possess the same properties.

There are, of course, many other aspects of decision-making elements which properly belong in a chapter devoted to quantitative models. However, we believe that the problem section that follows speaks for itself. In the problem section many different kinds of qualitative and quantitative models are developed. The emphasis is on quantitative models. But all the models are designed to handle the very great number of different situations that can arise when objectives, strategies, states of nature, competitive strategies, outcomes, and payoffs interact with each other in the decision-making framework.

PROBLEMS

1. Suppose you have the following probability distribution of truck arrivals at a loading dock:

TRUCKS PER 15-MINUTE INTERVAL	PROBABILITY
0	0.135
1	0.270
2	0.270
3	0.180
4	0.090
5	0.055

You want to know the probability distribution of truck arrivals on an hourly basis. One way to do this is by Monte Carlo. Assign three digit numbers to each number of truck arrivals in the above table in proportion to the probability of occurrence. Thus, for example, we can assign the numbers 000–134, inclusive, to zero arrivals. Then use the table of random numbers to select a series of samples of four 15-minute interval arrivals. The total number of arrivals in the four intervals is the number of arrivals in one hour. Continuing in this way one can get a sample of as many hours as is desired and can determine the desired probability distribution. Take a sample of 100 hours and find the probability distribution.

2. It is often the case that a new system is planned for processing some work load. The arrangement of the system is new but the individual components of the system are familiar and information is available concerning their performance individually. Under such circumstances it is often worthwhile to use Monte Carlo methods to determine how the system will operate as a whole.

Suppose there are two processes with the following probability distributions of time necessary to process one unit:

PROCESS A		PROCESS B	
MINUTES REQUIRED	PROBABILITY	MINUTES REQUIRED	PROBABILITY
1	0.10	1	0.11
2	0.20	2	0.45
3	0.40	3	0.15
4	0.20	4	0.10
5	0.10	5	0.08
		6	0.05
		7	0.04
		8	0.02

The system being considered requires that each unit shall be processed first on A and then on B. The average time required on A is three minutes and the average time required on B is three minutes. A unit arrives at A every three minutes. Use Monte Carlo procedures to run a sample of 50 units through the system. You will be interested in such characteristics of the system as the average time it takes a unit to go through and the waiting times before either process. [Assign numbers to A's processing times in proportion to the given probabilities and do likewise for B's processing times. You will need two separate samples of 50 random numbers: the first will represent A's processing times; the second, B's processing times. It is now only necessary to work through the sample, keeping track of the time when each unit actually starts processing on A and B.]

3. Here are 65 outcomes:
   01101101001111010101011011101101101111010101110111010101011
   011010011
   a. Determine the entropy and the redundancy of the frequencies of the two outcomes.
   b. Determine the entropy and the redundancy of the one step transitions. The limiting probabilities are: $p(0) = 0.348$, $p(1) = 0.652$.

4. An executive has two personal objectives: income and leisure time. He spends 77 hours per week in the routine activities of sleeping, commuting, etc., so his leisure time is $168-77 = 91$ hours minus the time he spends on his job. He is currently working 48 hours per week for $20,000 per year. He has turned down a job offer of $24,000 which would require him to work 54 hours per week. He accepts an offer of $33,000 which requires 62 hours per week. What can you say about the weighting of his two objectives, assuming that the three jobs were similar in all other respects? What would be his salary requirements if a job demanded 72 hours per week?

5. A graduating business student has received a variety of job offers. He has three objectives: salary, opportunity for advancement, and location. He measures opportunity for advancement by the number of executive positions in the company and he is interested in location only in terms of distance from

his home city—the farther it is, the less he likes it. There are three job offers which he considers to be equally good:

Job offer	Salary	Executive positions	Distance
A	$7200	200	500
B	7500	300	2000
C	8500	200	1000

How is the student weighting his objectives?

PART 3

DECISION-PROBLEM PARADIGMS

Chapter nine

Of Marketing

Marketing is that subject which treats all of the conditions under which the supplier meets the consumer. It is the testing ground where the cumulative effect of many previous decisions can be observed. If sales are good, then the marketing effort is said to be successful, and vice versa. Of course, it is usually understood that the marketing objective is not only sales. It is sales at a sufficiently low cost so that a good profit can be realized. At the same time, few companies are solely interested in profit today, or profit this month. The ability to continue to make profit far into the future is of prime importance. It is hard to make marketing decisions that take both present profit and future profit into account. For this reason, marketing problems are prone to serious temporal sub-optimization. But this is only one of the difficulties that management experiences in formulating marketing decision problems.

First of all, there are an enormous number of strategic possibilities. The dimensions of marketing strategies are so varied that it is inconceivable to include all of them in a formal analysis. The controls that exist for achieving different market strategies begin with the design of the product and include naming the brand, packaging the product, pricing the product, choosing types of outlets, and advertising the brand. In other words, they consist of product characteristics, price, distribution, and communication with consumers.

The second major difficulty is the effect of competition. Formulating the strategic possibilities of a rational competitor is as difficult as, if not more difficult than, formulating our own strategies. Creativity plays such an important part in the development of marketing strategies that it is quite often impossible to analyze the effects that competitive strategies will have on the outcomes. Many times, more than a single competitor exists. Each competitor has so great a number of possible strategies that the resolution of the decision problem is impossible. In the same way, the states of nature that affect the outcomes are hard to detail. The economy can change in too many ways to catalog them all. Consumer attitudes are dynamic and respond to factors that are outside the ordinary scope of consideration. All told, detection and listing of all relevant columns in the decision matrix cannot be a reasonable approach to the problem. To illustrate this, imagine that the decision-maker's strategy includes 5 possible product designs, 5 prices, 5 patterns of distribution, and 5 methods of communicating with the consumer. This is a total of 625 strategies. If there are 4 competitors, it is not unreasonable to assume that each of the competitors has 625 strategies available. Presuming that there are 5 states of nature, then the number of different conditions that can prevail is 476,837,158,203,125. Ironically, the only ludicrous thing about this number is that it is far too small to describe the actual situation.

The third difficulty is the determination of outcomes. Even if we could write down all of the important strategies, competitive strategies, and states of nature, we could not hope to find one outcome that would suffice to describe completely each box in the payoff matrix. We have already mentioned that a multiple objective exists. That is, we are interested in both short- and long-term profit. Usually, we cannot determine either of these two kinds of profit for every box. The situation is simply too complex for us to conceive of what would happen to profit if one or several factors changed. For example, suppose the decision-maker changed his package; at the same time, one competitor lowered his price; meanwhile, the state of nature changed so that it was warmer than usual; and the cost of living rose—how would the two kinds of profit be affected? Even the most deliberate and painstaking attempts to formulate this problem must result in failure.

How, then, do we handle these three types of difficulties? One approach is to consider only a few factors at a time, i.e., parts of strategies, states of nature, and so on. These few factors are related either to the profit outcomes or to suboutcomes that are believed to influence profit. For example, we relate color of the package and the expressed preferences of consumers for various colors. The connection between the consumers' preference and profit cannot be formalized. The executive believes that increasing consumer preference is a means of increasing profit. Similarly, the executive tries to minimize the cost of communicating the brand name to x number of consumers, or he attempts to increase sales volume. The profit objectives are not forgotten in these cases. The general relationships between cost and profit—between the size of an advertising campaign and profit—between sales volume and profit, and so on are kept in mind even though they cannot be included in the explicit formulation of the problem.

Another approach to the problem is to consider outcomes and suboutcomes without attempting to find relationships between them and the strategies, competitive strategies, and states of nature. We have previously discussed this kind of analysis of outcome data which treats outcomes as information. The purpose of the investigation is to find patterns and regularities that permit us to predict future outcomes although we do not know the way in which these results occur. Neither this approach nor the one that considers parts of strategies is entirely satisfactory. The use of parts of strategies results in suboptimization, and a great deal of caution must be exercised to prevent the suboptimization from producing outcomes that lower the degree of achievement of the objectives. The danger always exists that a few factors isolated from the total environment in which they appear will behave in an entirely different manner under the conditions of isolation. The recourse to suboutcomes is another cause of suboptimization. We presume that the suboutcome is related to profit in a manner that we can intuit. If we are wrong, then the achievement of the optimal suboutcome can lead to lower rather than higher profit. However, since we can observe only certain kinds of factors that relate to the marketing objectives, we have no alternative but to use suboutcomes. For the most part it is better than doing nothing at all. The danger in just studying outcome data arises from the possibility that significant changes might have taken place during the period in which the data were collected. Since the outcomes are not analyzed in conjunction with strategies and states of nature, the effects of changes are observed in the data without the knowledge of what caused them. Sometimes, the fact that a significant change took place can be detected and traced to its source by means of statistical control techniques. In general, however, the assumption is made that no significant changes took place during the period and that the outcome process is essentially stable. If a competitor, or the decision-maker, introduces an important change, then it is possible to attempt to determine the effect of that change by studying the outcome data before and after the change. All of the above remarks will apply in one form or another to the discussion of specific marketing models, which follows.

78. BRAND-SHARE MODEL

The portion of the market that each company obtains is an important measure of the relative success of the respective brands. This portion is usually called the *brand share*. Certainly, one company can have 90 per cent of the market and still be making less profit than five other companies, each of which has 2 per cent of the market. But, in general, the executives of a company can tell whether or not they are making a reasonable profit on what they sell. They want to know whether they are selling as much as they should be selling, and how much more they could be selling. Brand-share measurements, which can be obtained from consumer surveys or by services that record brand sales in stores, provide some answers to these questions.

When a company introduces a change in strategy, it is usually with the intention of achieving an increase in brand share. Sometimes the change is made with the hope of reversing a downward trend in brand share. Perhaps a competitor introduces the first change, and the marketing decision-maker believes that it will result in a decreasing brand share for his company. However, changes in brand share can occur without any change at all in strategies, competitive strategies, and states of nature. A company that experiences a decreasing brand share may well be better off to wait and see, rather than to take immediate action. The reason is that the decision-makers cannot be sure what effect their action may have on both short- and long-range profit. In other words, their first job is to predict what will happen if they do nothing to change their present course.

The brand-share model succeeds in describing both short- and long-term brand-share outcomes. Although brand share may not be as direct an outcome as short- and long-term profit, nevertheless it is a most useful description of general conditions. It is also one way in which the effect of a change in a complex strategy, competitive strategy, or state of nature can be examined on both a short- and long-term basis.

To begin with, we determine the brand shares of each of the several brands that are defined as the market. The definition of "the market" is not as straightforward as it might seem. The kind of problem that develops when we attempt to construct a brand-share model for automobiles is representative. Is it sufficient to consider cars that are in the same price field, or should we consider all prices of automobiles? Are small three-wheel cars part of the market? If so, are motor scooters also to be considered? Should we group all convertibles together? And so forth. Empirical data gathered from the consumer by surveys is one means of approaching this problem. In effect, we are attempting to define the relevant product class. Groupings by function and then subgroupings by outlets, users, price, quality, and so on are a reasonable means of defining a product class. Once it is learned what the consumer considers to be competitive brands, the marketing executive can generally apply his experience and intuition to the job of defining the market.

One other kind of information is required. We need to know brand-switching characteristics. In other words, some consumers use one brand all of the time while others switch continually from one brand to another.

Brand-switching may be influenced by a variety of factors such as the effect of consumer leaders who cause consumer followers to imitate their choice. Meanwhile, the leader may meet up with an even more dominant leader who will succeed in switching the former to the latter's brand. Dissatisfaction with a product can lead to switching. The dissatisfaction may be caused by a chance event which occurs once in every n products. It may occur because of special circumstances, such as ill health or bad weather which the consumer thereafter associates with the product. Another possibility is the effect of boredom with any brand after a given number of uses. Consumers would have different tolerances for such boredom. No matter what the reasons, surveys detect the brand-switching phenomena by observing the last two purchases that the consumer has made. There are many refinements required in order to collect meaningful and useful data. We obviously cannot dwell on such topics because it would shift us from our purpose, which is to construct the general model.

Let us assume that 5 brands constitute "the market." These 5 brands, at the time we begin our study (t_0), have brand shares, $S_i(t_0)$. In this case i stands for the brand $(i = 1, 2, 3, 4, 5)$. We know that the sum of the brand shares must equal 100 per cent of the market, or 1.00.

$$S_1(t_0) + S_2(t_0) + S_3(t_0) + S_4(t_0) + S_5(t_0) = 1.00$$

We must convert the switching data so that the sum of the probabilities of changing from one specific brand to any other brand, or not changing at all, is equal to one.

$$p_{11} + p_{12} + p_{13} + p_{14} + p_{15} = 1.00$$

$$p_{21} + p_{22} + p_{23} + p_{24} + p_{25} = 1.00$$

$$\cdots$$

where p_{11} = probability that a consumer of Brand 1 does not switch to another brand, and

p_{12} = probability that a consumer of Brand 1 switches to Brand 2 —and so on.

Let us assume that we have collected the following information.

i	$S_i(t_0)$	From Brand	To Brand 1	2	3	4	5	
1	0.20	1	0.57	0.03	0.13	0.16	0.11	1.00
2	0.15	2	0.15	0.47	0.15	0.08	0.15	1.00
3	0.10	3	0.09	0.06	0.55	0.15	0.15	1.00
4	0.30	4	0.07	0.01	0.14	0.64	0.14	1.00
5	0.25	5	0.10	0.05	0.14	0.19	0.52	1.00
	1.00							

These probabilities are obtained by treating each row of the original switching data as a frequency distribution (with 5 classes) and converting the frequencies to probabilities by dividing by the total frequency for the row. Each entry in the body of the table is the probability that a consumer of the brand represented by the row will switch from that brand to the brand represented by the column. Thus, the probability that a consumer of Brand 2 will switch to Brand 5 is 0.15. The column headed $S_i(t_0)$ shows the original share of the market of each brand. The diagonal of this matrix (0.57, 0.47, 0.55, 0.64, and 0.52) represents the probability that no change will occur. This is the proportion of consumers who stay with the same brand for two successive purchases. Consequently, the diagonal is one possible definition of brand loyalty. We will have occasion, later on, to discuss the question of brand loyalty again.

We can now use the transition matrix to derive successive states of brand share. This is accomplished in the following way. Brand 1 starts out with 20 per cent of the market. For convenience, let us say that the market consists of 1000 consumers. Then Brand 1 has 200 of these consumers at time t_0. What happens at time t_1? About 57 per cent of 200 consumers, or 114, do not change their brand. Brand 2 has 150 consumers at time t_0. Since 15 per cent of Brand-2 users become Brand-1 users, we calculate that 22.5 Brand-2 consumers become Brand-1 users. In the same way we find that 9 Brand-3 consumers become Brand-1 users, 21 Brand-4 consumers become Brand-1 consumers, and 25 Brand-5 users become Brand-1 consumers. This means that at time t_1, Brand 1 has

$$114 + 22.5 + 9 + 21 + 25 = 191.5$$

which represents a loss of 8.5 consumers. We can perform the same calculations for each of the brands and, in this way, determine brand share at time t_1. The operations to find brand share at time t_2 are identical in all respects. Of course, we begin with the brand-share situation of time t_1 instead of time t_0. For our assumed case, we find that brand share changes in the following way.

i	$S_i(t_0)$	$S_i(t_1)$	$S_i(t_2)$	$S_i(t_3)$	...	$S_i(t_L)$
1	20.00	19.15	18.41	17.93	...	17.29
2	15.00	9.80	7.72	6.88	...	6.32
3	10.00	18.05	21.31	22.63	...	23.54
4	30.00	29.85	30.06	30.27	...	30.63
5	25.00	23.15	22.50	22.29	...	22.22
	100.00	100.00	100.00	100.00		100.00

Three transitional steps are shown together with the limiting distribution. These limiting values picture the long-term situation that will occur if nothing happens to disturb the evolution of the system. The limiting values are derived by repeatedly going through the process that we described above to determine successive brand-share states. However, we must keep on doing this until no more change takes place in the brand shares. This procedure would be too time-consuming unless we used a computer. Fortunately, it is possible to express this problem in mathematical terms. There are six relationships that we can write. The first five are the basic computations which are used to derive the next set of brand-share values. The sixth is the relationship we previously mentioned to describe the fact that the sum of the brand shares must equal 1.00.

$$S_1' = 0.57\,S_1 + 0.15\,S_2 + 0.09\,S_3 + 0.07\,S_4 + 0.10\,S_5$$
$$S_2' = 0.03\,S_1 + 0.47\,S_2 + 0.06\,S_3 + 0.01\,S_4 + 0.05\,S_5$$
$$S_3' = 0.13\,S_1 + 0.15\,S_2 + 0.55\,S_3 + 0.14\,S_4 + 0.14\,S_5$$
$$S_4' = 0.16\,S_1 + 0.08\,S_2 + 0.15\,S_3 + 0.64\,S_4 + 0.19\,S_5$$
$$S_5' = 0.11\,S_1 + 0.15\,S_2 + 0.15\,S_3 + 0.14\,S_4 + 0.52\,S_5$$

$$S_1 + S_2 + S_3 + S_4 + S_5 = 1.00$$

Under equilibrium conditions, the brand share at time t_{n+1} will be exactly the same as the brand share at time t_n. In other words, as much is going out as is coming in, and the brand share of each company remains the same. To express this fact mathematically, we set $S_i(t_{n+1}) = S_i(t_n)$. In the above equations, this means that $S_1' = S_1$, $S_2' = S_2$, $S_3' = S_3$, $S_4' = S_4$, and $S_5' = S_5$. From this, we derive a new set of equations.

$$-0.43\,S_1 + 0.15\,S_2 + 0.09\,S_3 + 0.07\,S_4 + 0.10\,S_5 = 0$$
$$0.03\,S_1 - 0.53\,S_2 + 0.06\,S_3 + 0.01\,S_4 + 0.05\,S_5 = 0$$
$$0.13\,S_1 + 0.15\,S_2 - 0.45\,S_3 + 0.14\,S_4 + 0.14\,S_5 = 0$$
$$0.16\,S_1 + 0.08\,S_2 + 0.15\,S_3 - 0.36\,S_4 + 0.19\,S_5 = 0$$
$$0.11\,S_1 + 0.15\,S_2 + 0.15\,S_3 + 0.14\,S_4 - 0.48\,S_5 = 0$$

$$S_1 + S_2 + S_0 + S_4 + S_5 = 1.00$$

(*Note:* $0.57\,S_1 - 1.00\,S_1 = -0.43\,S_1$; $0.47\,S_2 - 1.00\,S_2 = -0.53\,S_2$; and so on.) Any four of the five switching equations together with the equation which denotes that the sum of the brand shares must equal one are solved by methods of algebra. The results are the brand shares in the limit. Figure 9.1 shows the alteration of brand shares in graphical form. Let us observe the changes in brand position that occur over time.

BRAND	RANKING AT t_0	RANKING AT t_L
1	3	4
2	4	5
3	5	2
4	1	1
5	2	3

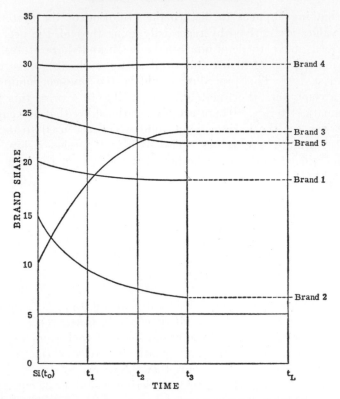

Figure 9.1 Successive brand share conditions including the limiting conditions at t_L.

Brands 5, 1, and 2 drop one position in their rankings. Brand 3 climbs three steps, going from the lowest ranking to the position of second largest brand in the market. How long does it take for this change to occur? The answer to this question will depend on the characteristics of the switching probabilities, the initial brand distribution, and the speed with which switching takes place. Now, let us consider for a moment the problem of Brand 4. It is the leader in the market with 30 per cent brand share. The sales manager observes that a decrease in sales takes place at time t_1. He asks himself whether the decrease is the first sign of a new trend for his company. After studying the brand-switching model, the sales manager knows that the setback is temporary. He also knows that if everything stays the same, his company will continue to obtain a little more than 30 per cent of the total market. This fact may not please him, in which case he will attempt to find a new strategy that will bring about a change in the brand-switching characteristics.

A more intensive view of this problem leads us to question how reasonable the assumption is that the matrix of switching probabilities is ever constant and unchanging. Successive consumer surveys can produce transition data for the transition data of the switching matrix. The problem becomes much more complex when it is considered in this way, but the utility of the solution increases as well. In particular the influence of a new strategy can be examined in terms of the changes it induces in the dynamic system of transition probabilities.

Another point of interest is the fact that below some level of brand share it may not be economical for a company to remain in business. Of course, the level will vary by industry, product, and many special circumstances. On Figure 9.1 we have drawn this level at 5 per cent. Brand 2 is not very far from being a marginal brand. It is therefore reasonable for the other companies to attempt to analyze what will happen to their respective shares of the market if Brand 2 should not survive. For this situation, data must be collected to indicate what would happen to Brand-2 users if Brand 2 ceased to exist. Another situation arises when a new brand is about to enter the market. Data from test markets can then be analyzed in this same way. The fact that a new brand starts out slowly does not mean that it will not succeed eventually in obtaining a reasonable share of the market. On the other hand, if a new brand obtains a substantial market position this does not mean that it will be able to keep it. Sometimes wide oscillatory behavior occurs before brand shares settle down to equilibrium values (see Figure 9.2). In this hypothetical case, only one brand exists initially and then two new brands enter the market. Especially in such oscillatory situations, observations of brand share that are limited to one particular interval of time can be misleading. It is possible to observe brand-share position at a time when brand share is swinging down or when it is very low, without considering the nature of such swings and with the misguided belief that they represent trends or permanent conditions. Many times, when a strong downtrend occurs action is taken that alters the situation. Such action, since it is taken for the wrong reasons, will seldom improve upon the brand position that would have occurred at equilibrium under the original conditions.

One way of incorporating transitions of transitions is to represent the switching probabilities for each brand as lambda (λ), and mu (μ). We let λ_i be the probability that one or more consumers will switch to Brand i in some period of time and μ_i be the probability that one or more consumers will switch from Brand i to some other competitive brand in the same period. The period of time is presumed to be small enough so that it is quite unlikely that more than one switch of either kind will take place. Figure 9.3(a) depicts the situation for Brand i. λ and μ will change over time depending upon such factors as brand share, relative

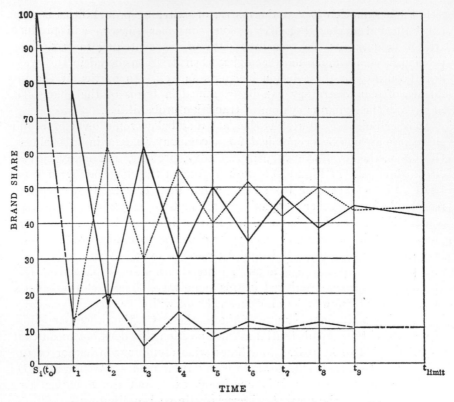

Figure 9.2   *Wide oscillations can occur in the brand share overtime.*

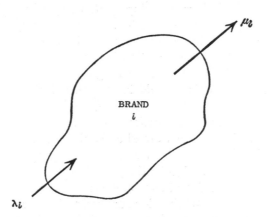

Figure 9.3a Representation of brand switching to and from (λ_i and μ_i) brand i.

advertising expenditures, price changes, changes in quality, number of competitors, strategies of competitors, degree of market saturation. The μ factor increases when competitive strategies are effective with the result that more consumers flow out of the Brand-i set of consumers. In other words μ represents, in part, the elements that are under the control of the competitors. At the same time changes can occur in states of nature that will result in an increased μ. However, it is important to note that a competitor's strategy may not be directed at increasing μ but rather at decreasing λ. Similarly, the decision-maker's strategy might be aimed at increasing λ, but it will usually also include strategic elements to decrease or stabilize μ. Changes in the state of nature can also affect λ.

The sales of Brand i can be put into terms of brand share, so that 100 per cent would be its maximum value at any time. One hundred per cent represents complete market domination and saturation. A mathematical model can be constructed to describe the probability that Brand i will have different shares of the market. We will not derive this model here, since it requires a complex derivation which does not shed additional light on the class of model with which we are dealing. It is worthwhile noting, however, that this class of model applies to general conditions which are known as birth and death processes. It is clear that the relevant analogy is that new customers are being born all of the time as described by λ while old customers pass along to other brands as described by μ. The mathematical model is

$$P_{S_i} = \frac{S!}{S_i!(S - S_i)!} \left(\frac{\lambda}{\mu}\right)^{S_i} P_0$$

$S =$ market saturation limit,
$S_i =$ brand share of i,
$P_{S_i} =$ probability of Brand i obtaining a brand share S_i,
$P_0 =$ probability of Brand i obtaining a zero brand share.
$S! = S(S - 1)(S - 2) \ldots (2)(1)$ and is read "S factorial."

The market saturation limit is 100. Figure 9.3(b) depicts the resulting distributions for two competing brands A and B with (λ/μ) values of $\frac{1}{2}$ and 2 respectively. (With two brands the expected brand shares will sum to 1. When more than two brands are involved it is necessary to adjust the brand shares so that the expected values will sum to 1.) We can observe that the distributions in Figure 9.3(b) are quite narrow, indicating that the resulting brand shares will not vary by any great amount from the expected brand-share values, 0.33 for Brand A and 0.67 for Brand B. Models of this type can be used to simulate brand share in the limit. Therefore, they are essentially predictors of outcomes. It should be emphasized that λ and μ can be made dependent on the size of

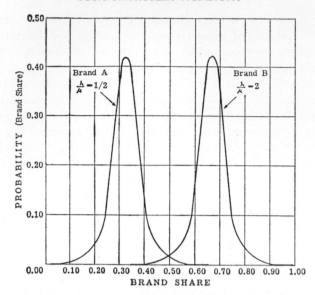

Figure 9.3b Brand share probability distributions for brands A and B.

the brand share S_i, or they can be made dependent on each other, and they can be dependent upon time, and so on. Many of the relationships are complex feedback rules. The decision-maker can employ a model of this sort not only to try to obtain predictions of reality, but to determine the probable outcomes of strategies in a completely formal sense. It would be absurd to interpret the results derived from such models in any manner other than a qualitative one. Nevertheless, the extreme complexity of the marketing field normally prevents the decision-maker from tracing through complex interdependent situations. For this reason, qualitative interpretations of quantitative models can play an important role in assisting the marketing decision-maker.

79. BRAND-LOYALTY MODEL

Students of marketing describe problems, strategic factors, states of nature, and outcomes by the use of many phrases that produce intuitive understanding but lack specific definition. This situation seriously handicaps the development of useful marketing models. One such term which is frequently used in marketing is *brand loyalty*. Previously, we called attention to the diagonal of the switching matrix as a possible definition of brand loyalty. The boxes along the diagonal expressed the probability that the consumer would make no change in his brand choice between two successive purchases. It is generally understood that loyalty refers to some kind of consumer constancy to a particular brand. If a survey reveals that 15 per cent of all the consumers in a given market use Brand X and only Brand X, how much consumer loyalty to Brand X does this connote? On the face of it, the decision-maker might be tempted to answer that 15 per cent of the consumer market is 100 per cent loyal to Brand X. In saying this, the decision-maker implies that 15 per cent of the market likes the product characteristics and the brand image of X. (The brand image is the total set of associations that characterizes X in the consumer's mind.) The decision-maker does not want to include in his estimates of loyalty consumers who are actually indifferent to whether they use Brand X or Brand Y. Such indifferent consumers would appear to be 50 per cent loyal to Brand X and 50 per cent loyal to Brand Y. On the other hand, a number of the indifferent consumers, by chance alone, might have always used X and never used Y. Therefore, the first question that must be resolved is the scale by which we measure brand loyalty. The second aspect of the problem we will consider is the way in which brand loyalty can appear to exist even when the consumer has no preference for one brand over another.

The importance of the brand-loyalty analysis is that if brand loyalty actually exists, then marketing strategies must take this fact into account. If a company assumes, on the basis of data which it collects, that a certain amount of brand loyalty exists for its product in the market—when, in fact, that amount of brand loyalty could have arisen by chance—the company is in danger of committing serious strategic errors. The degree of brand loyalty will influence the extent to which advertising and other controllable marketing elements can be used to increase a company's share of the market.

Let us first look at the scale on which we measure brand loyalty. Figure 9.4 presents the situation of two competing brands which define "the market." It seems right that a consumer with 100 per cent loyalty for Brand X will have zero loyalty for Brand Y. However, the notion of

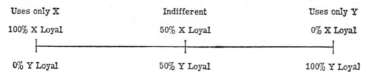

Figure 9.4 *A misleading scale for brand loyalty.*

50 per cent loyalty, which we recognize as an equiprobable chance condition, raises the question of whether this scale is an appropriate description of brand loyalty. The midpoint of the scale, 50 per cent loyalty, portrays a completely indifferent consumer. This completely indifferent consumer is the epitome of the conception of no loyalty. Therefore, we

can change our scale so that it will measure loyalty as the extent to which the consumer exhibits selectivity in his brand choice above the degree of selectivity that appears if the consumer is indifferent. Figure 9.5 represents this scale.

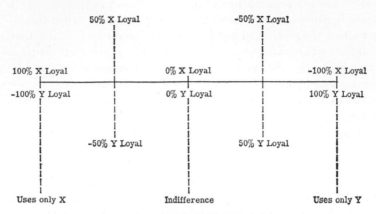

Figure 9.5 A reasonable scale for brand loyalty.

We can now consider the problem. We begin with the premise that there is such a thing as brand loyalty. However, we have no definite idea with respect to how it comes about. We do not know how to control it. Let us assume that there are two brands that are identical in every respect except that one brand is marked X and the other is marked Y. We can accept the fact that consumers have no greater preference for the symbol "X" or the symbol "Y." Since the two companies use identical brand strategies, the consumer, in this hypothetical case, is known to be completely indifferent as to which brand he uses. The decision-maker would like to know how many totally indifferent consumers could, *by chance*, appear to be 100 per cent loyal.

The brands and brand strategies being identical, it is reasonable to expect, and to find, that 50 per cent of total sales go to each brand. However, we will investigate a number of ways in which each brand could achieve an equal share of the market. The first case which we will consider is that in which consumer surveys tell us that consumers use both X and Y with equal probability. According to our second scale, this is 0 per cent loyalty. It is the result that would be expected for the example that is being used. In effect, each consumer tosses a coin before he makes a purchase. If the coin comes up heads, then the consumer buys X; if it comes up tails, then he buys Y. As long as we do not describe the situation as 50 per cent loyalty to each brand, the outcome is in keeping with our intuition. However, suppose the consumer survey reports that two sets of consumers exist. Each set, we are told, appears to be 100 per cent loyal. In other words, half of the market is 100 per cent loyal to X and the other half is 100 per cent loyal to Y. This is our second case. We know that the consumers are actually totally indifferent to which brand they use, but their buying habits appear to refute this fact. How can this come about? If half of the consumers shop in one kind of store which carries only Brand X while the other half use a different kind of store which carries only Brand Y, this appearance of complete loyalty would occur without any foundation in fact. All we need assume is that the stores are willing to carry only one brand. Since the choice of brand carried is a chance selection, 50 per cent of the stores carry Brand X and 50 per cent carry Brand Y. Granted, in reality it is unreasonable to assume that half of the market shops in one kind of store while the other half shops in another kind of store. Granted also that it is unlikely that Brand X and Brand Y would have such totally different distribution patterns. Nevertheless, it can be recognized that to some extent this situation arises. When it does, greater loyalty can appear by chance than actually exists.

Neither of the above two cases fits the majority of results that have been observed for brand loyalty. For our third case, we will continue to insist that the consumer is totally indifferent to which brand he buys. However, we will propose the following behavior pattern for the consumer: if he has seen more people buy X than Y, he buys X; if he has seen more people buy Y than X, he buys Y. Since each company has 50 per cent of the total market, the consumer is as likely to see another consumer buy X as Y. If the consumer is motivated by this rule, his behavior is hardly what the decision-maker means when he speaks of brand loyalty for his company's product.

Let us look more carefully at this rule and its effect on apparent loyalty. At any time, the consumer is aware only of the fact that one brand is ahead of the other in sales that he has observed. He may see someone buying one or the other brand in the store. He may observe the brand in a friend's home. He could, for example, have five friends who purchase in this product class. If three friends use X and two friends use Y, he will purchase X. However, while he is waiting his turn in the store he observes three people who buy Y and one person who buys X. This results in a total of four people who bought X and five who bought Y. According to our rule, the consumer switches to Brand Y. In this way, the consumer's choice will switch back and forth between the brands. Figure 9.6 charts a typical series of events.

In the figure, X leads Y by four to one in seven observations. Using intuition, we are led to the conclusion that, since for each observation that the consumer makes there is an equal probability of observing another consumer purchase X or purchase Y, the most probable result will

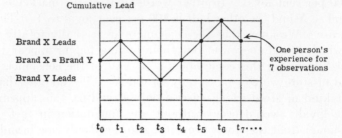

Figure 9.6 *One consumer's experience—seven observations are made of a Brand X sale or a Brand Y sale. The lead of one brand over another in sales is shown over all seven observations.*

be that Brand X will lead Brand Y as many times as Brand Y leads Brand X. From this, we would conclude that the consumer will purchase Brand X half the time and will therefore exhibit the zero loyalty that we anticipate. Allowing for chance variation, we would then expect that the observed loyalty in the total market would be distributed as shown in Figure 9.7.

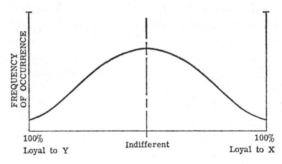

Figure 9.7 *Distribution of loyalty in the total market, based on intuition, for the example given in the text.*

Now, in fact, this is not the distribution of loyalties that is generally observed in the market. Therefore, we might erroneously conclude that this third case plainly shows there must be real brand loyalty in the market in order to account for the discrepancies between the intuited distribution and the one that is generally observed (see Figure 9.8).

However, our intuition has misled us. The phenomenon that we are describing is one that very few people without previous knowledge of the situation can properly intuit. The distribution that arises from our example looks precisely like that shown in Figure 9.8. Although at first it

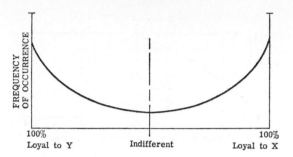

Figure 9.8 Distribution of loyalty in the total market which is sometimes observed.

may seem surprising, there is a high probability that for any one consumer either Brand X or Brand Y will take the lead over the other brand and never relinquish it. To explain this result, we will first look at Figure 9.9 which shows the probability tree of all possibilities. According

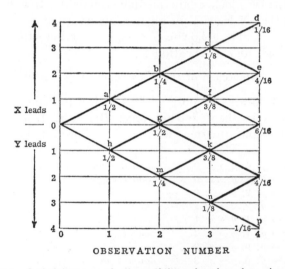

Figure 9.9. Probability tree of all possibilities based on four observations.

to Figure 9.9 there is a $\frac{1}{16}$ probability that X leads Y by 4 after four observations. That is, there is a $\frac{1}{16}$ probability that in four encounters the consumer will observe in every case that product X was purchased. There is a $\frac{1}{4}$ probability that X leads Y by 2 after four observations have been made. And, there is a $\frac{3}{8}$ probability that X does not lead Y after four observations. These are the results which we had previously intuited. They are pictured in Figure 9.10.

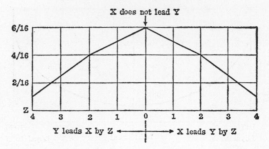

Figure 9.10 *Probability distribution for X leads Y and Y leads X by a number Z after four observations.*

But the fact of the matter is that we do not want to ask for the probability that X leads Y by Z after n observations. We want to know the probability that X leads Y in four out of four observations, three out of four observations, two out of four observations, and so on. To obtain this probability we look again at the probability tree of Figure 9.9. Now we find that X leads Y in all four observations with a probability greater than $\frac{1}{16}$. The following sequences describe situations in which X leads Y for all four observations:

oabcd, oabce, oabfe (each of these sequences has a probability of $\frac{1}{16}$)

thus X leads Y in all four observations with a probability of $\frac{3}{16}$. We will denote this in the following way: $P(x \to y: 4, y \to x: 0) = \frac{3}{16}$. Then for all possible situations we find the following:

1.	$x \to y: 4, y \to x: 0$	*oabcd, oabce, oabfe*	$\frac{3}{16}$
2.	$x \to y: 3, y \to x: 0$	*oabfj, oagfe*	$\frac{2}{16}$
3.	$x \to y: 2, y \to x: 0$	*oagfj*	$\frac{1}{16}$
4.	$x \to y: 2, y \to x: 1$	*ohgfe*	$\frac{1}{16}$
5.	$x \to y: 1, y \to x: 1$	*oagkj, ohgfj*	$\frac{2}{16}$
6.	$x \to y: 1, y \to x: 2$	*oagkl*	$\frac{1}{16}$
7.	$x \to y: 0, y \to x: 2$	*ohgkj*	$\frac{1}{16}$
8.	$x \to y: 0, y \to x: 3$	*ohmkj, ohgkl*	$\frac{2}{16}$
9.	$x \to y: 0, y \to x: 4$	*ohmnp, ohmnl, ohmkl*	$\frac{3}{16}$
			$\overline{1.00}$

Line 1 expresses the probability that the consumer will always have seen more people buy Brand X than Brand Y. Line 2 denotes the probability that in three out of four observations the consumer will have seen more people buy Brand X. We can see that the distribution goes up at the ends, which indicates that 100 per cent use of only one product is the most probable condition. Figure 9.11 shows the shape of the curve for 20 successive observations.

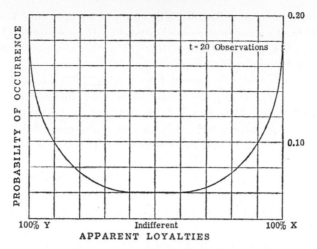

Figure 9.11 Distribution of apparent loyalties based on twenty observations.

As the number of observations increases, the probability that one or the other brand will always lead becomes more marked. Based on 20 observations we find the following distribution of pseudo or apparent loyalties.

6 per cent have no loyalty—they use both X and Y equally
12 per cent lie between 0 and 20 per cent loyalty
13 per cent lie between 20 and 40 per cent loyalty
15 per cent lie between 40 and 60 per cent loyalty
19 per cent lie between 60 and 80 per cent loyalty
35 per cent lie between 80 and 100 per cent loyalty

Figure 9.12 depicts the way in which the apparent loyalty to either brand is distributed in the total market. Our assumption that an indifferent consumer (who is about to make a purchase) buys Brand X whenever he has observed that more people purchase X than Y leads to this unexpected result. If the decision-maker learns that 15 per cent of all

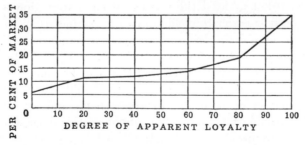

Figure 9.12 Distribution of apparent loyalty to either brand in the total market.

Brand-X users never use Brand Y, he cannot conclude that this group is 100 per cent sold on the virtues of Brand X.   If he attempts to find out in what ways his loyal customers differ from the rest of the market, he will find no significant differences.

Of course, this model is purely hypothetical.   There is, if anything, less reason to believe that such relationships hold than there is to believe in a loyal consumer.   However, it is interesting to find that the distribution of apparent loyalties derived in this manner comes fairly close to a number of observed distributions.   Other hypotheses can also be used to obtain this same result, including the notion that there is a cumulative impact of advertising.   The point is that before an outcome, such as brand loyalty, can be used as a meaningful measure of the effectiveness of strategies, it is important to consider what values of the outcome might be expected by chance.

80. THE MEDIA PROBLEM

One of the areas of marketing that involves enormous expenditures of money, most of which are based on intuitive decisions, is media selection. Media selection is one of the major, controllable strategic variables. Why then, we can ask, are media selected intuitively?   Either the problems of media are simple enough so that formal methods are unnecessary or else they are so difficult that formal methods cannot easily be devised. Unfortunately, the latter is the case: media problems are very difficult. However, if they are viewed in the decision framework, certain analytic possibilities become apparent.

We recognize that media are the instruments by means of which communication or advertising strategies can be fulfilled.   The decision problem here is to choose the best alternative from a number of possible strategies.   What are the different kinds of strategies that are available? We have magazines, newspapers, radio, television, direct mail, billboards, and others.   This is a major classification.   Within each class there are large differences but at least the method of communication is the same. For this reason it is easier to compare two magazines than to compare a magazine with television.   In order to make a comparison between two dissimilar channels of communication it is necessary to find outcomes or suboutcomes that result from each and that can be compared along the same dimension.   Ideally, we would like to be able to discriminate between two media in terms of the different short- and long-range profit outcomes that result from each.   We cannot do this even when the type of medium is the same.

Why can't we derive the expected profit from the use of each medium? In the first place, the medium by itself is like a rifle without bullets.   It has certain capabilities. In the hands of a marksman with excellent bullets the rifle functions magnificently. At the other extreme, this same rifle becomes ineffective when used by a rookie in training. Even the finest marksman will do better with superior ammunition. With a medium, the problem is of the same type. We are forced to evaluate the medium without the message. It is not feasible to create art and copy for magazines and to develop programs for TV and radio in order to compare their outcomes. And it is not possible, even then, to obtain profit outcomes. We can find out how many consumers noticed the advertisements and we can ask them how much they liked them. On the basis of these and other similar outcomes we can compare two medium-message sets. However, when we attempt to choose the medium without the message, we do not even have the advantage of these kinds of outcomes.

The choice of a medium interacts with the creation of a message. Brilliant art and copy may be devised but, because of poor media selection, it can be directed to the wrong audience. A more appropriate medium with an inferior message may well be more effective. This line of approach, in which the medium and message are evaluated together, cannot be followed for very long because there are too many possible combinations of media and messages to permit us to choose an optimal combination. Our problem will be to choose initially between media alone. In order to do this, we must presume that we know something about how effective and how ineffective the message for a particular medium might be. We will, in fact, presume that some measure of the average performance of copy, program and so on is known. We will then want our method of media selection to allow us to vary the effectiveness of the message in order to determine whether this consideration affects our choice of media. In this way, we will not seriously diminish our ability to find an optimum solution. In other words, we will determine the outcomes for some average strategy with respect to message. After we have located the optimum media strategy we can see whether this strategy would shift to a different media strategy if the effectiveness of the message we used was less than we expected. Similarly, we can determine the effect of a better-than-average message on a less-than-optimal media selection.

We must now discuss the problem of which outcomes to use when comparing different media strategies. Let us consider the question of optimal rifle selection again. We can presume that one gun might be selected in preference to another if it could shoot farther. Distance is important. But accuracy is important too. Therefore, if one gun has distance and the other accuracy, we must reach some compromise in order to select the "best" gun. We have previously examined such situations involving multiple outcomes and we have presented a way of handling these problems. We are now in a different situation, however, since we can mix our strategies and thereby obtain mixed-multiple outcomes. That is, we can simultaneously use two media in order to achieve a better resultant outcome.

Let us look at an example. Assume that we wish to begin an advertising campaign. For convenience, we will limit our possible choices to two different media. They could be two different magazines or two different TV stations, or the comparison could be made between one magazine and one TV station. For each medium, we know certain characteristics. After all, a medium is nothing more than a communication channel that can be observed. One of the main distinguishing features, therefore, is the audience with which each channel communicates. The advertiser attempts to study his market. He learns that people with intelligence $\bar{I}$ are most likely to buy his product. That is, he finds out that the average intelligence of his customers is $\bar{I}$. Similarly, the average income is $\bar{S}$. The proportion of males to females is $\bar{M}$, and so on. On the basis of this analysis, he decides that he would like his media mix to conform to these characteristics. There are a great variety of demographic and psychological factors that can be included in the decision-maker's prescription. Occupation, years of schooling, number of children, social poise, degree of tension, credit standing, and frugality are just a few examples of other possibilities.

All of these factors are treated by the decision-maker as though they were legitimate outcomes or suboutcomes. The distribution of some of these characteristics in the various media audiences is known. In other cases audience characteristics must be obtained by survey. Let us assume for our example that each medium has the data which the decision-maker requests. This will include the following—for medium j.

1. The size of the audience, A_j.
2. A distribution of noting scores, α_j. (These noting scores will measure the per cent of the total audience that "notes" any advertisment. It is never expected that everyone in an audience will see, and be aware of having seen, an advertisement.) $\bar{\alpha}_j$ is the expected value of the distribution. Thus, $\bar{\alpha}_j A_j$ is the expected value of the number of exposures delivered by medium j.
3. The average intelligence, $\bar{I}_j$, of the audience.
4. The average income, $\bar{S}_j$, of the audience.
5. The proportion of female readers, $\bar{F}_j$, of the audience.
6. The average age, $\bar{G}_j$, of the audience.
7. The cost per unit of the advertising medium C_j, such as cost of a page per issue, cost of an evening program, cost of a two-minute TV spot.

With this information, the advertising decision-maker can determine his optimal media strategy. How does he consider his problem? Even with only two media there are an endless number of possible strategies. That is, the jth medium can be used once, $M_j = 1$, and the kth medium can be used 50 times, $M_k = 50$. Or, j can be used 322 times, $M_j = 322$, and k can be used 8547 times, $M_k = 8547$. In theory, any combination of numbers is a possible strategy. Therefore, the decision-maker starts out by listing a number of conditions and restrictions which he believes will make his campaign more effective and at the same time will limit the number of possible strategies he can employ. For our example, we have chosen intelligence, income, per cent of females, and age. This is, of course, only one possible list. Other factors can be included if they seem important.

A way in which the decision-maker can help himself determine which factors are important is by means of multiple regression analysis. It is far from being the case that regression analysis will always help the decision-maker. Nevertheless, this statistical technique can provide some information regarding which variables are relevant and which are not.

By whatever means he employs, including intuition, the decision-maker selects certain characteristics which he believes are important attributes of potential customers. He must also be prepared to specify how much of each characteristic is desirable. It is not enough for him to state that intelligence is a significant variable with respect to the sales potential of the consumer; he must also specify that some intelligence level—say four, rated on a scale from one to ten—characterizes the best level of consumer intelligence for his purposes. In doing this, the decision-maker is choosing what he believes to be the most favorable state of nature. On what basis does he make these selections? There are a number of bases. For example, he can analyze previous sales in order to determine the characteristics of previous customers. Or he may conclude that he has exhausted the potential of the group from which his previous sales were derived; in this case, he may attempt to address a new market segment chosen on the basis of survey results. He may wish to choose a group which he feels exerts great influence on the rest of the market. Still another example would be the choice of a group that spends freely and makes full use of installment purchasing. In each case, the decision-maker by his choice of a media strategy attempts to obtain the state of nature that will be most likely to produce an optimal payoff.

Having specified as best he can the state of nature, the decision-maker then tries to find that combination of media which will meet his requirements. Another way of stating this situation is that the state of nature is in reality a suboutcome derived under certainty. The fact is that his choice of media yields an outcome which becomes a state of nature for the message. We will view the choice of media (and later on the choice of message) as the strategies available to the decision-maker. The restrictions will be considered as suboutcomes achieved under certainty. It should be noted that suboutcomes of many kinds will occur in each box of the decision matrix. None of these outcomes is profit because we cannot find the resultant profit to be gained from each strategy. For example, if we use M_1 of medium 1, and M_2 of medium 2, then we obtain the following:

SELECTED CHARACTERISTICS OF THE MEDIUM

$S1:\ M_1$ $\overline{I}_1, \overline{S}_1, \overline{F}_1, \overline{G}_1, A_1, \overline{a}_1, C_1$

$S2:\ M_2$ $\overline{I}_2, \overline{S}_2, \overline{F}_2, \overline{G}_2, A_2, \overline{a}_2, C_2$

We want to use M_1 of medium 1 and M_2 of medium 2 in such a way as to achieve our objectives $\overline{I}$, $\overline{S}$, $\overline{F}$, $\overline{G}$, E, and minimum cost. At the expense of some repetition let us clarify what all of the symbols given above mean. $\overline{I}_1$ is the average intelligence of the audience, A_1, of medium 1. $\overline{I}_2$ is the average intelligence of the audience, A_2, of medium 2. $\overline{I}$ is the level of average intelligence the media selector would like to achieve for the total number of exposures,* E, which his campaign will yield. Similar discussions apply to $\overline{S}_1$, $\overline{S}_2$, and $\overline{S}$; $\overline{F}_1$, $\overline{F}_2$, and $\overline{F}$; and $\overline{G}_1$, $\overline{G}_2$, and $\overline{G}$. C_1 and C_2 represent some unit cost of the advertising medium. A method is required such that the seven outcomes in each box can be mixed together to produce superior outcomes. The description of the superior outcomes is given by $\overline{I}$, $\overline{S}$, $\overline{F}$, $\overline{G}$, and E. The assumption is implicit that these five restrictions describe the characteristics that should bring maximum sales. As a matter of fact, knowing the approximate size of E, we can estimate the sales volume that should result. In other words, some per cent of E exposures will result in sales. That per cent should be maximized by meeting the conditions $\overline{I}$, $\overline{S}$, and so on. In this way the advertiser expresses his inventory situation and production capabilities by choosing a reasonable E. Otherwise, he might find that he has oversold or undersold his ability to meet demand. Of course, the estimate of sales volume for a given E is, at best, a rough approximation. The decision-maker can, if he chooses, specify that E should be greater than some number of exposures and less than some other number of exposures. By so doing, he expresses a range of campaign sizes which, according to

---

* An "exposure" occurs whenever a consumer becomes *aware* of a message from a particular medium. Therefore, by our definition, if a consumer is aware of the same or different advertisements for one brand in two different magazines, it is the equivalent of two exposures. This is *duplication,* which we will consider later. Also, by our definition, if a consumer is aware of the same or different advertisements for one brand in two different issues of the same magazine, it is the equivalent of two exposures. This is *replication,* which we will consider later. If the consumer sees the same advertisement in the same magazine several times, we will consider this a single exposure. Exposures derived from radio, TV, newspapers, billboards, and so on can be defined in the same way.

the information available and his considered judgement, represents some appropriate range of sales volume for his chosen $\bar{I}$, $\bar{S}$, and so on.

As we have mentioned, sales volume alone cannot be our objective. The cost of achieving any particular level of sales volume can be so exorbitant that profit is too low. Therefore, the advertiser states that for the conditions, he wishes to minimize his costs. In this way, he attempts to achieve at least one part of his multiple objective: optimal short-range profit. (For long-range profit other characteristics might be more desirable. For example, higher intelligence might result in lower immediate sales but in the long run it might win acceptance in a leader group. In this case the objective is different and the appropriate outcomes are correspondingly altered.) The point to notice is that the relationships between the outcomes of media selection—such as intelligence, income, and number of exposures—and the objectives must be intuited. They cannot be formally stated.

The advertiser is now ready to analyze his problem. He must choose media that correspond to the criteria he has chosen. In other words, if the average incomes of the media that he selects as possible components of his strategy are all below the average income that he considers important, he cannot hope to obtain the result he wants. Consequently, logical media selection has already posed certain fundamental requirements. Once the advertiser has chosen his media, the analysis can begin. We have chosen a very simple case which permits us to illustrate in a geometric fashion the underlying elements of the solution. The same kind of problem may be solved in other ways, and these other methods will be discussed in the chapters which follow. The geometric solution can be used only when no more than two media exist or when no more than two restrictions exist. With three, we can build a three-dimensional model and solve the problem geometrically, but it is no longer worth the effort. With four dimensions, analytical techniques must be used. We have chosen to illustrate this problem in geometric terms so that when operations of the same type are encountered at a later point, the underlying factors of the analytical methods will be easier to comprehend.

In analogy to the candy manufacturer's problem of Chapter 8 we can present the relevant information concerning the media and the decision-maker's restrictions in tabular form:

	M_1	M_2	RESTRICTIONS
Number of exposures	$\bar{a}_1 A_1$	$\bar{a}_2 A_2$	E
Average intelligence	$\bar{I}_1$	$\bar{I}_2$	$\bar{I}$
Average income	$\bar{S}_1$	$\bar{S}_2$	$\bar{S}$
Proportion of females	$\bar{F}_1$	$\bar{F}_2$	$\bar{F}$
Average age	$\bar{G}_1$	$\bar{G}_2$	$\bar{G}$
Cost per medium use	C_1	C_2	minimize

It should be pointed out that this is not a decision matrix. The arrangement being used is a general form for presenting the information of a programming problem. The strategy will be some combination of values for M_1 and M_2. Therefore, in decision terms, the format would be as follows:

Possible strategies	One state of nature
First combination of $M_1 + M_2$	First outcome values for $\bar{I}, \bar{S}, \bar{F}, \bar{G}, E, C$
Second combination of $M_1 + M_2$	Second outcome values for $\bar{I}, \bar{S}, \bar{F}, \bar{G}, E, C$
Third combination of $M_1 + M_2$	Third outcome values for $\bar{I}, \bar{S}, \bar{F}, \bar{G}, E, C$
.	.
.	.
nth combination of $M_1 + M_2$	nth outcome values for $\bar{I}, \bar{S}, \bar{F}, \bar{G}, E, C$

Some of the outcome values violate the decision-maker's restrictions. Accordingly, he will eliminate strategies that produce unwanted outcomes. Next, he will look at the cost outcome of all the remaining strategies. Since he wishes to minimize cost, he will choose that strategy which produces the minimum cost. We have seen in Chapter 8 similar sets of linear conditions. In this case, they can be written as follows:

Row

$$
\begin{aligned}
1: &\quad \bar{\alpha}_1 \cdot A_1 \cdot M_1 &+&\quad \bar{\alpha}_2 \cdot A_2 \cdot M_2 &\geqslant E \\
2: &\quad \bar{\alpha}_1 \cdot A_1 \cdot \bar{I}_1 \cdot M_1 &+&\quad \bar{\alpha}_2 \cdot A_2 \cdot \bar{I}_2 \cdot M_2 &\geqslant E\bar{I} \\
3: &\quad \bar{\alpha}_1 \cdot A_1 \cdot \bar{S}_1 \cdot M_1 &+&\quad \bar{\alpha}_2 \cdot A_2 \cdot \bar{S}_2 \cdot M_2 &\geqslant E\bar{S} \\
4: &\quad \bar{\alpha}_1 \cdot A_1 \cdot \bar{F}_1 \cdot M_1 &+&\quad \bar{\alpha}_2 \cdot A_2 \cdot \bar{F}_2 \cdot M_2 &\geqslant E\bar{F} \\
5: &\quad \bar{\alpha}_1 \cdot A_1 \cdot \bar{G}_1 \cdot M_1 &+&\quad \bar{\alpha}_2 \cdot A_2 \cdot \bar{G}_2 \cdot M_2 &\geqslant E\bar{G} \\
6: &\quad C_1 \, M_1 &+&\quad C_2 \, M_2: &\text{MINIMIZE}
\end{aligned}
$$

The first inequation is a direct statement of the restriction on exposures. The other inequations result from the fact that the averages of the characteristics, $\bar{I}, \bar{S}, \bar{F}, \bar{G}$, are specified. Thus, for example, the average level of intelligence delivered by the media mix of M_1 and M_2 will be:

$$
\frac{(\bar{\alpha}_1 \cdot A_1 \cdot M_1)\bar{I}_1 + (\bar{\alpha}_2 \cdot A_2 \cdot M_2)\bar{I}_2}{(\bar{\alpha}_1 \cdot A_1 \cdot M_1) + (\bar{\alpha}_2 \cdot A_2 \cdot M_2)} = \bar{I}
$$

From this expression in conjunction with Inequation 1, Inequation 2 follows directly. Similarly, from the analogous expressions for the averages of the other characteristics in conjunction with Inequation 1, the other inequations follow. Now we will use the following set of data for our example. The decision-maker specifies that he would like his campaign to include at least ten million exposures, $E = 10^7$. Media 1 and 2 furnish the information which the decision-maker requests:

	$\bar{a}_j$	A_j	$\bar{I}_j$	$\bar{S}_j$	$\bar{F}_j$	$\bar{G}_j$	C_j
M_1:	0.3	$3\frac{1}{3} \times 10^6$	3	4	0.8	40	8,000
M_2:	0.4	5×10^6	7	8	0.1	20	12,000

The decision-maker then specifies his conditions: $\bar{I} = 4$, $\bar{S} = 5$, $\bar{F} = 0.4$, $\bar{G} = 30$. From this, we can write the necessary inequations which reduce to the following simple forms when the above values are substituted in Inequations 1–5 and Equation 6.

$$
\begin{aligned}
\text{Row} \\
1:\ & M_1 + 2M_2 \geqslant 10 \\
2:\ & 3M_1 + 14M_2 \geqslant 40 \\
3:\ & 4M_1 + 16M_2 \geqslant 50 \\
4:\ & 8M_1 + 2M_2 \geqslant 40 \\
5:\ & 4M_1 + 4M_2 \geqslant 30 \\
\text{Minimize } 6:\ & 8000M_1 + 12{,}000M_2 = \text{Total cost}
\end{aligned}
$$

Each of these linear conditions can be depicted graphically. They are interpreted in the same way as the inequations we have already studied. Each point of intersection can be determined by solving the appropriate set of simultaneous equations (these values specify the possible corner points of the polygon). But a large problem would require an impossible amount of work. For this simple example we have tabulated the solutions of all possible pairs of equations. It should be noted that two additional equations must be included.

$$
\begin{aligned}
\text{Row} \\
7:\ & M_1 \geqslant 0 \\
8:\ & M_2 \geqslant 0
\end{aligned}
$$

In other words, we cannot permit negative quantities of media to be part of the solution. For each pair of values for M_1 and M_2 the appropriate cost is determined and entered in the table. Also, each of the restrictions is tested with the derived values. If a violation of the restriction is found, it is circled.

We find that there are seven solutions that do not violate the restrictions. Further, the intersection of equations 1 and 5 provides the minimum-total-cost solution. Figure 9.13 portrays the conditions and the solution in a graphical form. The intersection of equations 1 and 5 is point f. We know that any possible solution must lie on or above *defgh*.

Any combination of M_1 and M_2 that lies below *defgh* must violate at least one of the restrictions.

Whatever method we use to solve a problem of this kind must move the cost line into a variety of positions until the optimal position is located. For example, every combination of M_1 and M_2 that falls on the cost line A–A' results in a total cost of $24,000, but all these points violate the restrictions. All values of M_1 and M_2 lying on the cost line B–B' result in a total cost of $48,000, but only some of the restrictions are met. The cost line D–D' has a total cost of $106,640. All points to the left of the intersection j violate the restriction $8M_1 + 2M_2 \geqslant 40$. That is, they do not provide a large enough proportion of females in the audience. Cost line C–C' passes through point f. It produces the minimum cost while holding to all of the restrictions. In effect, analytic methods for obtaining a solution

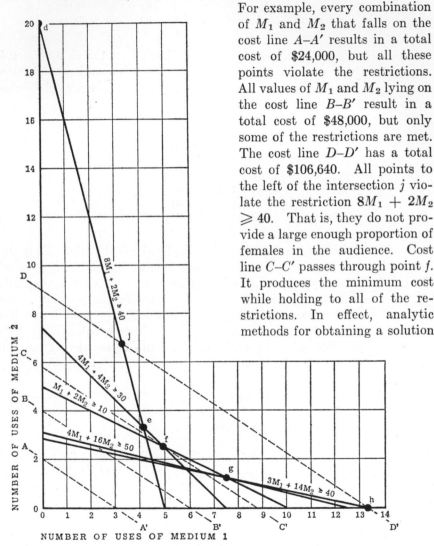

Figure 9.13 Graphical solution of the media problem.

pass the cost line through the points of the solution polygon since one of these must represent the optimal solution. The point that falls on the minimum cost line is then selected as the solution.

Table 9.1 presents an additional column for the cost per exposure. Thus, when $M_1 = 5.0$ and $M_2 = 2.5$, which is our optimal solution, the number of exposures is

$$E = (0.3)(3\tfrac{1}{3} \times 10^6)(5.0) + (0.4)(5 \times 10^6)(2.5) = 10 \times 10^6 = 10^7$$

Then, the cost per exposure is

$$\frac{\$70,000}{10^7} = \$0.0070$$

Table 9.1 Solution of all possible pairs of equations, the resultant cost, values and violations of the restrictions, and cost per exposure.

				VALUES OF EQUATIONS					
EQUATIONS	M_1	M_2	C	1	2	3	4	5	C/E
1–2	7.50	1.25	75,000	10	40	50	62.5	35	0.0075
1–3	7.50	1.25	75,000	10	40	50	62.5	35	0.0075
1–4	4.29	2.86	68,640	10	52.9	62.9	40	(28.6)	
1–5	5.00	2.50	[70,000] ←	10	50	60	45	30	0.0070
1–7	0	5.00	60,000	10	70	80	(10)	(20)	
1–8	10.00	0	80,000	10	(30)	(40)	80	40	
2–3	7.50	1.25	75,000	10	40	50	62.5	35	0.0075
2–4	4.53	1.89	58,920	(8.3)	40	(48.5)	40	(25.7)	
2–5	5.90	1.60	66,400	(9.1)	40	(49.2)	50.4	30	
2–7	0	2.86	34,200	(5.7)	40	(45.6)	(5.7)	(11.4)	
2–8	13.33	0	106,640	13.3	40	53.3	106.7	53.3	0.0080
3–4	4.50	2.00	60,000	(8.5)	41.5	50	40	(26)	
3–5	5.83	1.67	66,680	(9.2)	40.9	50	50	30	
3–7	0	3.13	37,560	(6.3)	43.8	50	(6.3)	(12.5)	
3–8	12.50	0	100,000	12.5	(37.5)	50	100	50	
4–5	4.17	3.33	73,360	10.8	59.1	70	40	30	0.0068
4–7	0	20.00	240,000	40	280	320	40	80	0.0060
4–8	5.00	0	40,000	(5)	(15)	(20)	40	(20)	
5–7	0	7.5	90,000	15	105	120	(15)	30	
5–8	7.50	0	60,400	(7.5)	(22.5)	(30)	60	30	

Now, we notice that this cost per exposure is not the minimum cost per exposure. Although we have minimized total cost, we have not minimized cost per exposure. Here we have a striking example of how important it is for the decision-maker to know what he wants and to state it clearly as his objective. The minimization of total cost will be very important to the decision-maker if his company does not have large reserves of cash. Consequently, he sacrifices some efficiency in order to spend the least amount possible. For a small additional amount ($3,360) he can save $0.0002 per exposure. This necessitates using M_1 4.17 times instead of 5, and M_2 3.33 times instead of 2.5. There is still another possibility. If the decision-maker is willing to spend $240,000 he can then cut the cost per exposure from $0.0070 to $0.0060.

If we had begun this problem with the notion of minimizing the resultant cost per exposure, we would have tried to write an objective function similar to our previous cost function, $C_1M_1 + C_2M_2$. This new objective function would have been

$$\text{MINIMIZE:} \quad \text{cost per exposure} = \frac{C_1M_1}{\bar{a}_1A_1M_1 + \bar{a}_2A_2M_2}$$
$$+ \frac{C_2M_2}{\bar{a}_1A_1M_1 + \bar{a}_2A_2M_2}$$

But this form would not meet the requirements of our programming method since M_1 and M_2 are in the denominator of each term. The decision-maker cannot expect to solve every problem with formal and direct methods. He may be forced to apply one objective function in order to derive another by cut-and-try methods such as we previously used to obtain the smallest reasonable cost per exposure. At other times a different analytic technique can be used to obtain a solution. In any case, the decision-maker gains valuable insights by studying a problem with formal tools—even though he may not entirely achieve his objective in the form of a single answer. For example, the cost per exposure has an interesting relationship to the media mix. Figure 9.14 shows that lines of constant cost per exposure fan out from the origin. Point f, which was our optimal point, is located on the 0.0070 line. The decision-maker finds that as he uses more of medium 2 the cost per exposure decreases. He knows that the total-cost lines produce increasing total cost as they move further away from the origin. If he wishes to minimize total cost he will choose point f. Otherwise, he can select a point on a less expensive cost-per-exposure line, which will produce a greater total cost—so long as he does not violate the restrictions.

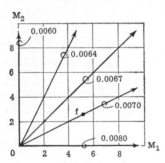

Figure 9.14 *Relationship of media mix to cost per exposure.*

If the objective was to minimize total cost subject to the restrictions, we have solved the problem. Our solution tells us to use 5 issues (or programs, or whatever) of M_1 and 2.5 of M_2. This should give us 10^7 exposures, an average intelligence of 5, an average income of $6000, a proportion of 45 per cent females in the audience, and an average age of 30 years. The total cost will be $70,000 for this campaign, and it will produce a total of ten million exposures (10^7).

However, a number of subjects must yet be considered. The decision-maker will have an idea of the media to be chosen and the extent to which each can be used. But he will want to know whether the example can be extended to include a number of basic media problems. In particular, he will request more information about the following:

1. How many media can be considered at one time and how many restrictions?

2. What does an answer of 2.5 uses for M_2 mean?

3. How can the effects of unusually good or unusually bad copy and art, or programming, be included in the analysis?

4. What can be done about the effects of duplication?

5. What can be done about the effects of replication?

6. Can media discounts be considered in writing the total cost function?

We will answer these six questions in order.

1. The number of media that can be considered at one time is limited only by the ability to deal with vast numbers of calculations. It would be unusual if the decision-maker wanted to work with more than 50 media at one time, and problems of this size can be handled by computers. Solutions concerning up to ten media can be obtained by hand if the number of restrictions is not too great. However, graphical methods, as mentioned before, cannot be used with more than two media or two restrictions. A more general method for solving these problems will be explained in the next chapter. The fundamental theorem of the programming method states that the number of media appearing in the final solution cannot exceed the number of restrictions employed. The only limitation on restrictions is, therefore, the computational problem. But it must also be borne in mind that if only a few restrictions are written, only that number of media, or less, will be mixed in the final solution.

2. We should use medium 1 five times, but how can we use medium 2 the two and one-half times required? Let us assume that each use of M_2 represents a full page in magazine 2. Then the number of exposures obtained through the use of M_2 is as follows:

$$M_2 \text{ exposures} = \bar{a}_2 A_2 M_2 = \bar{a}_2 A_2 (1) + \bar{a}_2 A_2 (1) + \bar{a}_2 A_2 (\tfrac{1}{2})$$

The question is, what fraction of a page will result in one-half the number of exposures obtained by a full page? Figure 9.15 depicts the hypothetical relationships between page size, Z, and the proportion of exposures that Z obtains in comparison with a full page. It also shows the proportion of the full-page cost that Z entails. We see that $\tfrac{1}{2}$ the number of exposures is obtained with $\tfrac{3}{4}$ of a page. Therefore, two full pages and $\frac{3}{4}$ of a page of medium 2 fulfill the M_2 part of the media program. However, from Figure 9.15 we now observe that $\frac{3}{4}$ of a page requires

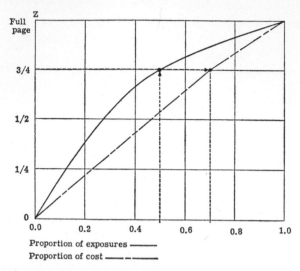

Figure 9.15 *Proportion of exposures which Z part of a full page obtains and proportion of the full-page cost for Z.*

$\frac{7}{10}$ of the full-page cost instead of the $\frac{5}{10}$ which the original cost equation used. This requires an additional $2400.

$$(12,000)\,(0.7) - (12,000)\,(0.5) = \$2400$$

Therefore, the real total cost of this media plan is $72,400. Similar adjustments can be made at other corner points in order to compare different media strategies involving fractional media use. But this can only be done when the effect is small. Whenever the number of times a medium is used is reasonably large, the effects of fractional uses on the cost can be disregarded.

3. It will be remembered that for each medium a distribution of α (message effectiveness) measurements was obtained, as in Figure 9.16. The mean value, $\bar{\alpha}$, was used for each medium. If the decision-maker believes that he has an especially effective message, α^*, for one medium, he will want to include the increased effectiveness of this campaign in his comparison of media strategies. Medium 1 had an $\bar{\alpha}_1$ value of 0.3. If the creative department has prepared an advertisement that should have an effectiveness of 0.6, i.e., $\alpha_1^* = 0.6$, then the decision-maker will use this larger value of α in his calculations. The change in α value has the effect of shifting the scale on the M_1 axis for all of the restrictions and, in this case, doubling the slope of each of the lines. The slope of the cost line

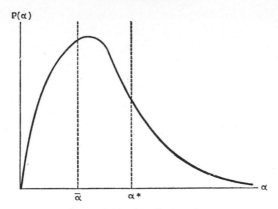

Figure 9.16 Distribution of α.

remains the same, and a new solution results. For our example, the optimal solution of minimum total cost has shifted to the transformed point g.

TRANSFORMED POINT	$M_1{}^*$	M_2	TOTAL COST
e	2.09	3.33	56,680
f	2.50	2.50	50,000
g	3.75	1.25	45,000

All of these points meet the restrictions. We can see that the change in α_1 leaves the M_2 values unchanged, but alters M_1 in accordance with the ratio

$$\frac{\overline{\alpha_1}}{\alpha_1{}^*} = \frac{M_1{}^*}{M_1}$$

where $M_1{}^*$ is the new value of M_1. It is important to bear in mind that although the optimal solution can change when the message effectiveness increases or decreases, the solution will still be given by one of the points of the transformed polygon.

4. Duplication is a major problem affecting the choice of media strategies. First of all, let us consider how duplication arises. Some of the audience of medium 1 are part of the audience of medium 2. These individuals may be exposed to the same message in both media. If three media are involved, duplication and triplication can occur. Assuming that duplication, triplication, quadruplication, and so on are not desirable, we must define how undesirable they are and how much of each we can expect to occur. First, we must define some terms.

Let A_j = total audience of medium j,

a_j = total unduplicated audience of medium j,

K = total adult population of the country,

$A_{ij} =$ number of duplicates in the audiences of medium i and medium j,

$A_{ijk} =$ number of triplicates in the audiences of media i, j, and k,

$D_{ijk} =$ number of duplicates in the audiences of i, j, and k,

$U_{ijk} =$ total unduplicated audience for i, j, and k, and

$T_{ijk} =$ total number of different consumers that are reached.

Based on probability considerations requiring that duplication, triplication, and so on occur by chance, we find that for three media, 1, 2, and 3,

$$A_{12} = \frac{A_1 \cdot A_2}{K}$$

$$A_{13} = \frac{A_1 \cdot A_3}{K}$$

$$A_{23} = \frac{A_2 \cdot A_3}{K}$$

$$\text{and } A_{123} = \frac{A_1 \cdot A_2 \cdot A_3}{K^2}$$

Therefore, total number of duplicates for all three media will be

$$D_{123} = A_{12} + A_{13} + A_{23} - 3A_{123} = \frac{A_1 \cdot A_2 + A_1 \cdot A_3 + A_2 \cdot A_3}{K}$$

$$- 3\frac{A_1 \cdot A_2 \cdot A_3}{K^2}$$

Total unduplicated audience will be

$$U_{123} = a_1 + a_2 + a_3 = A_1 + A_2 + A_3 - 2D_{123} - 3A_{123}$$

and the total number of different consumers reached will be

$$T_{123} = U_{123} + D_{123} + A_{123}$$

Let us consider an example before we return to our original media problem. When $K = 50,000,000$ consumers, and $A_1 = 10$ million, $A_2 = 8$ million, and $A_3 = 5$ million, the audience sizes of three hypothetical media, then

$$A_{123} = \frac{(10 \times 10^6)(8 \times 10^6)(5 \times 10^6)}{(50 \times 10^6)^2} = 160,000$$

$D_{123} = [(10 \times 10^6)(8 \times 10^6) + (10 \times 10^6)(5 \times 10^6) + (8 \times 10^6)(5 \times 10^6)]$
$\div (50 \times 10^6) - 3(160,000) = 2,920,000$

$U_{123} = (10 \times 10^6) + (8 \times 10^6) + (5 \times 10^6) - 2(2,920,000)$
$- 3(160,000) = 16,680,000$

$T_{123} = 16,680,000 + 2,920,000 + 160,000 = 19,760,000$

Many times, there is more or less duplication than would occur by chance. For example, two fashion magazines would undoubtedly produce more duplication than one fashion magazine and a men's sporting magazine. For these cases, where information is available, adjustments must be made in the estimates of duplication. Equations for situations that involve more than three media can be derived with no difficulty and can be used to estimate quadruplication, quintuplication, and higher values when necessary. It should be noted that for any given total audience size, $A_i + A_j + \ldots + A_n$, duplication will be greatest when each medium has about the same audience size, i.e., $A_i = A_j = \ldots = A_n$. Also, duplication increases as the K value decreases. The choice of an appropriate K value is dependent upon the ability to define the size of the group from which the media audiences are drawn. The K value for fashion magazines would be quite small, and this results in a higher level of duplication. On the other hand, no adjustment of K will compensate for the fact that all individuals in the total population do not have equal likelihood of reading either fashion magazines or sporting magazines.

We must now consider the question of how duplication affects the media problem. Duplication (we will henceforth use this single term to include triplication, and so on) is an outcome derived from using a given set of media. If it is an outcome that diminishes the degree of achievement of the objective, then we must know by how much it decreases the effectiveness of any strategy. We know that with two media the duplication is $\bar{a}_1 \cdot A_1 \cdot \bar{a}_2 \cdot A_2 / K$. However, we must take into account the number of times each medium is used. The resultant number of exposures from any combination of our two media will be

$$\text{Total exposures with duplication} = \bar{a}_1 \cdot A_1 \cdot M_1 + \bar{a}_2 \cdot A_2 \cdot M_2$$

$$+ (\beta - 2) \frac{\bar{a}_1 \cdot A_1 \cdot \bar{a}_2 \cdot A_2 \cdot M_2}{K}$$

where M_2 is equal to or less than M_1, and β is equal to the effectiveness of a duplicate. If a duplicate is fully effective, then it will count as two exposures. If duplication were desirable, it would count as more than two exposures. If a duplicate is a complete waste, then it can be considered as one exposure. We will choose a hypothetical β of 1.5, which means that each duplicate counts as 1.5 exposures. We can now observe the effect of duplication on our possible media strategies.

Point	M_1	M_2	Cost	Total Exposures With Duplication	Total Exposures Without Duplication	Per Cent Loss
d	0	20	240,000	40,000,000	40,000,000	0
e	4.17	3.33	73,360	10,763,400	10,836,666	0.7
f	5	2.5	70,000	9,950,000	10,000,000	0.5
g	7.50	1.25	75,000	9,975,000	10,000,000	0.3
h	13.33	0	106,640	13,333,333	13,333,333	0

In this case, the effect is not too marked; nevertheless, duplication causes our optimal strategy (point f) to violate the restriction on the minimum number of exposures. It is not a severe violation, so usually the decision-maker will continue with his plan to use M_1 five times and M_2 two and one-half times. If a serious duplication effect is felt, it can lead to significant violations of the original restrictions; and the decision-maker may want to continue his search for a better solution. By so doing, he may find that cut-and-try methods are the most rewarding since he knows he is somewhere near an optimal solution. All media solutions should be checked for duplication effect if the sizes of the $\bar{a}_j A_j$ are relatively large in comparison to K.

5. Replication occurs when the same individual receives two or more messages from the same medium and the same advertiser, but spaced in time. Usually, the messages are not identical. The replication effect is much easier to handle than the duplication effect since the former is re-

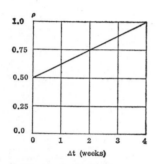

Figure 9.17 Replication effectiveness ρ as a function of the spacing between replicates.

lated to only one medium at a time. Let us assume, for example, the relationship shown in Figure 9.17. It tells us that if M_1 is spaced two weeks apart, then successive uses of M_1 result in an effectiveness of 0.75. If the messages were spaced one month apart, then the effectiveness would be 1.00. This function is purely hypothetical, of course. It can be recognized that ρ is an additional characteristic similar to a. In order to use this replication effect, a can be multiplied by ρ and ρa can be used throughout the original formulation of the problem. Replication is another outcome that needs to be considered only if it affects the achievement of the objective.

6. We have tried to present an over-all view of the media problem, making it evident that complex decision problems can be examined in parts. The need to consider the problem in bits and pieces arises because we could not start out with a simple relationship explaining long- and short-term profits as a function of the strategic variables and the states of nature. Instead, we have looked at a number of suboutcomes and examined the way in which they affect other suboutcomes. These suboutcomes have, in each case, been produced by the relatively simple possibilities of different strategic combinations of media.

We will now consider how a transformation of the strategic variables permits us to further our analysis. This transformation will be, in effect, the breaking down of each strategic variable into subvariables—or parts of the original variables.   The need to do this comes about as a result of media discounts.

Our original cost function, \$8000 M_1 + 12,000 M_2, does not describe what happens when a medium costs less per use as the number of uses increases.   Discounting is common in the media field, and its effects will generally be far greater than the effects of duplication.   Figure 9.18 illustrates two hypothetical discount functions.   In this chart the cost

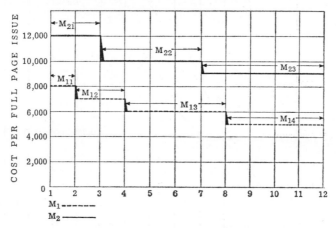

Figure 9.18   Hypothetical discount functions for M₁ and M₂.

per full-page issue of medium 1 is discounted in four steps. M_1 costs \$8000 per full page for one or two issues, \$7000 per full page for three or four issues, \$6000 per full page for 5, 6, 7, and 8 issues, and \$5500 from there on.   Similar discounts apply to M_2.   In order to allow for these discounts, we will break M_1 and M_2 into smaller units and write the cost function as follows:

$$\text{Total cost} = 8000\ M_{11} + 7000\ M_{12} + 6000\ M_{13} + 5500\ M_{14} + 12{,}000\ M_{21} + 10{,}000\ M_{22} + 9000\ M_{23}$$

We can also write the restrictions for the parts of M_1 and M_2.

$$2 \geqslant M_{11} \geqslant 1 \qquad\qquad 3 \geqslant M_{21} \geqslant 1$$
$$4 \geqslant M_{12} > 2 \qquad\qquad 7 \geqslant M_{22} > 3$$
$$8 \geqslant M_{13} > 4 \qquad\qquad M_{23} > 7$$
$$M_{14} > 8$$

Our graphical method for developing the minimum cost subject to the constraints can no longer be applied.   There are too many dimensions now. The problem is larger and more difficult to compute, but the solution can still be analytically derived by the methods described in the next chapter.

Let us look at the shape of the total-cost equation with respect to M_1, assuming that M_2 is zero. Figure 9.19 shows clearly that the total-cost function with discounts is not linear—as was our original cost function (without discounts). That is why we have broken it into the smaller parts M_{11}, M_{12}, and so on. But we cannot always break up a nonlinear

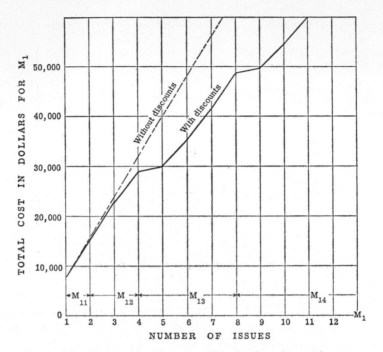

Figure 9.19 *Total cost for* M$_1$ *issues with and without discount function.*

function in this way. It is clear that we would pick M_{14} in preference to M_{13} and similarly M_{13} in preference to M_{12}, and M_{12} in preference to M_{11}. However, we will not select M_{14} if the restrictions can be met with M_{13} since that would mean a lower total cost. The method must never select two or more of the fractions of M_1 at the same time and it will not, since one fraction will always represent a preferred solution and the use of this fraction would be increased to the maximum instead of being divided between that fraction and a higher-cost fraction. But the method will not work when the discounts are not stated retroactively (see below). For example, it will not work if the first two issues cost \$8000 per issue, and the next two issues cost \$7000 per issue, and the next four issues cost \$6000 per issue, and issues after that cost \$5500 per issue. Let us compare the two ways of stating discounts.

Retroactive	Average cost per issue	Cumulative	Average cost per issue
1 issue @ $8000 = $8000	$8000	1st issue @ $8000 : $8000	$8000
2 issues @ 8000 = 16,000	8000	2nd issue @ 8000 : 16,000	8000
3 issues @ 7000 = 21,000	7000	3rd issue @ 7000 : 23,000	7667
4 issues @ 7000 = 28,000	7000	4th issue @ 7000 : 30,000	7500
5 issues @ 6000 = 30,000	6000	5th issue @ 6000 : 36,000	7200
6 issues @ 6000 = 36,000	6000	6th issue @ 6000 : 42,000	7000
7 issues @ 6000 = 42,000	6000	7th issue @ 6000 : 48,000	6857
8 issues @ 6000 = 48,000	6000	8th issue @ 6000 : 54,000	6750

If discounts are normally given in the cumulative manner then we cannot write a linear cost equation that will meet the conditions we described above. That is, with cumulative discounts we will pick M_{14} in preference to M_{13} but M_{14} should not appear unless M_{13} is included. The problem would be resolved if we could transform cumulative discounts to retroactive discounts by stating the average cost per issue for each interval. Under some circumstances it is awkward to do this, since the average cost per issue changes with each additional issue under the cumulative method.

Our analysis of media techniques shows that the problem of choosing an optimal strategy is too involved to permit an entirely straightforward approach. At the same time, it should be reasonably evident that the decision-maker has a great number of analytical techniques at his disposal for determining important suboutcomes. In the process, if he combines his intuition with the results of these techniques, he should improve upon the degree to which the company's objectives are achieved.

81. OPTIMIZING MESSAGE EFFECTIVENESS

Once a set of media have been selected, another decision problem appears. What message should we send through the medium? This is another aspect of marketing strategy. If we assume that the medium has been selected, then this problem resolves itself into the usual decision matrix form. Let us consider a television programming example. The strategies will be the different amounts of money, t_i, which the decision-maker can commit to creating the message. This cost will be over and above the cost of the medium which he has already agreed to buy. The state of nature will be described in terms of the medium. Specifically, the total expected audience, N_j, of the network j for the time of day, day of the week, and so on, will be one important factor. We will represent the cost of network j as C_j. Both of these factors are fixed. If they were the only factors to be considered, the problem would be one of decision-making under certainty. However, another characteristic of the medium and its audience is the fact that the ratings, r_i, for different programs, i, will differ. The ratings are measurements of the proportion of people who are in j's audience group and who tune in the program i. The states of nature vary with different values of r_i. An approximate description of r_i as a function of t_i is given by

$$r_i = (1 - e^{-kt_i})$$

where r_i = rating for talent i,
    t_i = cost for talent i, and
    k = constant.*

The relationship described above is shown in Figure 9.20. We will assume that the three values of k occur with uncertainty. Since the three

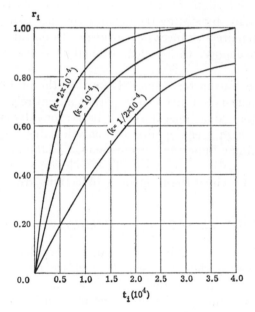

Figure 9.20 *Relationship between ratings for talent* i, (r_i), *and cost for talent* i, (t_i), *for three* k *values.*

values, to the best of our knowledge, are equally probable we will use the Laplace decision criterion.

The decision matrix for our specific case is as follows:

* e is a frequently occurring mathemathical constant which equals 2.7183.

	$k_1 = 2 \times 10^{-4}$	$k_2 = 10^{-4}$	$k_3 = \frac{1}{2} \times 10^{-4}$
$S1: t_1$	T_{11}	T_{12}	T_{13}
$S2: t_2$	T_{21}	T_{22}	T_{23}
$S3: t_3$	T_{31}	T_{32}	T_{33}
$\cdot$	$\cdot$	$\cdot$	$\cdot$
$\cdot$	$\cdot$	$\cdot$	$\cdot$
$\cdot$	$\cdot$	$\cdot$	$\cdot$
$Sn: t_n$	T_{n1}	T_{n2}	T_{n3}

T_{ij} is the total cost per thousand exposures. That is, it includes the cost of talent t_i and the cost of the network C_j. Clearly, the decision-maker wants to find that strategy which will minimize T_{ij}. The relationship of T_{ij}, t_i, C_j, and N_j can be expressed mathematically.

$$T_{ij} = 10^3 \left[\frac{t_i}{N_j r_i} + \frac{C_j}{N_j r_i} \right] = \frac{10^3}{N_j} \left[\frac{t_i + C_j}{(1 - e^{-kt_i})} \right]$$

We can find the minimum of this equation by taking the derivative and setting it equal to zero. For simplicity, the following approximation to this derivative can be used:

$$\frac{dT_{ij}}{dt_i} = (kt_i)^3 + 3(kt_i)^2 - 6C_j k = 0$$

This is a cubic equation which for our case will always have one real root. The value of the root can be approximated by

$$t_i[\text{MIN } T_{ij}] = \frac{1}{k} (\sqrt[3]{6C_j k - 2} - 1)$$

In this way, the decision-maker has located for each row and column the minimum value of T_{ij}, and that strategy which brings it about. It is interesting to notice that the choice of an optimal t_i strategy which results in a minimum T_{ij} is only determined by C_j and k. The size of the audience, N_j, is not a factor in this choice, as the decision-maker might have believed. The values of k and t_i fix the proportion of the audience which will view the program.

Let us now complete the matrix where $C_j = \$50,000$, $N_j = 10^6$ and k takes on the three values given before.

MIN t_{ij}	$k = 2 \times 10^{-4}$	$k = 10^{-4}$	$k = \frac{1}{2} \times 10^{-4}$
$S1: t_1 = \$14,350$	$\$68^*$	$\$84$	$\$125$
$S2: t_2 = \$20,360$	$\$72$	$\$81^*$	$\$110$
$S3: t_3 = \$23,510$	$\$74$	$\$81$	$\$106^*$

The payoffs are the T_{ij} values which are the costs per thousand exposures for each combination of a strategy and a state of nature. The minimum

T_{ij} is shown with an asterisk. We can now determine the strategy to use by applying the Laplace criterion. The solution is the third strategy —spend \$23,510 for the program. This is the same solution that would result if we applied the maximin criterion.

We can observe how the minimum T_{ij} value changes by plotting the relationships for any fixed k. The network cost per thousand decreases as more people are added to the audience. The talent cost, on the other hand, increases as more viewers are added. After a while, we must spend exorbitant amounts of additional money in order to add a few new viewers. In other words, we have approached the saturation level. Figure 9.21 illustrates the way in which MIN T_{ij} occurs for $k = 10^{-4}$.

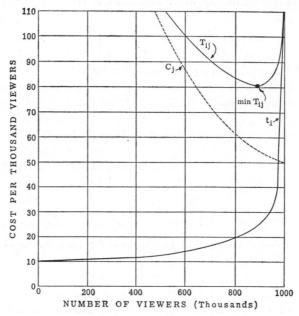

Figure 9.21   *Network cost per thousand plus talent cost per thousand yield a minimum total cost per thousand when the number of viewers is about 870,000.*

These same methods can be used to examine the results of buying different networks. In this case, we would obtain different MIN T_{ij} values as C_j was changed.

82. COMPETITION AND MIXED STRATEGIES

One of the major characteristics of the marketing area is the fact that intelligent competition exists. We have not ignored competition up to this point, but neither have we singled it out as a subject for analysis. In the brand-share model, competition accounts in great part for the values of the switching matrix. In fact, the brand-share model has no meaning if competition does not exist. Similarly, our discussion of loyalty included competition between brands. The media problem involved many estimates on the part of the decision-maker which are influenced by his knowledge of competitive strategies. For example, the characteristics of the audience which the decision-maker specified are reflections of his evaluation of his company's position in the market. The decision-maker may try to reach the consumers who generally buy a competitor's brand. On the other hand, he may try to avoid reaching this group because of the belief that it would be too costly to convert some of the competitor's market to his own. In the optimization of message effectiveness the decision-maker took as his objective the minimization of total cost per thousand of exposures. He observed a number of different k values. As the k value decreased, it became more and more costly to enlarge the viewing audience. It is quite apparent that, at least in part, k is a competitive factor. If the decision-maker spends $23,510 for talent on network j and his competitor buys the same time and high-priced talent on network m, then the programs will strongly compete with each other. Consequently, the k factor for both of them will be lower.

Sometimes, the effect of an intelligent competitor is to produce a situation in which the optimal strategy for the decision-maker is a mixture in time of the strategies which are available to him. This is not the same kind of mixture which we previously considered in the media problem. In that case the mixture was made at one point in time. M_1 of the first medium and M_2 of the second were used. The decision-maker could employ this same mixture again, at a later period in time, if none of the factors on which the choice was based had changed. However, if the decision-maker's strategies are defined so that he can use only one of the available alternatives at a time, then a mixture over time can be developed. For example, if the available strategies are (1) raise the price, (2) keep the price unchanged, and (3) lower the price, it is obvious that we cannot simultaneously use more than one of these strategies. However, over a period of time we could employ each of these strategies in different proportions. The choice of which strategy to employ at any moment is made on a purely chance basis, but in keeping with the optimal proportions. The methods for determining the optimal mixtures of strategies over time should be used when the decision-maker and the competitor find themselves in a repetitive situation which has a particular structure. Suppose that the following matrix applies:

DECISION-MAKER	COMPETITOR		
USES	USES $C:1$	USES $C:2$	USES $C:3$
$S:1$	−30	40	−32
$S:2$	−60	20	−15
$S:3$	35	−35	30
$S:4$	65	25	−10

Let us assume that the decision-maker and the competitor are representatives of competing department stores. Each day the stores advertise items in the local newspaper which are on sale. Depending upon which items they advertise and the prices they ask, one store will gain sales at the expense of the other store. This assumption is necessary, as was discussed in an earlier chapter, in order to have a zero-sum game. The matrix describes the gain in sales to the decision-maker. Negative entries signify a gain to the competitor and a loss to the decision-maker. Of course, a realistic matrix would be much larger, since a great number of items and prices for these items are involved. However, for our example, this matrix will suffice.

The decision-maker's maximin solution is the selection of strategy $S:4$ with a payoff of −10. The competitor's minimax solution is $C:3$ with a payoff of 30. Since these two payoffs are not the same, there will be two mixed strategies—one for the decision-maker and one for the competitor—which will result in an improvement in the payoff for both. It is the fact that the payoffs are not equal which determines that a mixed strategy should be employed in repetitive decision-making problems.

As we examine the matrix we observe that strategy $S:4$ always yields a better payoff to the decision-maker than strategy $S:2$. That is, no matter what the competitor does, $S:4$ is better than $S:2$. Therefore, the decision-maker will have no use for $S:2$ and he discards it. We describe this situation by saying that $S:4$ dominates $S:2$. Whenever one strategy dominates another, it simplifies the decision problem. Next, as we continue our examination, we find that column $C:3$ dominates $C:1$. The dominating relationship does not hold in the original matrix, but it does hold after we discard $S:2$.

	$C:1$	$C:2$	$C:3$
$S:1$	−30	40	−32
$S:3$	35	−35	30
$S:4$	65	25	−10

In this case, dominance is expressed in the reverse direction—because it is the competitor who is considering it and he prefers smaller payoffs. Since $C:3$ always yields less payoff to the decision-maker than $C:1$ does, the competitor will never choose to use $C:1$. Thus, we can rewrite the payoff matrix.

		(Y_2) $C:2$	(Y_3) $C:3$
(X_1)	S:1	40	−32
(X_3)	S:3	−35	30
(X_4)	S:4	25	−10

Dominance of strategies undoubtedly provides an intuitive means for discarding large numbers of strategies from consideration. However, we can see that with complex strategies and a great number of possibilities, it would be hard for the decision-maker to examine all the possibilities in his mind. Even on paper there can be difficulty in spotting dominance when the matrix includes many rows and columns.

We must now obtain the solution to this mixed strategy problem. We remember that the decision-maker's maximin is −10 and the competitor's minimax is 30. A mixed strategy will be some combination of the pure strategies which are chosen at random according to the probabilities which optimize the payoff for both parties. This mixed strategy will result in an equal value of the expected payoff for both the decision-maker and the competitor. To begin,

let S:1 be used X_1 per cent of the time by the decision-maker,
    S:3 be used X_3 per cent of the time by the decision-maker,
    S:4 be used X_4 per cent of the time by the decision-maker,
    C:2 be used Y_2 per cent of the time by the competitor, and
    C:3 be used Y_3 per cent of the time by the competitor.

Then we can write the following five inequations and two equations.

$$40X_1 - 35X_3 + 25X_4 \geqslant v \tag{1}$$

$$-32X_1 + 30X_3 - 10X_4 \geqslant v \tag{2}$$

$$X_1 + X_3 + X_4 = 1.00 \tag{3}$$

$$40Y_2 - 32Y_3 \leqslant v \tag{4}$$

$$-35Y_2 + 30Y_3 \leqslant v \tag{5}$$

$$25Y_2 - 10Y_3 \leqslant v \tag{6}$$

$$Y_2 + Y_3 = 1.00 \tag{7}$$

v is the expected value of the payoff after many repetitions of the decision problem. If the competitor uses either his pure strategy, $C:2$, or $C:3$, and the decision-maker uses the mixed strategy (S:1 being used X_1 per cent of the time, S:3 is used X_3 per cent of the time, and S:4 X_4 per cent of the time), then either Equation (1) or Equation (2) results. These equations, which describe the expected value of the payoff to the decision-maker, are set equal to or greater than v since the decision-maker wants to maximize the payoff measure. The competitor, in turn, wants to minimize the size of the payoff measure, and so equations 4, 5, and 6 are set equal to or less than v. Thus the value of v will be as large as possible for the decision-maker and as small as possible for the competitor. Equations (3) and (7) express the fact that for both the decision-maker and the competitor, the per cent of time that each of their available strategies is used must sum to 100 per cent.

Since we are dealing with five inequations, the solution of the unknowns is not straightforward. One method is to treat the inequations as though they were equations and then to test the results to see if they violate the inequalities on v. We have seven equations and six unknowns. Therefore six equations can be solved at a time and the results tested by the seventh equation. This procedure can be quite lengthy, since each set of six must be solved until the solution does not violate the one remaining equation. For example, if we solve equations 1, 2, 3, 4, 5, and 7, we obtain the following values:

$$v = \frac{80}{137} = 0.585 \qquad\qquad X_1 = \frac{65}{137} = 0.474$$

$$Y_2 = \frac{62}{137} = 0.453 \qquad\qquad X_3 = \frac{72}{137} = 0.526$$

$$Y_3 = \frac{75}{137} = 0.547 \qquad\qquad X_4 = 0$$

When the appropriate values are substituted in Equation (6), we find

$$25\,\frac{62}{137} - 10\,\frac{75}{137} \leqslant \frac{80}{137}$$

or
$$\frac{1550 - 750}{137} = \frac{800}{137} \leqslant \frac{80}{137}$$

which is a violation of the restriction. Consequently, the values given above are wrong and a new attempt must be made. Equations 1, 2, 3, 5, 6, and 7 produce values which fulfill all of the requirements. These are

$$\begin{array}{ll} v = 4.00 & X_1 = 0.00 \\ Y_2 = 0.40 & X_3 = 0.35 \\ Y_3 = 0.60 & X_4 = 0.65 \end{array}$$

When the appropriate values are substituted into Equation (4), we observe

$$40\,(0.40) - 32\,(0.60) \leqslant 4$$
or
$$-3.2 \leqslant 4 \qquad \text{(which is a fact)}$$

The same solution for the Y and v values can be obtained by graphical methods. The reason is that, in this example, there are only two dimensions in the Y plane. Figure 9.22 portrays the graphical solution.

Since $Y_2 = 1 - Y_3$, we rewrite equations 4, 5, and 6 in these terms.

$$40\,(1 - Y_3) - 32Y_3 = 40 - 40Y_3 - 32Y_3 = 40 - 72Y_3 = v_1$$

$$-35\,(1 - Y_3) + 30Y_3 = -35 + 35Y_3 + 30Y_3 = -35 + 65Y_3 = v_3$$

$$25\,(1 - Y_3) - 10Y_3 = 25 - 25Y_3 - 10Y_3 = 25 - 35Y_3 = v_4$$

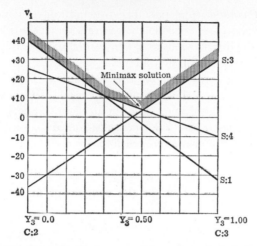

Figure 9.22 Graphical representation of a mixed strategy.

We determine v_1, v_3, and v_4 when $Y_3 = 0$ and when $Y_3 = 1$.

Y_3	v_1	v_3	v_4
0	40	−35	25
1	−32	30	−10

Next we plot these points, drawing straight lines to connect each v_i pair. The competitor prefers minus values, which represent his gains. Accordingly, he chooses the minimax solution. When we inspected the payoff matrix before deriving the mixed strategy result, we found the competitor's minimax payoff was 30 which he achieved with his strategy C_3. We can see that this is the top point on the righthand side of the graph. Also, this point is lower than the top point on the lefthand side of the graph. That is why it is the minimax solution for pure strategies. But we observe that other points along the top surface lie still lower than the righthand point. The lowest top point falls at $Y_3 = 0.60$ and $v = 4$ which was the value of the solution we previously derived. The competitor will mix his strategies in order to obtain this large benefit. On the average, instead of losing 30 he will lose only 4. The decision-maker, on the other hand, by using his mixed strategy will change his maximin solution from a loss of 10 to a gain of 4. Although we cannot present the decision-maker's situation in a visual form, the same considerations apply and can, of course, be derived analytically.

Why should the competitor enter this competition with the decision-maker if he must expect a loss? Presumably, if he does not advertise in the newspaper, he will take an even greater loss. The competitor will search for new strategies which can be added to the decision matrix in an attempt to shift the advantage over to his side. Thus, a creative act is required on the competitor's part because nothing else will improve his lot. This is true if the decision-maker randomizes his mixed strategy. What might happen if he doesn't do so? Let us assume that he sets up a schedule to specify when each advertisement will appear and the competitor learns the information on this schedule. Then every time the decision-maker uses his S:3, the competitor uses his C:3, with a resultant gain each time of —35. Every time the decision-maker uses his S:4, the competitor parries with his C:3, and the resultant gain per time will be —10. Then, the decision-maker will lose—and the competitor will gain:

$$-35\,(0.35) - 10\,(0.65) = -18.75$$

which is an increase of 22.75 for the competitor at the expense of the decision-maker.

83. PRICING PROBLEMS

One of the fundamental marketing decision-problems is the determination of the "best" price for a product or service. This is also one of the most complex problems in the marketing field. The determination of price is, in classical economic theory, the result of supply-and-demand relations. But many factors which influence the demand for a product cannot be accounted for in such broad terms. It is not meaningful to consider a large number of brands as being differentiated solely by price. At the same time, any one brand is competing with every other choice that the consumer has as to where he should spend his money. In many cases, price is an integral part of the brand image. A change in price can shift the market to an entirely different group of consumers rather than adding or subtracting consumers from the same basic group. Psychological factors play an extremely important part in the determination of the value which a consumer imputes to any particular product. The values are not static and can change quite rapidly for reasons which are apparent only long after the effects of the change have been felt. It is clear that the heart of the pricing problem is broader than price alone. A wide spectrum of consumer values most of which cannot be stated in numerical terms are involved in every pricing decision. These are some of the reasons why, in spite of its importance, a genuine, practical pricing model has not yet been evolved. Some interesting aspects of pricing can be illuminated, however, by utilizing the brand-share model which we have previously developed.

The switching probabilities of the brand-share model can be examined in terms of their responses to price changes. For example, in a given test area, it might be expected that as price is lowered, the changes in the switching probabilities would be proportional, in some sense, to the difference in price between the brands. Then an optimal change in price would be one which yielded the maximum profit. At least in theory, very large market shares could be obtained by lowering the price to cost or below. Such a situation might, in fact, be the objective of the marketing decision-maker who is willing to operate without profit for some period of time in the belief that competitors will be driven out of business. However, if we analyze this situation we see that the decision-maker is really not interested in brand share as an end, but rather as a means. The payoff that he is interested in is his competitors' profit.

We have assumed certain hypothetical relationships to hold between the switching probabilities and the prices of two competing brands such that an increase in the price of either brand increases the number of customers who will switch from that brand to the other brand. At the same time, it decreases the number of customers who will switch to the brand which has increased its price. Of course, a decrease in price works in the other direction. If both brands change their price there is a resultant influence on the switching probabilities. One other factor has to be considered. As the prices of the brands rise, the size of the total market decreases. Even when only one brand raises its price a significant amount, some customers in preference to switching their brand drop out of the market. On the basis of these assumptions, the brand-share model can be used to simulate profit positions for the brands in question.* We find that for any constant price of one brand, there is an optimal price for the other brand. That is, there is a price which yields optimum profit to the brand which varies its price. For example, where profit = market size · brand share · (price — cost):

PRICE OF BRAND A	BRAND SHARE	MARKET SIZE	(PRICE — COST)	BRAND A'S PROFIT
$1.00	0.560	100,000	$0.50	$28,000
1.10	0.517	100,000	0.60	31,000
1.20	0.477	99,000	0.70	33,100
1.30	0.434	98,000	0.80	34,000
1.40	0.388	96,000	0.90	33,500
1.50	0.336	94,000	1.00	31,600

* The price relationships which were used to determine brand switching and total market size are of the form:

$$P_{ij}(2) = f\left[\frac{P_i(1) - P_i(2)}{P_i(1)}, \frac{P_j(2) - P_j(1)}{P_j(1)}, P_{ij}(1)\right]$$

and

$$M(2) = g\left[\frac{P_i(1) + P_j(1)}{P_i(2) + P_j(2)}, M(1)\right]$$

where $P_i(1)$ = price of Brand i at time 1,
$M(1)$ = market size at time 1, and so on.

We observe that at the price of \$1.30, Brand *A* obtains maximum profit although it has less brand share than it would obtain at a lower price. Figure 9.23 illustrates the typical curve which occurs when Brand *B* holds its price constant. However, assuming that Brand *A* was originally priced at \$1.00, Brand *B* also gained in profits. Brand *A* has increased its profit from \$28,000 to \$34,000 while Brand *B*'s profits have been raised

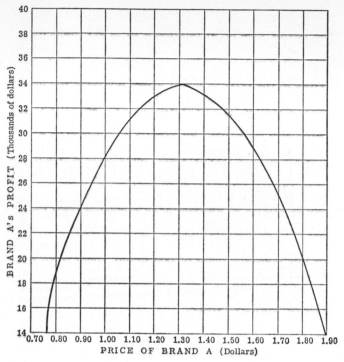

Figure 9.23   The relationship of brand A's *profit to its price, when brand* B *holds its price constant at \$1.20.*

from \$25,000 to \$30,000. This increase has taken place although Brand *B* has done nothing. How can we explain this? Brand *A* has raised its price and decreased its market share. Brand *B* has picked up this additional market share. Of course, when the competitor's prices become unreasonably high a further increase in his prices will result in no advantage to the competitor. If both brands are overpriced, a change by either one can result in a considerable shrinkage in the size of the market and a loss in profits to both. Figures 9.24 and 9.25 present "isoprofit lines" (lines of equal profit) for each brand.

Figure 9.24 shows Brand *A*'s profit for various combinations of Brand-*A* and Brand-*B* prices. Figure 9.25 depicts Brand *B*'s profits. Let us first look at Figure 9.24. We shall assume that the original prices of the two brands are $P_A = \$1.00$ and $P_B = \$1.20$. Brand A changes its price from $1.00 to $1.30. This moves it to its optimal position with Brand B priced at $1.20. We see that Brand A has raised its profit from $28,000 to $34,000. Figure 9.25 shows us that Brand B has experienced increased profits—from $25,000 to $30,000. Now Brand B wants to optimize its profit position with respect to A's new price of $1.30. Accordingly, Brand B can move anywhere up and down the $1.30 line of A's price, and it will choose a price of $1.48 which optimizes its profit at $45,000. Brand A now finds its profit level at $35,000. However, once again, Brand A looks for its optimal position which occurs at either $1.16 or $1.62. The process of hunting and alternating would continue until a mutually satisfactory point was reached. In this example there is one point available

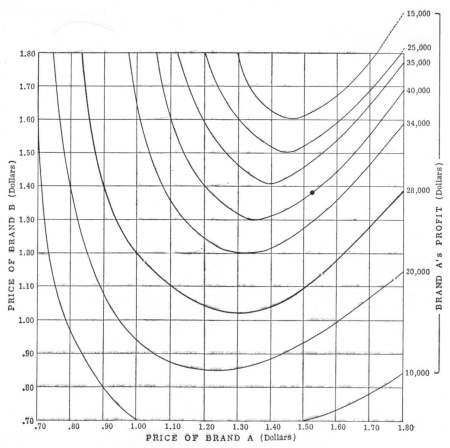

Figure 9.24 Lines of equal profit for brand A, for different combinations of prices.

at which both brands achieve their absolute maximum profits. That point is reached when A charges \$1.52 and B charges \$1.38. Their respective profits would then be \$40,000 for A and \$45,000 for B. A slight alteration in the shape of the curves could easily result, however, in a situation where the two brands could never simultaneously achieve their

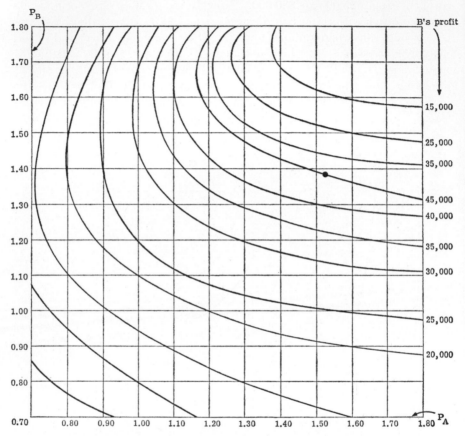

Figure 9.25   Lines of equal profit for brand B, for different combinations of prices.

absolute maximum prices. In theory, under these circumstances each brand would indefinitely continue to shift its price. In game-theory terms, we see that this is a nonzero-sum game; each set of strategies creates a different amount of wealth for each brand. We can also observe that if it were practical, a mixed strategy would be used by both the decision-maker and his competitor since their respective optimals do not coincide. For our example a mixed strategy is not necessary since the lines of optimal profit do cross each other at one point.

We have presented this example to illustrate the possible advantages to be gained by using a simulation model, such as the brand-share model, to investigate the effect of price on profit. At the same time, we must caution the reader that such models capture only a small part of reality. The pricing problem is extremely complex. The model with its artificialities yields results that are conceptual aids and not solutions to problems. If a brand could alter its price as frequently as desired, without creating side effects, it might be possible to begin to learn the real nature of price-profit relationships.

84. COMPETITIVE BIDDING

Competitive bidding is another kind of pricing. In competitive bidding each firm bidding on a particular contract must submit a sealed bid, and the firm which submits the lowest bid, or price, is awarded the contract. This is a perfectly realistic and extremely illuminating kind of pricing problem. How should a firm determine price when engaged in competitive bidding, and what would constitute an optimal pricing policy? * Granted that this is a very specialized marketing problem, nevertheless it is of crucial importance to firms which do not deal with large numbers of consumers, and which have relatively few opportunities to sell their goods or services.

The best strategy for a firm to follow, of course, depends upon the objective of the firm. We can evaluate different pricing policies or strategies only by considering the degree to which they contribute to the firm's objectives. Any one of a considerable number of completely reasonable objectives might motivate a particular firm at a particular time. For example, we can list the following possibilities:

1. maximize immediate profit. 2. maximize long-run profit. 3. obtain a given return on investment. 4. minimize profits of competitors. 5. minimize risk of excessive losses. 6. obtain a greater share of the market. 7. strengthen the position of management.

In this discussion we will assume that the firm pursues only the first of these objectives, the maximization of immediate profits. A different objective might require a pricing policy different from the one we are going to develop.

Since the objective of the firm on which our analysis will be based is to maximize its immediate profit, we must ask: What do we mean by "immediate profit" in this type of situation? Consider a firm which sub-

---

* The competitive bidding model was developed by Lawrence Friedman. See his article, "A Competitive Bidding Strategy." Operations Research, Volume 4, No. 1, February 1956, page 104.

mits a bid on a contract. If the firm is awarded the contract, it will cost the firm a certain amount to fulfill its contractual obligations. The profit will be the difference between the bid and the cost to the firm. This is what we mean by the firm's immediate profit. We can write this symbolically.

Let $x =$ amount of bid, and $c =$ cost of fulfilling obligations under contract.

Then $\qquad\qquad x - c =$ Immediate profit to the firm

This may, of course, be negative, in which case the firm has suffered a loss. We have ignored the cost of making the bid, partly for purposes of simplicity. However, since bidding costs are "sunk costs" which are not affected by whether or not the firm wins the contract it follows that it is not unreasonable to ignore them.

We have offered an unambiguous statement of what we mean by immediate profit but, unfortunately, there is a vital qualification in our verbal statement of which we have not taken account in our symbolic representation. The difficulty is the seemingly innocuous word "if" in the phrase "if the firm is awarded the contract." The presence of this word makes it necessary for us to revise our phrasing of the firm's objective. The "if" simply expresses the fact that one will not know the result of any particular bid. It is clear that after the contract has been awarded one of two things will have occurred: either the firm will have gotten the contract for its bid of x and will have made a profit of $x - c$ or it will not have gotten the contract, in which case its profit will be 0. But what can we say about the profit on a particular contract before the firm makes its bid on that contract? We can't say that the profit will be $x - c$ because it may be 0. Correspondingly, we can't say that the profit will be 0 because it might be $x - c$. This basic uncertainty about results is at the heart of the problem—as it is in so many other business decision problems. It should occasion no surprise that the method which we must apply is that of *expected* profits.

Let us consider a marketing situation in which we have two possible strategies, A and B, with the following possible outcomes and corresponding probabilities:

$S{:}A$		$S{:}B$	
OUTCOME	PROBABILITY	OUTCOME	PROBABILITY
$2000	0.5	$3500	0.4
600	0.2	400	0.3
−500	0.3	−2000	0.3

Assuming that our objective is to maximize return, which strategy should we choose? The answer should be easy to derive in terms of our previous discussions of expected value. We reason exactly as we have before.

$S:A$ can produce a return of \$2000 with a probability of 0.5, \$600 with a probability of 0.2, and a loss of \$500 with a probability of 0.3. The expected return is then

$$0.5(\$2000) + 0.2(\$600) + 0.3(-\$500) = \$970$$

Similarly, for $S:B$ we have an expected return of

$$0.4(\$3500) + 0.3(\$400) + 0.3(-\$2000) = \$920$$

Since the expected return from $S:A$ is greater than that from $S:B$, we conclude that we should select A.

The relevance of these familiar operations entailed in deriving expected values for the competitive bidding problem can now be made apparent. Generally, for a given contract, the higher the bid the less the probability of being awarded the contract. We can readily take this fact into account by using the notion of expected profit from a contract. Suppose, for example, that the cost of fulfilling a particular contract is \$20,000, i.e., $c = \$20,000$. Let us also suppose that the decision-maker knows that a bid (x) of \$40,000 has a probability of 0.3 of being awarded the contract and that a bid of \$30,000 has a probability of 0.7 of being awarded the contract. Which of these two bids should the decision-maker choose? He reasons as follows: The profit on a bid of \$40,000 will be $x - c$ or \$40,000 — \$20,000 = \$20,000 if the contract award is won. If the contract award is not won, then the return is zero. The profit on a bid of \$30,000 will be \$10,000 if the contract award is won; if not, the return is zero. When $x = \$40,000$ the expected return will be

$$\$20,000(0.3) + \$0(0.7) = \$6000$$

and the expected return when $x = \$30,000$ will be

$$\$10,000(0.7) + \$0(0.3) = \$7000$$

Since the bid of \$30,000 has the larger expected profit, it is the bid which should be submitted.

This concept of expected profit must be used in our formulation of the problem of competitive bidding. For this reason we change the statement of the objective from "maximize immediate profit" to "maximize expected immediate profit." This change in the wording will serve to emphasize the necessity for introducing the idea of probabilities of being awarded the contract. It also states precisely what we intend to do.

Let us now explain this in terms of the notations we introduced earlier. If the firm is awarded the contract it will make a profit of $(x - c)$. If it is not awarded the contract it will make a profit of 0. Suppose that we know the probability that the firm will be awarded the contract for its bid of x. Let this probability be p. Since the firm will either be awarded the contract or not, it follows that the probability that it will not be awarded the contract is simply $(1 - p)$. Therefore, with probability of p the firm will be awarded the contract for its bid of x and will make a profit of $(x - c)$. With probability of $(1 - p)$ the firm will not be awarded the contract and will make a profit of 0. We can now write the expression for the firm's expected profit in the following terms:

$$\text{Expected profit} = p(x - c) + (1 - p)(0) = p(x - c)$$

since, of course, $(1 - p)(0) = 0$. Let us reiterate once more the meaning of this expected profit. The expected profit represents the average return per bid which the firm could expect if (1) it repeated the same bid on a large number of contracts with precisely the same cost, and (2) the probability of being awarded the contract remained fixed at p. It is clear that expected profit can be calculated if we know the probability of the firm's being awarded the contract for a given bid. Our first step towards reality in the situation with which we are dealing comes when we note that the probability of being awarded the contract is related to the size of the bid. This is obvious since, on the one hand, the decision-maker could certainly make a bid on a contract which would be so high that the probability of being awarded the contract would be zero. On the other hand, he could make a bid so low, zero for example, that his company would be virtually certain to be awarded the contract. (In this last case we would say that the probability of being awarded the contract for that bid was 1.) This means that the probability of award varies with the size of the bid. For a given contract, the higher the bid the less the probability of being awarded the contract—though other factors might affect the outcome. In short, there is some relationship between probability of award and size of bid. This sort of relationship can be expressed as a cumulative probability distribution. Suppose that all the necessary information were available and the relationship between the probability of award and the size of bid were known. What would the cumulative probability distribution look like?

Let us take an example. Assume that a firm is bidding on a contract which will cost \$8000 $(= c)$ to complete. For simplicity we will assume that all bids on this contract must be in thousand-dollar units. Then the relationship between the probability of award and the size of the bid might be presented as the following cumulative distribution.

BID (x)	PROBABILITY OF AWARD (p)
\$7000	1.00
8000	0.95
9000	0.85
10,000	0.60
11,000	0.30
12,000	0.10
13,000	0.00

For each allowable bid there is a given probability of being awarded the contract if that bid is made. This probability gets smaller as the bid gets larger, as it should. An actual distribution, to be useful, would give probabilities of award for smaller intervals of the size of bid than we have done but the principle would be the same. The data indicate that a bid of $7000 would certainly win the contract but that a bid of $8000 has only a probability of 0.95 of winning the contract. Why? Because there is a probability of $1.00 - 0.95 = 0.05$ that there would be a competitive bid of $7000, which would beat the bid of $8000. Similarly, the probability of award at $9000 goes down to 0.85 because there is a probability of $0.95 - 0.85 = 0.10$ of a competitive bid of $8000. We can continue in this way and determine, by successive subtractions, the probability of each bid, as implied by the above cumulative distribution. We get:

BID	PROBABILITY OF BID
$7000	0.05
8000	0.10
9000	0.25
10,000	0.30
11,000	0.20
12,000	0.10
13,000	0.00

This sort of presentation is the probability distribution with which we are familiar. The sum of the probabilities is 1 since one of these bids must occur—no other is possible. The relationship between the cumulative distribution and the corresponding probability distribution permits us, if we are given one of them, to immediately deduce the other. They simply represent two different ways of presenting the same information. Sometimes one is more useful, sometimes the other. In this case, the cumulative distribution is the probability of a bid of x dollars or greater which is the equivalent of the probability of award for a bid x if we ignore ties.

Now, we have not given even a hint as to how a firm might have obtained the appropriate cumulative distribution, but let us continue to assume that, somehow, the firm does have it. Given this information we are able to calculate the expected profit for any bid. We will ignore the possibility of ties (equal bids) since they do not affect the principle involved, and since the possibility of ties looks more serious here than it would usually be because of the large interval of bids we have used in presenting our data. Consider a bid of $9000. If the firm is awarded the contract for this bid it will make $9000 - $8000 = $1000 profit. This corresponds to the $(x - c)$ we used above. Since we now know that the probability of the firm's being awarded the contract for this bid is 0.85, we can calculate the expected profit exactly as we did above. Our equation, given above, was

$$\text{Expected profit} = p(x - c)$$

For the \$9000 bid we have, therefore, an expected profit of $0.85(\$9000 - \$8000) = \$850$.

Proceeding similarly we can calculate the expected profit for each bid.

BID	EXPECTED PROFIT
\$7000	$1.00(\ 7000 - 8000) = -\$1000$
8000	$0.95(\ 8000 - 8000) = \quad 0$
9000	$0.85(\ 9000 - 8000) = \quad 850$
10,000	$0.60(10,000 - 8000) = \quad 1200$
11,000	$0.30(11,000 - 8000) = \quad 900$
12,000	$0.10(12,000 - 8000) = \quad 400$
13,000	$0.00(13,000 - 8000) = \quad 0$

The maximum expected profit is \$1200, at a bid of \$10,000. This is therefore the bid the firm should make. Why? Because the firm has the stated objective of maximizing its expected profit and this bid, if repeated a large number of times under identical circumstances, would give the firm an average return of \$1200 per bid. This is greater than that from any other bid.

We have made the assumption in our calculations that the cost of fulfilling the contractual obligations was known, in our example \$8000. What effect does the undoubted fact that the decision-maker doesn't know the exact cost have on the problem? The answer is that if the wrong cost is used it can lead to the selection of a nonoptimal strategy. To avoid this, the decision-maker can accumulate information on the relationship between the estimates and the actual costs of the contracts which were awarded. This can be done, most conveniently, by recording for each completed contract the ratio between the estimated cost, on which the bid was based, and the actual final cost. By this means, a distribution of these ratios can be obtained which will be useful in many calculations concerning a firm's over-all position. Analytical methods can be used to determine the sensitivity of expected profit to errors in cost estimation. For example, we find the value of cost (C_1) which will switch the bid from \$10,000 to \$9000 in the following way:

$$0.85(9000 - C_1) = 0.60(10,000 - C_1) : C_1 = \$6600$$

Similarly, we obtain the value of cost (C_2) which will switch the bid from \$10,000 to \$11,000.

$$0.30(11,000 - C_2) = 0.60(10,000 - C_2) : C_2 = \$9000$$

We next take the ratios

$$\frac{8000}{6600} = 1.21$$

$$\frac{8000}{9000} = 0.89$$

and consult the distributions of ratios. Assuming that this distribution is stable, we can observe the probability that a ratio of 1.21 or greater will occur. In the same way, we can obtain the probability that a ratio of .89 or less will occur. If the probabilities of either or both eventualities are high, then it is quite likely that the decision-maker will initiate additional cost studies to refine the estimates. On the other hand, if it appears that the amount of error which is likely to occur will not affect the bid decision, then the decision-maker can ignore the uncertainty of cost since it does not affect his bidding strategy. Other techniques, including Monte Carlo, can be used if the sensitivity of expected profit to errors of estimation is high. In these cases, the variability of actual costs with respect to estimated costs can be included in the decision model. Consequently, the problems connected with estimation of cost can be handled. All that the decision-maker needs to know is the distribution of probabilities of award as a function of the amount of the bid; his firm can then utilize the procedures of this competitive bidding model to optimize its position.

But we can very well ask at this point: How can a firm determine the distribution? First, the *complexities* of trying to determine this distribution should be distinguished from the fundamental method as outlined above. The method itself is quite simple, at least in conception, despite any difficulties which may be involved in attempting to determine the crucial distribution of probabilities of award as a function of the amount of the bid.

We are, then, going to consider practical ways in which a decision-maker can obtain the necessary information about the distribution of the probabilities of award as a function of the amount bid. Since it is customary to announce the bids on contracts after they have been awarded, it is possible to learn the bidding behavior of competitors. We will consider three cases: first, the competitors for a particular contract are known; second, the identities of one's competitors are unknown but it is known how many there are; third, the competitors are unknown and their number is also unknown.

First we will consider the case where the competitors bidding for a particular contract are known. Let us study competitor A. The information we have about A consists of every previous contract on which A bid and for which the decision-maker's firm made a cost estimate. For every such contract we can determine the ratio of A's bid to the decision-maker's *cost* estimate (not his "bid"). For example, part of the data on A might look like this:

CONTRACT	DECISION-MAKER'S ESTIMATED COST	A'S BID	RATIO
1	$8500	$10,200	1.2
2	22,000	33,000	1.5
3	11,000	15,400	1.4
4	35,000	38,500	1.1
5	9000	9000	1.0

The ratio is simply A's bid divided by the decision-maker's cost estimate. We would continue this procedure for all contracts on which we had the necessary information: the cost estimate and A's bid. We would then summarize all of this information in a table in which we would give the total number of times that each ratio occurred. The table would look like this:

RATIO OF A'S BIDS TO THE DECISION-MAKER'S COST ESTIMATES	NUMBER OF TIMES IT OCCURRED
0.9	1
1.0	3
1.1	5
1.2	11
1.3	15
1.4	8
1.5	4
1.6	3
	—
	50

Of course, we would search to discover some influence other than the variability of the decision-maker's costs to account for the differences in the ratios. It might turn out that A bid lower than the cost estimate when he had not obtained a contract award for 12 months or more; that he bid much more than the decision-maker's costs when he had recently won a contract that gave him a heavy backlog of work. We have a total of 50 such ratios, and this table gives the frequencies of the various ratios' occurrences. This table contains all of the information available to us for estimating the probability of occurrence of each of the ratios. Consider the ratio, 1.2. Out of 50 ratios we find that this ratio occurred 11 times, which indicates that the probability of occurrence of the ratio 1.2 is $11/50 = 0.22$. Similarly, the probability of occurrence of the ratio

1.4 is $8/50 = 0.16$. In short, we can convert the above table into a table of probabilities of occurrence of the various ratios simply by dividing each of the frequencies in the righthand column by the total number, 50. This gives:

RATIO OF A'S BIDS TO THE DECISION- MAKER'S COST ESTIMATES	PROBABILITY OF RATIO
0.9	0.02
1.0	0.06
1.1	0.10
1.2	0.22
1.3	0.30
1.4	0.16
1.5	0.08
1.6	0.06

The sum of the probabilities is 1, as it must be. This table is to be read as follows: With a probability of 0.22, or 22 per cent of the time, competitor A has submitted bids on contracts which were 1.2 times the decision-maker's cost estimate for the contract. We note again that we have used a crude interval in our breakdown of the ratios. This is done solely for the purpose of simplicity in the example. In actual practice a more refined breakdown of the ratios would be used, but the principle would remain exactly the same.

A comparison of this table with the one previously given will show that they are identical in form. This table is, as that one was, a probability distribution. As we pointed out, at that time, to each probability distribution there corresponds a cumulative probability distribution, and vice versa. Therefore, from the table on competitor A we can immediately determine the cumulative probability distribution for competitor A. This cumulative distribution will show the probability that a particular bid, expressed as a multiple of the decision-maker's cost estimate, will be lower than the bid of competitor A. Thus, for example, a bid of 0.9 times the cost estimate will be lower than the bid of competitor A with probability of $1.00 - 0.02 = 0.98$. But this would leave the possibility of tie bids, chiefly because of the large interval we have used in presenting the ratios. To eliminate this possibility let us simply lower the bid slightly. Thus, we can say that a bid of 0.89 times the cost estimate will be lower than A's bid with probability of 1.00. A bid of 0.99 times the cost estimate will be lower than A's bid with probability of $1.00 - 0.02 = 0.98$. A bid of 1.09 times the cost estimate will be lower than A's bid with probability of $1.00 - 0.02 - 0.06 = 0.92$. Proceeding similarly we can obtain the following table:

BID, AS MULTIPLE OF COST ESTIMATE	PROBABILITY THAT BID IS LOWER THAN BID OF A
0.89	1.00
0.99	0.98
1.09	0.92
1.19	0.82
1.29	0.60
1.39	0.30
1.49	0.14
1.59	0.06
1.69	0.00

This is the required cumulative probability distribution. For any given bid, expressed as a multiple of the cost estimate, it gives the probability that that bid will be lower than the bid of A. Or, if A is the decision-maker's competitor in bidding for a particular contract, we can say that this table gives the probability of award as a function of the amount bid. This should mean that the decision-maker already has sufficient information to determine the bid which will give him the maximum expected profit, if A is his only competitor.

Let us see if this is so. Suppose the decision-maker is bidding on a contract and A is his only competitor. As usual, we will let c denote the cost estimate on this contract. Suppose the decision-maker bids $1.09c$ on this contract. According to the table the probability will be 0.92 that he will win the contract. If he wins the contract he will make a profit of $1.09c - c = 0.09c$. This, of course, is simply the $(x - c)$ we used above, where $(x = 1.09c)$. We know that the expected profit is the probability of award times $(x - c)$. In this case, then, $0.92(0.09c) = 0.0828c$. If he bids $1.19c$ we have

$$\text{Expected profit} = 0.82(1.19c - c) = 0.82(0.19c) = 0.1558c$$

Proceeding similarly, using the probabilities from the table above we obtain:

BID, AS MULTIPLE OF COST ESTIMATE	EXPECTED PROFIT WHERE A IS ONLY COMPETITOR
0.89	$1.00(0.89c - c) = -0.11c$
0.99	$0.98(0.99c - c) = -0.0098c$
1.09	$0.92(1.09c - c) = 0.0828c$
1.19	$0.82(1.19c - c) = 0.1558c$
1.29	$0.60(1.29c - c) = 0.1740c$
1.39	$0.30(1.39c - c) = 0.1170c$
1.49	$0.14(1.49c - c) = 0.0786c$
1.59	$0.06(1.59c - c) = 0.0354c$

Clearly, a bid of $1.29c$ gives the maximum expected profit, $0.1740c$. If we use $c = \$8000$, as in an earlier example, this would give a bid of \$10,-

320 and an expected profit of $1392. Consequently, it can be seen that empirically obtained information is sufficient to enable us to determine the bid which will maximize expected profit in the case where A is the only competitor.

What does the decision-maker do if there is more than one known competitor against him? Let us assume that he is faced with two competitors on a particular contract: A, as above, and B. We could go through precisely the same procedure for obtaining information about B as we did for A. We will not repeat these steps because they are in no way different from those illustrated for A above. Granting that we have done this, we would end up with a cumulative probability distribution for B which would be similar to, but different from, that for A. Now that we have this, it will be convenient to present the two cumulative probability distributions, one for A and one for B, in one table.

BID, AS MULTIPLE OF COST ESTIMATE	PROBABILITY THAT BID IS LOWER THAN BID OF:	
	A	B
0.89	1.00	1.00
0.99	0.98	0.94
1.09	0.92	0.83
1.19	0.82	0.65
1.29	0.60	0.37
1.39	0.30	0.20
1.49	0.14	0.10
1.59	0.06	0.03
1.69	0.00	0.00

The distribution for A is the same one that was used before. From this table we are able to say immediately that, for example, a bid of 1.09 times the cost estimate has a probability of 0.92 of being lower than A's bid and a probability of 0.83 of being lower than B's bid. Can we deduce from this statement the probability that a bid of 1.09 times the cost estimate will simultaneously be lower than A's bid and B's bid, or, in short, that it will win the award of the contract? Yes, we can do this very simply. The probability of the joint occurrence of two independent events is the product of the probabilities of the two events separately. For example, the probability of throwing heads on one coin is $\frac{1}{2}$. What is the probability of obtaining two heads if you throw two coins simultaneously? On each coin the probability is $\frac{1}{2}$ of obtaining heads, so the probability of getting two heads is $\frac{1}{2} \times \frac{1}{2} = \frac{1}{4}$. Similarly, the probability that a bid of 1.09 times the cost estimate will be simultaneously lower than A's bid and B's is $0.92 \times 0.83 = 0.76$. The probability that a bid of 1.19 times the cost estimate will be simultaneously lower than A's bid and B's bid is $0.82 \times 0.65 = 0.53$. Proceeding in this way we can obtain, for each bid, the probability that it is lower than both A's bid and B's bid. To do this requires only that we multiply the entries on the same row in the columns under A and B in the table above. This gives:

BID, AS MULTIPLE OF COST ESTIMATE	PROBABILITY THAT BID IS SIMULTANEOUSLY LOWER THAN BIDS OF A AND OF B
0.89	$1.00 \times 1.00 = 1.00$
0.99	$0.98 \times 0.94 = 0.92$
1.09	$0.92 \times 0.83 = 0.76$
1.19	$0.82 \times 0.65 = 0.53$
1.29	$0.60 \times 0.37 = 0.22$
1.39	$0.30 \times 0.20 = 0.06$
1.49	$0.14 \times 0.10 = 0.01$
1.59	$0.06 \times 0.03 = 0.00$
1.69	$0.00 \times 0.00 = 0.00$

The probability that the decision-maker's bid is simultaneously lower than the bids of A and of B is equivalent to the probability of award if A and B are the only competitors, as we are assuming. In other words, the table above gives the cumulative probability distribution for obtaining the contract as a function of the amount of the bid. Therefore, once again, we have the necessary information to enable us to determine which bid has the greatest expected profit. The calculations of the expected profit for each bid are made exactly as in the example we have given earlier. If we bid 1.09 times the cost estimate, the table shows that the probability of award will be 0.76. The expected profit is, therefore, $0.76(1.09c - c) = 0.0684c$. The expected profit from a bid of $1.19c$ is $0.53(1.19c - c) = 0.1007c$. The expected profit from a bid of $1.29c$ is $0.22(1.29c - c) = 0.0638c$. Similarly, the expected profit from each bid can be calculated. The maximum expected profit comes from a bid of $1.19c$ and is $0.1007c$. In terms of the earlier example, where $c =$ \$8000, this would mean that the bid should be \$9520 with an expected profit of \$805.60.

We see that if we have the necessary data on the past performances of competitors, the method will work equally well for any number of known competitors. For each competitor we must obtain the appropriate cumulative probability distribution showing the probability that a given bid of the decision-maker will be lower than the bid of that competitor. The final cumulative probability of award distribution is then determined by multiplying, for each bid, the entries given for each competitor for that bid. This distribution gives the necessary information for calculating the expected profit for every bid, which then enables us to choose the bid with the maximum expected profit. This procedure, therefore, handles the case where the competitors are known.

What can the decision-maker do when he doesn't know whom his competitors are? In this event we are no longer able to obtain specific information about the bidding behavior of each competitor as we did above. Our lack of information about the identity of the competitors on a particular contract forces us to utilize less precise information than otherwise. Instead of using information based on specific competitors we will have to be satisfied with information about an "average" or "typical" competitor. In other words, the best available information in this case is the past behavior of competitors on those contracts for which the decision-maker made cost estimates. The procedure to be followed is the same as before except that we lump all competitors together. We simply combine all the previous ratios of a competitor's bid to our cost estimate into one probability distribution. For example, *A* and *B*, as above, would be lumped into one probability distribution along with all the other competitors for which we had ratios. From this over-all probability distribution of ratios we can then obtain, as before, the cumulative probability distribution. The resulting cumulative probability distribution might look like this:

BID, AS MULTIPLE OF COST ESTIMATE	PROBABILITY THAT BID IS LOWER THAN BID OF AVERAGE COMPETITOR
0.89	1.00
0.99	0.97
1.09	0.90
1.19	0.79
1.29	0.58
1.39	0.35
1.49	0.21
1.59	0.08
1.69	0.02
1.79	0.00

This table is equivalent to the table for a single specific competitor, given above. The only difference is that this table is for a single unspecified competitor—the average competitor. This table should, therefore, be interpreted as follows: for a bid of 1.19 times the cost estimate the probability is 0.79 that it would be lower than the bid of any single competitor picked at random.

Suppose, for example, that, on a particular contract, the decision-maker is faced with only one competitor but that he doesn't know the identity of this competitor. Then he would use this table to determine the expected profit for each bid. The calculations would be exactly the same as those which have been shown several times above. Notice that the important difference in using this table is that we do not know the identity of the competitor. If we knew that our only competitor was *A* then we would use the table for *A*. Otherwise *we must use the best information we have:* the cumulative probability distribution for the average competitor.

Suppose that the decision-maker does not know the identity of his competitors but that he does know how many of them there are on a particular contract. He can use the above table to determine the probability of award for each bid. He simply assumes that this average cumulative distribution applies to each of the unknown competitors. He then proceeds as in the case of known competitors. This table shows, for example, that a bid of 1.19 times the cost estimate has a probability of 0.79 of being lower than the bid of any one competitor picked at random. Suppose there are two such competitors. The probability that a bid of 1.19 times the cost estimate will be simultaneously lower than the bids of both the competitors is $0.79 \times 0.79 = 0.6241$. If there are three competitors the probability is $0.79 \times 0.79 \times 0.79 = 0.4930$. If there are four competitors the probability is $0.79 \times 0.79 \times 0.79 \times 0.79 = 0.3895$. And similarly for each other possible bid. For example, the necessary probability of award cumulative distribution based on three unknown competitors is:

BID, AS MULTIPLE OF COST ESTIMATE	PROBABILITY THAT BID IS LOWER THAN BIDS OF THREE UNKNOWN COMPETITORS
0.89	$1.00 \times 1.00 \times 1.00 = 1.0000$
0.99	$0.97 \times 0.97 \times 0.97 = 0.9127$
1.09	$0.90 \times 0.90 \times 0.90 = 0.7290$
1.19	$0.79 \times 0.79 \times 0.79 = 0.4930$
1.29	. . . 0.1951
1.39	. . . 0.0429
1.49	. . . 0.0093
1.59	. . . 0.0005
1.69	. . . 0.0000
1.79	. . . 0.0000

Of course, the probability that a bid is lower than the bids of three competitors is precisely the probability of award in bidding against the three competitors. Therefore, this table is the required cumulative probability of award distribution as a function of the size of the bid. We can immediately calculate the expected profit for each bid in the usual way. The expected profit for a bid of $1.09c$ is $0.7290(1.09c - c) = 0.0656c$. The expected profit for a bid of $1.19c$ is $0.4930(1.19c - c) = 0.0937c$. The expected profit for a bid of $1.29c$ is $0.1951(1.29c - c) = 0.0566c$. The maximum expected profit is $0.0937c$ and is obtained for a bid of $1.19c$. In terms of our earlier example, where $c = \$8000$, this would mean that the maximum expected profit is \$749.60 and is obtained by bidding \$9520. It is clear that the same procedure can be followed for any given number of competitors.

What should we do if we don't know the number of competitors on a particular contract? The answer is that we must find some way of obtaining an estimate of the number. Let us consider the effect on our bid as the number of competitors increases. It is easy to show that, as the number of competitors increases, the maximum expected profit will be obtained with smaller bids. We can illustrate this, using the cumulative probability distribution function of the "average" competitor, given above. We calculate the following:

NUMBER OF COMPETITORS	BID WITH GREATEST EXPECTED PROFIT	AMOUNT OF EXPECTED PROFIT
1	$1.29c$	$0.1682c$
2	$1.19c$	$0.1386c$
3	$1.19c$	$0.0937c$
4	$1.19c$	$0.0750c$
5	$1.19c$	$0.0585c$
6	$1.09c$	$0.0478c$
7	$1.09c$	$0.0430c$
8	$1.09c$	$0.0387c$

It is clear that, as the number of competitors increases, the bid with the maximum expected profit becomes smaller and the amount of expected profit becomes steadily smaller. As the number of competitors gets even larger the amount of expected profit goes down steadily towards the breakeven point. This means that the number of competitors is a most important variable in determining the bid with the maximum expected profit. In the case of an unknown number of competitors it is of paramount importance to obtain an estimate of the number. Once an estimate is available the above procedure is followed, using the estimated number of competitors.

We will not discuss in detail any of the various possible methods of estimating the number of competitors. It is similar to other estimation problems and has all the difficulties associated with such problems. One possibility is to determine whether there has been a relationship between number of bidders and size of contract. If so, it would be possible to use estimated cost as a means for estimating the number of competitors. Perhaps the experience of the decision-maker will suffice to provide good estimates. Whatever the method of estimation, once the estimate has been obtained the procedure given above for a known number of competitors is then followed to determine the bid with the maximum expected profit.

The competitive bidding pricing model is of such a fundamental nature that it is only natural to consider extending it to the situation in which many consumers are involved. In other words, can the competitive bidding model be applied to the pricing of a consumer item? The answer is that it cannot be used for the selection of an optimal brand price. The major reason is that in competitive bidding the bids are unknown, whereas prices of competitive brands are usually available. Also, if price were the only factor determining the consumers' choice—as it is, for the most part, in competitive bidding situations—the problem of finding optimal pricing policies would be considerably easier. In the competitive bidding case the probability of award is directly related to the probability that bids of different sizes will be made for a contract entailing a certain level of cost. In the consumer pricing case, the probability of award is involved with price, variety, taste, habit, and many other factors. Consumer marketing problems are so intimately involved with behavioral factors that in many cases, qualitative models represent a big step forward. The bidding model is more typical of a production model. The production chapter which follows this one presents an interesting contrast with respect to the degree of development of decision-making in the field of production as compared to the field of marketing.

PROBLEMS

1. Two national coffee brands, B and C, are the major competitors of a regional brand A. The regional company undertakes a market survey from which it obtains the following brand-share and brand-switching information.

BRAND SHARE		BRAND SWITCHING		
		A	B	C
0.12	A	0.1	0.3	0.6
0.40	B	0.1	0.5	0.4
0.48	C	0.1	0.3	0.6

What will be the limiting distribution of brand shares? If the switching matrix applies to a period of one month, how long will it take for the situation to come to equilibrium? If the market is of fixed size, say 100,000 sales per month, and each company makes a profit of $0.30 on every sale, what will be the average monthly profit at the end of six months for each of the three companies?

Brand A's sales manager is distressed by the results of the analysis. He believes that the assumption of a fixed market size is unrealistic. He reasons that Brand A will be hard pressed to take a larger share of customers from the two national brands but he feels that Brand A should obtain a larger share of new customers as they enter the market. The sales manager asks for a report on the change in population size, by age groups, for the region, as well as a report on population mobility. The latter tells him how many consumers move in and out of the marketing region. He receives the requested information from his marketing department. On the basis of these data the sales manager determines that 10,000 new sales will be made each month while 5000 sales from repeat customers will be lost to the market. The sales manager conceives of an advertising campaign which will bring Brand A the largest share of the new sales and the lowest loss from attrition of old customers. He sets down the situation in the following way:

NEW SALES PER MONTH		STARTING POINT (SALES PER MONTH)	LOST SALES PER MONTH
A:	5000	12,000	1000
B:	2000	40,000	2000
C:	3000	48,000	2000

Using the same switching matrix as before, determine the average monthly profits of each of the three companies over a period of six months. If the growth in the size of the market stops, what is the long-term outlook for Brand A? Assuming no growth in market size, compare the limiting distribution previously derived with the limiting distribution of the matrix shown below. What could account for such a change?

BRAND SWITCHING

	A	B	C
A	0.3	0.2	0.5
B	0.1	0.5	0.4
C	0.1	0.3	0.6

2. Two airline companies have many corresponding routes. Company A has followed a policy of replacing existing equipment as soon as significant improvements are available while Company B's policy has been to utilize existing equipment as long as possible. Company B's management have always recognized the fact that their policy results in a smaller share of the market. On the other hand, Company B's costs are lower than Company A's, since Company A must borrow heavily in order to purchase new equipment. Company B's competitive position requires that it replan its schedules every time Company A introduces new equipment on its routes. Let us assume that such a situation is about to occur. Company B reasons that Company A can use the equipment that it is about to receive in only four different ways. In its turn, Company B has five reasonable strategies available to it. Company B's objective is to minimize its loss while Company A's objective is to maximize its gains. The following payoffs are determined for each combination of strategies:

	B'S STRATEGIES				
A'S STRATEGIES	B_1	B_2	B_3	B_4	B_5
A_1	30	35	40	45	50
A_2	60	65	20	30	70
A_3	35	40	35	40	55
A_4	25	45	25	20	10

What is the optimal strategy for each company to follow? B discovers an error in the calculations of the row A_3 and makes the following changes:

$$A_3, B_1 = 38 \neq 35$$
$$A_3, B_3 = 38 \neq 35$$

What is the new solution and what has brought this about?

3. A manufacturer of ball-point pens ships them in quantities of 25 of each of two colors. He observes that many retailers place reorders for only one color. However, the total number of requests are about equally divided between the two colors. That is, some retailers order only the first color, others order only the second color. He speaks to a number of the retailers and they explain that only one color sold well. He can find no regional or other differences to account for this result. What is the manufacturer doing that creates this situation? What should he do to correct the situation? Hint: $P_j =$ the probability that j pens of either color will be in stock when the clerk discovers that the last pen of the other color has been sold. $N =$ the number of pens of each of the two colors which the retailer receives in the shipment, and

$$P_j = \frac{(2N - j)!}{N!(N - j)!} \frac{1}{2^{2N-j}}$$

4. When a manufacturer decides to sell his product in a foreign market he is confronted with a variety of decision problems. Most of these problems are analogous to the situations he faces in his home market. Generally, however, the situations with which he has to deal are more extreme. Regional differences between consumers are relatively minor in comparison with national

Amount spent ($)	Expected sales ($) for				
	C_1	C_2	C_3	C_4	C_5
10,000	18,000	15,000	15,000	20,000	16,000
20,000	36,000	25,000	30,000	40,000	32,000
30,000	49,000	35,000	45,000	60,000	42,000
40,000	62,000	45,000	56,000	80,000	52,000
50,000	75,000	55,000	67,000	97,000	62,000
60,000	88,000	65,000	78,000	114,000	72,000
70,000	101,000	75,000	89,000	131,000	82,000
80,000	114,000	85,000	100,000	145,000	92,000
90,000	127,000	95,000	111,000	155,000	102,000
100,000	140,000	105,000	121,000	165,000	112,000
110,000	150,000	111,000	131,000	175,000	122,000
120,000	160,000	117,000	141,000	185,000	132,000
130,000	170,000	123,000	151,000	195,000	140,000
140,000	180,000	129,000	161,000	205,000	148,000
150,000	190,000	135,000	171,000	215,000	156,000
160,000	197,000	139,000	181,000	225,000	164,000
170,000	204,000	143,000	186,000	230,000	172,000
180,000	211,000	147,000	191,000	235,000	176,000
190,000	218,000	151,000	196,000	240,000	180,000
200,000	225,000	155,000	201,000	245,000	184,000

differences. We will consider a problem which confronts a manufacturer of radios. There are five countries in which he is considering marketing his line of products. His efforts in each country will produce different results because consumer taste varies in each country, different competitive products are sold in each country, and some of them compete more directly with the manufacturer's line of products. In the same way, advertising rates, media audiences, message effectiveness, tariffs, government regulations, and a host of other factors combine to yield different outcomes in each country. The manufacturer has allowed a budget of $200,000 for the international market. He sets up a table to indicate the estimated sales which might be expected for every $10,-000 he allocates to one of the five countries. Because of diminishing returns, the rate at which sales volume increases with each additional dollar becomes less as more and more dollars are spent in one country. The table above compares the expected sales for the five countries, C_1, C_2, C_3, C_4, and C_5. How should the manufacturer allocate the sum of $200,000 to the five countries in order to maximize his expected sales? What will the expected sales be? If the manufacturer decides to budget the larger sum of $300,000, what will the new allocation be? What will be the revised estimate of expected sales? How do the ratios of sales to expenditures compare for the two different budgeted amounts?

5. Variety is an important variable which must be considered in many marketing studies. A frequent problem is to determine the optimal amount of variety. Let us assume that the following hypothetical relationship has been derived as the result of a study conducted by a department store—namely, that the sales obtained from a specific counter are proportional to the expression $N^V V^N$, where V equals the number of varieties which appear on the counter and N equals the number of items of each variety which appear on the counter. It is assumed that it is the policy of the store to display equal numbers of whatever varieties are carried. We shall suppose that all of the items are of about equal size and the capacity of a counter is C. Then, $NV = C$.

What interpretation can be given for the relationship $N^V V^N$? What will the optimal variety be when the counter has a capacity of 120 items? ($C = 120$).

Hint: it is possible to rewrite the expression which we want to maximize in the following form:

$$\left(\frac{120}{V}\right)^V (V)^{120/V}$$

or
$$V(\log 120 - \log V) + \frac{120}{V} \log V$$

It is then possible to try different values of V until the maximum is found. However, note the shape of this function. There are two maxima. Try to plot this curve. The derivative of the function can be obtained and set equal to zero in order to derive the expression for the maxima. This result is given by

$$\log_e V = \frac{(120/V^2) + \log_e 120 - 1}{(120/V^2) + 1}$$

If the reader is familiar with natural logarithms (which have the base e), he can find the value of V which satisfies this equality. By substituting values other than 120 in the above expressions, the maxima can be found for counter capacities other than 120.

Comment on the credibility of the relationship $N^V V^N$, and whether its maximization would produce maximum sales.

6. Another variety problem can be formulated in the following terms. We are stocking $(V - 1)$ different items and we are considering adding one new variety. What is the probability that after S sales are made we will have sold none of this additional variety? The assumption is made that the sales of all varieties, including the new one, are equally likely.

The relationship we want is given by the equation

$$P = \left(\frac{V - 1}{V}\right)^S$$

Let us suppose that we sell refrigerators at the rate of 20 per month. What is the greatest number of varieties, V, which will give us a probability of 0.05 or less of selling none of the newest variety in the line, in a month?

7. A company collects information about the amount of time that each of its salesmen spends with customers. It also has information concerning how much each one of the customers orders. These data are given below. What conclusion might be drawn about the relationship between salesmen's time and customer orders?

CUSTOMER	TOTAL TIME SPENT PER MONTH	TOTAL ORDERS RECEIVED PER MONTH
1	2	$3500
2	2	2000
3	3	1500
4	3	4000
5	4	2500
6	4	3000
7	4	4500
8	5	5000
9	6	500
10	6	3500
11	7	3500
12	7	1500
13	8	2500
14	9	4500
15	9	3500
16	10	1500

8. A company which bids on many contracts has collected the following information:

Company's ACTUAL COST	Company's ESTIMATED COST	SIZE OF COMPETITOR'S BIDS
$16,000	$16,000	$24,000
18,500	15,400	20,000
10,000	10,000	16,000
28,300	25,700	36,000
10,500	15,000	24,000
10,000	12,500	15,000
15,300	13,900	25,000
12,000	12,000	18,000
8,300	9,200	12,000
9,000	10,000	14,000
5,000	5,000	10,000
8,600	6,600	8,000
4,600	4,200	8,000
3,400	4,300	6,000
9,600	10,700	15,000
36,700	36,700	55,000
32,300	26,900	35,000
18,000	20,000	22,000
3,800	3,800	6,500
11,000	10,000	15,000

How good a job has the company been doing in estimating contract costs? A new job presents itself which the company estimates will cost $10,000. What should the company bid on this job if there is only one competitor and assuming that the bids given above are those of that competitor? What should be the bid if there are two competitors and the bids given above represent both of them? What profit will the company make if it wins the award of the contract in each case? Develop a range of values within which the error in estimating costs is likely to fall. Use the extremes of this range to determine how profit might be affected.

9. A mail-order company buys lists for its direct-mail advertising. The population from which these lists are drawn is 20 million. The lists can be assumed to have been compiled by random selections from the population. If the company wants to mail 1 million pieces, which combination of lists should it select so as to minimize duplication? (We will ignore triplication, and so on, and assume that no duplication exists within a list.)

List 1   200,000
List 2   500,000
List 3   300,000
List 4   800,000
List 5   400,000
List 6   100,000

What is the least possible percentage of duplication?

Chapter ten

Of Production

Production refers to all the areas of company operations which are concerned with the manufacture or processing necessary in order to supply a product to the product's consumer. This statement is not intended as a definition, which might merely start a search for the exceptions. Rather, it is intended to indicate the subject matter of the decision problems we will be considering in this chapter.

As compared to the marketing area, production is characterized by the fact that it is more wholly within the control of the company. More of the relevant variables in production decision problems are subject to the control of the decision-maker than is the case with marketing decision problems. The relevant states of nature do not so often include competitive strategies and, generally, there are not so many hidden variables which may drastically affect the outcome. In production decision problems the objectives are likely to be more easily expressible in terms of costs or profit, and the necessary cost information will generally be available more easily and with greater accuracy. These statements are doubtless all overgeneralizations, but they are certainly more nearly true than their contradictions would be. They may therefore serve to suggest some of the general characteristics of production decision problems.

Any delimitation of the areas of marketing and production is to some degree arbitrary. Three major areas of mutual interaction are product quality, product price, and inventories. Obviously, the production process has a considerable effect on product quality and, of course, the production costs represent an inescapable limit on product price. But since production limitations on quality and price represent, at any point in time, a fact which must be accepted in marketing we have considered these to be in the marketing area. Similarly, marketing influences inventories but, at any given point in time, the level of demand represents a fact which must be accepted in production. We have therefore included inventory problems in this section on production.

85. OPTIMAL-LOT-SIZE PROBLEM

A good place to begin our discussion of some production problems will be with a consideration of the economic-lot-size problem. This problem is a basic one which arises frequently in a variety of production processes and, fortunately, is quite easy to solve. The basic elements of the problem can be presented quickly. Some part is produced to meet an anticipated demand. The amount of parts needed does not require the full-time capacity of the machine or machines used to produce the part. Therefore, one could schedule the production of the part in a variety of ways—at one extreme one could produce each day just enough to meet the demand for that day, and at the other extreme one could produce the part continuously until there was enough on hand to meet demand for a long time, perhaps a year. The problem, then, is: What is the best way to schedule the production of this part? This is the economic-lot-size problem.

The basic framework of this problem can arise in a great number of different situations and, hence, can require differing variants of the underlying decision-theory formulation. Since we cannot afford to get lost in a welter of special cases we will present a specific problem for analysis. Let us suppose that the part in question is a bolt which is subsequently used in an assembly and that 4000 of these bolts are used per day. This problem has been selected because it is simpler in two respects than some other problems which are, nonetheless, of the same type. First, we assume that demand for the part is known with certainty. Parts being produced for sale would, of course, have an uncertain demand. In our terms, we are stating a problem in decision-making under certainty. We will have ample opportunity below to find out how to deal with similar problems under risk and uncertainty. Second, the part is obviously a minor one and so the objectives can safely be assumed to be the minimization of costs. If, instead, we considered a similar kind of problem which involved a very expensive part we might have to introduce some measure of utility other than costs.

In decision-theory terms, then, this is a problem of decision-making under certainty. The strategies available are the various possible production lots of these bolts which might be scheduled. The objective is to minimize costs. What are the costs? On the one hand there is the set-up cost of the machine that produces the bolts. When the machine is not producing bolts it is producing something else and each time these bolts are put into production it requires time—and, hence, money—to set the machine up for production. On the other hand there are carrying costs associated with maintaining the part in inventory. At the very least there is the loss of use of the money tied up in inventory. Often, in addition, there are costs of storage space, insurance, deterioration, pilferage, obsolescence, and other things. It can be seen that these two costs are opposed in the sense that as one gets larger, the other gets smaller. Thus, if a great number of parts are run with one set-up it follows that the set-up cost is low but the carrying cost is higher. If very few parts are run with one set-up then the set-up cost becomes large but the carrying cost is low. In short, we have a cost picture as in Figure 10.1.

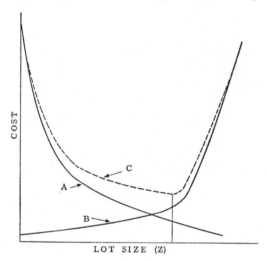

Figure 10.1   Cost as a function of lot size.

In the figure curve A represents the set-up cost, which decreases as the number of parts produced on one run increases. Curve B represents the carrying cost, which increases as the number of parts produced on one run increases. Curve C represents the total cost—the sum of A and B. The objective of minimizing the total cost is fulfilled by selecting the strategy of producing X parts on one run—where X is determined from the minimum of the total cost curve, C.

It should be noted that such opposing costs always exist. If there were no costs which increased as the number produced in one set-up increased (curve B) then it would be most reasonable to produce an enormous amount in advance—perhaps ten years' supply. If there were no costs which increased as the number produced in one set-up decreased (curve A) then it would be most reasonable to produce each part as it was needed. The unreasonableness of these two possibilities in almost all cases is due to the existence of both kinds of costs. In the present case we have already suggested what these costs are.

So the decision problem in question is solved as soon as the two curves in question are obtained and summed to get the total cost curve (C). The shape of the curves given in Figure 10.1 is arbitrary and is only meant to illustrate the general situation. For each specific problem the actual shape of these curves must be determined. This is the phase of the decision-problem analysis which we have called the determination of the relationship between the independent variable (the number of parts scheduled for production in one run) and the dependent variable (the associated cost). How do we measure the costs? The set-up cost consists essentially of the cost of the man-hours required for set-up plus the cost of having the machine idle while being set up. This is usually relatively easy to determine. Suppose in our case this cost is $40. The carrying cost includes several component costs, as indicated above. The costs of deterioration, pilferage, and obsolescence must be determined from historical records. The storage costs, including insurance costs, can usually be determined from cost-accounting data. But the cost of the loss of use of the money tied up in inventory is not so straightforward— and it is often the largest single cost component in this set of carrying costs. Basically, it can be measured in two ways—each of them a kind of opportunity cost. It can be considered to be measured by the cost of borrowing money (either from the bank or by bonds), under the assumption that if the money were not tied up in inventory then that much less would have to be borrowed. Or it can be measured by the current rate of profit being made by the company, under the assumption that if the money were not tied up in inventory it could be invested in the other company activities and would return the usual rate of profit. Let us assume that the company in question selects the first alternative and that it borrows at 7 per cent per year. Analysis of the other costs indicates that they total 3 per cent per year. Thus, total carrying costs are 10 per cent per year.

In order to make our costs comparable we need to express them all on the basis of some fixed unit of time. Any unit will do as long as all costs are put on an equivalent basis. Since carrying costs are already on a yearly basis ($1 in inventory for one year costs $0.10) we will use one year as our unit. The demand for the bolt amounts to 1,000,000 per year (we are assuming 250 working days per year). Therefore, if we produce Z bolts in one run we will need 1,000,000/Z runs at a set-up cost of (1,000,000/Z) · $40 = $40,000,000/$Z$. For example, if we produce 50,000 bolts in one run our set-up costs for one year will be $40,000,000/50,000 =

$800. This equation, then, expresses the relationship between our selection of strategy (choice of Z) and the objective (costs). This is curve A, graphed in Figure 10.3.

Carrying costs depend on the total inventory investment. What is the average inventory investment if Z parts are produced each run? Suppose $Z = 50,000$ are produced each run. Then the inventory will behave as graphed in Figure 10.2. This is the typical saw-toothed behavior of

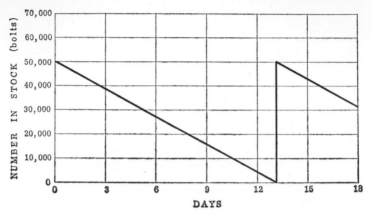

Figure 10.2 Inventory with constant rate of demand.

inventory under these circumstances. Starting out with 50,000 in stock the amount on hand goes down by 4000 (the daily usage) each day until it reaches 0. But just then, assuming perfect timing, another 50,000 comes into stock and the process repeats itself. It should be intuitively evident—and if it isn't, a little plane geometry will suffice to prove—that under these circumstances there will be an average stock on hand of 25,-000 bolts. Generally, the average year-round inventory will be $Z/2$, where Z represents the number of bolts produced in each run. The cost of each bolt must be determined in order to ascertain how much money is invested in the inventory. This cost will include the raw-material cost and the processing cost and can usually be determined from cost-accounting data. In our case we will presume that this cost is $0.08 per bolt. Then, our total carrying cost will be given by the average number in inventory times the cost per bolt times the carrying-cost rate (10 per cent). In our case this is

$$\frac{Z(\$0.08)(0.10)}{2} \quad \text{(curve } B\text{)}$$

For the case with $Z = 50,000$ this cost would be $200 per year. This curve is plotted on Figure 10.3.

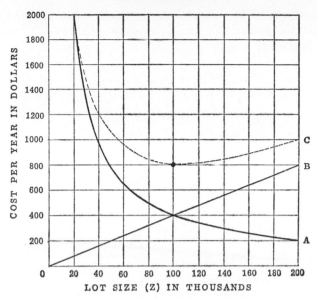

Figure 10.3 Costs for bolt inventory.

Our total-cost curve is simply the sum of these two costs:

$$\text{Total cost} = \frac{\$40,000,000}{Z} + \frac{Z\,(\$0.08)\,(0.10)}{2}$$

Which is graphed as curve C on Figure 10.3. The minimum point of this total-cost curve can be read directly from the graph and shows that the minimum cost is achieved by producing $Z = 100,000$ bolts at each run, with a total cost of \$800 per year. In other words, the minimum-cost scheduling requires production of 25 days' requirements in each run.

The same thing, however, can be accomplished mathematically, avoiding the necessity of graphing the three curves. In analogy to the above,

let $Z =$ number of parts produced in one run,

$p =$ cost of part,

$C_1 =$ set-up cost,

$C_2 =$ carrying cost per dollar of inventory investment per year, and

$D =$ yearly demand.

Then, it can readily be shown, by following the same reasoning as above, that

$$\text{Total cost} = \frac{DC_1}{Z} + \frac{ZpC_2}{2}$$

This equation can be minimized by taking the derivative of total costs with respect to Z and setting it equal to zero. This gives that Z which minimizes total costs as

$$Z = \sqrt{\frac{2DC_1}{pC_2}}$$

Putting in the values from our problem, we have

$$D = 1,000,000$$
$$C_1 = \$40$$
$$p = \$0.08$$
$$C_2 = 10 \text{ per cent or } 0.10$$

and
$$Z = \sqrt{\frac{2(1,000,000)(40)}{(0.08)(0.10)}} = 100,000$$

as before. Total costs are

$$TC = \frac{\$40,000,000}{100,000} + \frac{100,000(.08)(.10)}{2} = \$400 + \$400 = \$800$$

also as before.

This general expression for Z accomplishes the same purpose as the graph, is easier to use, and also is more informative. Thus, from the expression for Z we can see that Z gets larger (1) as D gets larger (naturally, the more needed the more we must produce), (2) as C_1 gets larger (the more it costs per set-up, the fewer set-ups we want to have), (3) as p gets smaller (the less the price, the less the carrying costs and the more we can carry in stock), and (4) as C_2 gets smaller (the less the cost of carrying a dollar in inventory, the more we can carry in stock). All of these relationships are in accord with what we would intuitively expect.

The procedure followed in solving this decision problem is an application of the marginal principle which is basic to most economic thinking. An economist who was presented this problem would immediately set out to find that value of Z for which the marginal cost of set up equalled the marginal cost of carrying stock in inventory. He would, upon solving for Z, get the same expression we have derived. The advantage of our procedure (the minimization of the total cost equation), is that it is readily applicable to more complicated variants of the same fundamental type.

This solution to the economic-lot-size problem leads naturally to a consideration of inventory problems in general. The two costs which entered into the formulation of the problem were the set-up and the carrying cost. Nothing prevents us from replacing "set-up cost" by "ordering cost"—leaving the carrying cost as before. This purely verbal change does not in any way affect the argument of our formulation of the decision problem in question, but it does show that the same solution is available for the case where an organization is ordering the item rather than producing it. As an example, suppose that all the conditions of the former problem remain the same except that the item is ordered and that the order cost is $10. Note that the order cost may not be just the cost of processing an order. It may also include costs associated with receiving and inspecting the incoming items if these costs are affected by the purchase quantity. The decision problem is to determine the minimum-cost order quantity and it has already been solved above. The numerical solution will be given by

$$Z = \sqrt{\frac{2\,(1,000,000)\,(10)}{(0.08)\,(0.10)}} = 50,000$$

In short, 50,000 bolts should be ordered each time. Total costs will be

$$TC = \frac{(1,000,000)\,(10)}{50,000} + \frac{(50,000)\,(.08)\,(.10)}{2} = \$200 + \$200 = \$400$$

And, of course, the fact that total costs are less in this case is owing to the lower cost of placing an order as compared to the previous set-up cost.

It is quite easy to incorporate various other costs in our model if these are relevant to the decision problem in question. For example, it is easy to include quantity discounts which may be available on the item to be purchased. Limitations on storage space (in the form of additional carrying costs if the quantity ordered requires more than the usual available space) can be readily built into this model. Anticipated price changes can also be included in the formulation of this decision problem. All of these various additional factors require only a little more algebraic complexity and manipulation. No basic difference in the model, or the argument leading to it, results from their inclusion.

86. RESERVE-STOCK PROBLEM

The two variants of the decision problem explained above afford a simple introduction to the approach which can be used in resolving this kind of inventory problem, with certain demand, but they suffer from a serious lack of realism in the majority of inventory problems. It is not that there are no actual problems which fit our description. On the contrary, the solution to the economic-lot-size problem has been used for many years in production scheduling. However, it is a fact that most inventory decision problems (whether the part is produced or ordered) cannot be handled by such a simple model as we have used above. The major single cause is that we have assumed that demand is known accurately in advance. This assumption, of course, is not valid for the majority of inventory problems.

The more typical situation is one in which we have some fairly good idea of about how large demand is going to be. But we are fully prepared to discover that actual demand is smaller or larger than we forecast. For example, we might expect that demand for a particular item would be about 1000 units per month. However, we would not be surprised if actual demand was 1150 or only 900. We might be surprised if demand went as high as 1400 or as low as 600 but we are aware that this is a possibility—even if not very likely. Under such typical circumstances as these how should we determine an optimal inventory policy?

We will assume that the objective remains the same: the minimization of the costs associated with procuring and carrying a stock of the item in question. Since demand is obviously one of the major variables affecting an inventory decision the first question we must answer is: How does the uncertainty about the exact level of demand affect costs? In order to answer this question we must first find means for expressing precisely what we know, or anticipate, about demand. The natural method for summarizing information of this kind is by means of a probability distribution. A probability distribution of demand shows, in shorthand form, the probability of occurrence of each specific level of demand. A probability distribution to describe our little example of the preceding paragraph would show that the probability of occurrence of a demand of 1000 units was relatively high, the probabilities of occurrence of demand of 1150 or 900 were lower, and the probability of a demand of 1400, or of 600, was definitely very small.

Probability distributions are used to describe a host of different kinds of phenomena for which there is no certainty about outcome. For example, if we toss ten coins we do not know how many heads will show. But we can very nicely summarize our information about the likelihood of the different possible outcomes by means of a probability distribution. Thus, we can present a table which shows the probability of each specific possible outcome.

NUMBER OF HEADS	PROBABILITY
0	1/1024
1	10/1024
2	45/1024
3	120/1024
4	210/1024
5	252/1024
6	210/1024
7	120/1024
8	45/1024
9	10/1024
10	1/1024

1

It will be noted that the sum of the probabilities is 1, as it must be, since one of the eleven possibilities must occur. This probability distribution presents in tabular form a summary of what we know about the outcomes of tosses of ten coins. In accord with our expectations we see that the most likely outcome is five heads and that the probabilities decrease as the outcomes depart in both directions from that value.

We can often express our information about demand in the form of a probability distribution. Since we can not usually hope to have such accurate information about demand as we have about the outcomes of coin tosses, we may group the possible demands into classes and give the probability for each class. Thus, for our example we might have this information:

Demand	Probability
500–699	0.05
700–899	0.20
900–1099	0.50
1100–1299	0.20
1300–1499	0.05
	1.00

This table, then, contains such information as we have concerning the probabilities of the various possible demands—in a manner analogous to that of the outcome of coin tosses.

Where does this information about demand come from? There are a variety of kinds of demands—each one characterized by some combination of the reliability and the accuracy of the information about it. At one extreme there are such kinds of demand as broken drill bits in a machine shop. Each time a drill bit breaks there is demand for a replacement—and, of course, the machine shop must maintain an inventory of bits to meet this demand. Here there is complete knowledge of the population from which the demand arises. In such a case historical records of demand may show a high degree of uniformity, and accurate probability distributions of demand can be drawn up directly from these records. For example, 500 days might show the following frequency distribution of demand:

Number of broken bits	Number of days
0	68
1	136
2	135
3	90
4	45
5	18
6	6
7	2
	500

From the frequency distribution a probability distribution can immediately be constructed by dividing by 500 the number of days for each given number of broken bits. This gives the probability distribution of demand directly.

Number of broken bits	Probability
0	0.136
1	0.272
2	0.270
3	0.180
4	0.090
5	0.036
6	0.012
7	0.004
	1.000

As a second type we can cite items for which the demand is inelastic with regard to most economic factors. Examples are lubricating oil, light bulbs, and the like. Generally, one cannot simply proceed as above in cases like these because there will be trends over time in the demand for these items and the probability distribution for demand must be measured around any trend which may exist—it should not include the trend. However, for basic items it is frequently the case that relatively simple analyses of the historical data will be sufficient to produce good approximations to the probability distribution of demand.

As a third type we can cite items for which demand is highly elastic with regard to many factors. Examples are luxury items of all kinds. In these cases it becomes quite difficult to separate fluctuations in demand which are due to changes in trend or changed economic factors from the probability distribution of demand around the level established by trend and economics. A variety of statistical techniques are used for this purpose but the accuracy of the resulting probability distribution is always somewhat in question.

Finally, we may have the case where a new product is being marketed and there is no historical information whatsoever. Under these circumstances it may often be useful to have the relevant executives simply pool their intuitions and estimate the probabilities for the various levels of demand. These probabilities will simply measure the subjective beliefs of the executives, but if this measurement is all that is available it can be used. The executives will reach their own decisions on the basis of these subjective probabilities anyway, so there is certainly no loss—and sometimes a gain—in making the probabilities in question explicit. And, after all, if one is going to be intuitive one may as well be as rational about it as one can.

Granting the use of probability distributions to express our information about demand, we can return to our original question: How does the uncertainty about the exact level of demand affect costs? The first point to be made in this regard is that it introduces two new costs. First, it is intuitively obvious that it will generally not be the best strategy to maintain enough stock to meet the maximum conceivable demand. Perhaps demand, although generally 1000 units per month, might reach 1600—with a very small probability. It would appear unlikely—but must be determined in each particular case—that the best strategy would be to maintain enough stock to meet this rare demand. But as soon as this is admitted as a possibility it follows as a corollary that the possibility exists of running out of stock and thus being unable to meet the demand which arises. Running out of stock has costs associated with it—for example, the loss of the profit on a sale (if the item is being sold), loss of customer goodwill, or loss of the production of a machine if a necessary spare part is out of stock. Second, the opposite result can also occur—namely, demand is smaller than the amount in inventory. In many inventory problems this only increases the carrying costs slightly and the surplus is sold in subsequent time periods. However, in some kinds of situations this is not possible and a sizable loss results from overstocks. In women's fashion clothing, for example, an overstock at the end of the season may require markdowns to far below cost. Similarly, in some lines of toys the overstock after Christmas can be almost a total loss. The overstock cost can, then, be of considerable importance in some inventory problems. Of these two kinds of costs which are introduced because of uncertainties in demand, the first is almost always a significant factor in the formulation of inventory problems. The second is of lesser importance but it is of great significance for certain kinds of items.

How are these costs determined? The overstock cost is usually fairly simple to measure. Under ordinary circumstances the loss owing to an overstock is some percentage of the amount paid for the item, and this percentage can usually be determined from historical data. But the more important out-of-stock cost is far more difficult to measure in a great many cases. Such possible components of this cost as expediting costs, loss of profit from forfeited sales, or loss of output from some machine not operating for lack of a spare part, are not difficult to measure. But the major intangible component of the cost of out-of-stock is, whenever customers are involved, the so-called loss of customer goodwill. The fact that inability to meet the requirements of a customer does lose goodwill cannot be denied. But how can this be expressed in the form of a dollar cost, comparable to the other costs? The answer is that sometimes ingenious methods can be used to estimate this cost, sometimes the estimates of informed executives have to be used, and sometimes there seems to be no way of getting a reasonable estimate. But let us hasten to add that in any case where this cost is involved it is *always* estimated when a decision is made regarding inventory policy. The only question is whether the estimate will be made explicitly or implicitly. Why this is so will be discussed shortly when we will consider the alternatives available when some of the relevant costs cannot be determined.

For an example we will take a situation which is not the most common or typical but which is particularly well suited to highlight the decision-problem formulation. Consider the purchase of some extremely complex and expensive piece of equipment: a large boiler, a large generator, a battleship, a nuclear submarine, or anything similar. Such a piece of equipment usually has a number of major component parts which have been especially designed for it. Often extra components can be ordered at far less cost when the piece of equipment is first purchased than if ordered subsequently. The reason is that the manufacturer can make the extra component parts with his original set-up far more cheaply than if he must set up again to make them. This being the case, there is a decision problem for the purchaser: How many extra component parts should he order with his original purchase?

The purchaser wants a reserve stock of component parts to protect himself from possible demand in the form of failure of the parts in the piece of equipment. We have the usual elements of decision problems. The possible states of nature are the various possible numbers of failures of the specific part in question during the lifetime of the piece of equipment. The strategies are the various numbers of units of the component part which might be ordered. The objective is to minimize total costs. Typically there is information available about the probabilities of the various states of nature, so we are dealing with decision-making under risk. The decision problem is, thus, fully characterized; all that is needed in order to determine the optimal strategy is to find the payoffs in each cell of the decision matrix.

Let us take a numerical example. Suppose a generator is being ordered for an atomic power plant and that a specific component part will cost $1500 for each extra unit ordered at the time of the initial purchase. If an additional unit is needed subsequently, however, it will cost $4000 to have it made to order. These are the basic costs of the component part in question. But the objective is to minimize total costs. Are there other costs which must be considered? Clearly there are. First, carrying costs will be involved for any extra units maintained in inventory. Second, there will be costs if the part fails and the generator cannot operate while a replacement is being ordered and manufactured. We will assume that the purchaser estimates that the down-time of the generator, while a replacement is made to order, will cost him $20,000. For simplicity we will assume that carrying costs are small and can be ignored.

These data are sufficient to enable us to evaluate the payoff in any cell of the matrix. The objective being to minimize total costs, the payoff measure is simply total costs. Suppose the strategy of carrying no extra units at all is followed. Then if no failure occurs there will be no cost. If one failure occurs there will be a cost of $4000 to have a replacement made to order plus a cost of $20,000 for the down-time of the generator, or $24,000 total. Two failures will cost $48,000 and, similarly, a greater number of failures will cost the corresponding multiple of the $24,000 for each failure. Suppose the strategy of carrying one extra unit is followed. Then if no failure occurs there will be a cost of $1500 for the unit purchased and never used (we assume that if the generator is replaced before a part is used the scrap value of the part is negligible). If one failure occurs the total cost is still $1500. If there are two failures the total cost will be the $1500 spent for the extra unit plus the $24,000 cost of the second failure, or a total cost of $25,500. All of the remainder of the cells of the matrix can be calculated in exactly the same way. For the first seven states of nature and the first seven strategies we get the payoff matrix:

		STATES OF NATURE						
		N_1	N_2	N_3	N_4	N_5	N_6	N_7
	EXTRA	FAILURES						
STRATEGIES	UNITS	0	1	2	3	4	5	6
S_1	0	$0	24,000	48,000	72,000	96,000	120,000	144,000
S_2	1	1500	1500	25,500	49,500	73,500	97,500	121,500
S_3	2	3000	3000	3000	27,000	51,000	75,000	99,000
S_4	3	4500	4500	4500	4500	28,500	52,500	76,500
S_5	4	6000	6000	6000	6000	6000	30,000	54,000
S_6	5	7500	7500	7500	7500	7500	7500	31,500
S_7	6	9000	9000	9000	9000	9000	9000	9000

At this point we have the decision problem in the familiar form. If we were completely uncertain about the probabilities of the various states of nature we would use one of the decision criteria available for decisions under uncertainty. Ordinarily, however, we have information about the probabilities of the states of nature. Generally such information is available in the form of a frequency distribution of the number of failures of the part in question during the lifetimes of similar generators. Otherwise it may be possible to get good estimates from engineers. Suppose we have a frequency distribution of the number of failures of the part and that this has been converted to the corresponding probability distribution.

STATE OF NATURE	NUMBER OF FAILURES	PROBABILITY
N_1	0	0.70
N_2	1	0.15
N_3	2	0.07
N_4	3	0.04
N_5	4	0.02
N_6	5	0.01
N_7	6	0.01
		1.00

This probability distribution gives the information concerning the probability of occurrence of the various states of nature which is necessary in order to have a problem in decision-making under risk rather than one under uncertainty. The probability of N_1, or zero failures, is 0.70; the probability of N_2, or one failure, is 0.15; and so on. We know that the decision criterion for decision-making under risk is the minimum (or maximum) expected value. This requires calculating the expected total cost of each strategy, using the probabilities of each of the states of nature. For S_1 we calculate

$$0.70\,(\$0) + 0.15\,(\$24{,}000) + 0.07\,(\$48{,}000) + 0.04\,(\$72{,}000)$$
$$+ \,0.02\,(\$96{,}000) + 0.01\,(\$120{,}000) + 0.01\,(\$144{,}000) = \$14{,}400$$

For S_2 we have

$$0.70\,(\$1500) + 0.15\,(\$1500) + 0.07\,(\$25{,}500) + 0.04\,(\$49{,}500)$$
$$+ \,0.02\,(\$73{,}500) + 0.01\,(\$97{,}500) + 0.01\,(\$121{,}500) = \$8700$$

Proceeding similarly we find:

STRATEGY	EXPECTED TOTAL COST
S_1	$14,400
S_2	8700
S_3	6600
S_4	6180
S_5	6720
S_6	7740
S_7	9000

According to our criterion we should select that strategy which has the minimum expected total cost. In our case this leads to the selection of S_4: 3 extra units should be ordered initially. The expected total cost of this strategy is $6180, less than that of any other strategy.

The original inventory decision problem has been solved by the determination of the optimal strategy, S_4. But it will be worthwhile to raise a question concerning the payoff matrix which we constructed. The matrix doesn't seem to reflect what we really had in mind in this decision problem—at least if we look at the situation in one way. Consider, for example, our evaluation of the various payoffs for S_5, the initial purchase of 4 extra units. We have calculated that the total cost of this strategy is the same, $6000, for all states of nature from N_1 to N_5. But, one might reason, for N_1 we have in some sense "wasted" the $6000 because we didn't need any replacement units at all. Similarly, for N_3 we needed only 2 units and, in the same sense, the other 2 units were "wasted." For N_5 we needed all 4 units so none were "wasted." By this line of reasoning it seems, somehow, incorrect to have given each of these five states of nature the same payoff measure, $6000. Furthermore, the payoffs for the other two states of nature, still assuming S_5, seem equally wrong. If N_6 occurs we are 1 unit short and must order it, at a cost of $24,000. This plus the $6000 for the 4 units originally purchased gives the $30,000 payoff for S_5 and N_6, as in our matrix. But consider the $24,000 component of this payoff. If we had had another unit in stock it would have cost $1500, so it seems that the $24,000 only represents an extra, or avoidable, cost of $24,000 − $1500 = $22,500. A similar argument applies to every entry in the payoff matrix except that for S_1 if N_1 occurs, which has a zero cost by any argument. In short, the whole payoff matrix seems wrong. What can we say to this?

The answer is that the counterargument we have just presented is perfectly correct—but so is the original argument. Further, both will lead to exactly the same selection of the optimal strategy although the payoff matrices are different for the two approaches. The reason that this is so is important enough to justify our devoting some space to explaining it.

The counterargument can be restated more briefly. Instead of considering total costs we should only concern ourselves with avoidable costs, that is, costs which might have been avoided had we had reliable advance information about the state of nature which would occur. In economic terms, we should use opportunity costs instead of total costs. An opportunity cost is that extra cost which results when we have selected a strategy which is not the minimum cost for the state of nature which actually occurs. Thus, consider S_5 again. By our counterargument we have "wasted" the $6000 if N_1 occurs because we didn't need any replacements. And in terms of opportunity costs we have, for S_5 and N_1, an opportunity cost of $6000 since we could have used S_1, which would have had zero cost for N_1 and $6000 − 0 = $6000. We may note that this opportunity cost is actually an overstock cost. If N_3 occurs our counterargument was that we had "wasted" two units and the payoff should have been $3000, (2 × $1500). The opportunity cost for this case would be $6000 minus the cost of the minimum-cost strategy for N_3, which is S_3 with a cost of $3000. Thus, the opportunity cost for S_5 if N_3 occurs is $6000 − $3000

= $3000, the same as by our counterargument. We leave it to the reader to verify that all of the other changes suggested by the counterargument are exactly those which result if we use opportunity costs rather than total costs.

It is very easy to determine the opportunity-cost payoff matrix. We want to measure each payoff as an opportunity cost against the minimum cost for the same state of nature. The reader should recognize that this amounts to subtracting the lowest cost in each column from every entry in that column. This is exactly the same procedure we used in constructing the regret matrix for the Savage decision criterion for decision-making under uncertainty. And, as a matter of fact, this is precisely what the regret matrix is in economic terms: an opportunity-cost matrix. Applied to our total-cost payoff matrix we get the opportunity-cost matrix.

	STATES OF NATURE						
	N_1	N_2	N_3	N_4	N_5	N_6	N_7
	PROBABILITIES						
STRATEGIES	0.70	0.15	0.07	0.04	0.02	0.01	0.01
S_1	$ 0	22,500	45,000	67,500	90,000	112,500	135,000
S_2	1500	0	22,500	45,000	67,500	90,000	112,500
S_3	3000	1500	0	22,500	45,000	67,500	90,000
S_4	4500	3000	1500	0	22,500	45,000	67,500
S_5	6000	4500	3000	1500	0	22,500	45,000
S_6	7500	6000	4500	3000	1500	0	22,500
S_7	9000	7500	6000	4500	3000	1500	0

We have changed the payoff measures but the decision problem remains the same in all other respects. In particular, it is still decision-making under risk and we will still use the expected value. But we can save ourselves some calculation by a little preliminary thinking. How does this matrix differ from the preceding one? We have subtracted from each entry in a column a fixed amount (the minimum cost for that column). The amounts subtracted from the various columns were

STATE OF NATURE	AMOUNT SUBTRACTED (MINIMUM COST)
N_1	$ 0
N_2	1500
N_3	3000
N_4	4500
N_5	6000
N_6	7500
N_7	9000

But this means that the expected opportunity costs for the various strategies (the expected values derived for our new matrix) will each be a constant amount smaller than the expected total costs we calculated previously. Specifically, the expected opportunity cost for each strategy will be

$$0.70\,(0) + 0.15\,(1500) + 0.07\,(3000) + 0.04\,(4500)$$
$$+ 0.02\,(6000) + 0.01\,(7500) + 0.01\,(9000) = \$900$$

less than the expected total cost previously calculated. For example, let us calculate the expected opportunity cost for S_7.

$$0.70\,(9000) + 0.15\,(7500) + 0.07\,(6000) + 0.04\,(4500)$$
$$+ 0.02\,(3000) + 0.01\,(1500) + 0.01\,(0) = \$8100$$

This is just $900 less than the expected total cost for the same strategy, as it should be. The reader may verify the relationship for other strategies if he has any doubts about its validity. We can, then, immediately write down the expected opportunity costs for each strategy by simply subtracting $900 from the corresponding expected total costs previously calculated. We get

STRATEGY	EXPECTED OPPORTUNITY COST
S_1	$13,500
S_1	7800
S_3	5700
S_4	5280
S_5	5820
S_6	6840
S_7	8100

Our criterion dictates the selection of that strategy with the lowest expected opportunity cost. It is S_4, with an expected opportunity cost of $5280.

Thus, the use either of total costs or of opportunity costs results in the selection of the same strategy. This will always be the case for decision-making under risk because the use of opportunity costs instead of total costs simply results in the subtraction of a constant amount from the expected total cost of each strategy. This cannot change the relative ranks of the expected costs of the strategies, and the smallest expected total cost will remain the smallest expected opportunity cost. Therefore, our criterion will always select the same strategy in both cases. Phrased in decision criteria terms, we see that the minimum expected value criterion selects the same strategy whether it is applied to the original matrix or to the Savage regret matrix (not the Savage criterion).

We will conclude our discussion of this kind of inventory decision problem by asking, and answering, two questions which may have already occurred to the reader. First, why did we ignore carrying costs in this example? Carrying, for example, units worth $6000 for the entire life of a generator could be quite costly. Why ignore such costs? The answer to this question is that these costs should not, and could not, be ignored in any actual decision problem. We ignored them because their inclusion complicates the calculation of the payoffs with a lot of details which do not in any way affect the basic procedure but which do quite thoroughly obscure it. In order to include them one must first have information about the lifetimes of generators, usually in the form of another probability distribution. Then one must have information concerning the lengths of time between failures, which may require several more probability distributions. Such information is necessary in order to determine how long the various units will probably have to be carried. The net effect of these complications is to hide a fundamentally simple and straightforward decision problem under a mass of arithmetical details. In short, we ignored carrying costs in order to spare the reader, and ourselves.

The second question is, why did we select an infrequently occurring kind of inventory problem as an example? Why not a more typical case, like the inventory problem of a manufacturer producing any product which has varying demand? The answer to this question is similar to that for the first question. The decision-theory structure of these kinds of inventory problems is like that in our example. Specific cases will have different kinds of costs, as we discussed earlier, but the procedure is always to determine the total costs for each cell of the matrix. In the case of most frequently occurring inventory problems the determination of the total costs requires manipulations of probability distributions and other mathematical devices which are too elaborate to present here. Our example was selected because, while it is identical in structure to the more usual kinds of inventory problems, it does not require any of these more advanced mathematical methods.

87. INVENTORY PROBLEMS WITH UNKNOWN COSTS

The above examples suffice to illustrate the procedure involved in formulating inventory decision problems. A great variety of different models have been constructed, and used, to handle the specific decision problems which arise as a result of the particular circumstances which can be involved in inventory problems: price discounts, anticipated changes in price, transportation costs depending on quantity, warehouse limitations, peculiarities of demand, and others.   But all of these different models are based on the same approach that we have followed here: the isolation of the opposing costs involved, the construction of the total-cost equation, and the determination of the minimum total cost.   Therefore, rather than developing various elaborations on this basic theme, we will consider in greater detail some of the questions involved in the determination of the various costs which we have seen are required in the total-cost equation.

The difficulties involved in determining some of the necessary costs, particularly the out-of-stock cost, are often considerable.   Nonetheless, the analysis of the decision problem depends on these costs.   It is therefore important to raise the question whether the analysis we have developed is of any use to the executive when these costs cannot be determined accurately.   In answering this question we will develop two related points.   First, as stated above, the costs in question are involved in every inventory decision, whether the decision-maker knows it or not. The costs used in the total-cost equation are not creations of the fertile imagination of the analyst.   Rather, every decision concerning inventory policy imputes a value to the relevant costs.   The only question is: Does the decision-maker profit from making these values explicit?   Second, the analysis of the inventory decision problem can be formulated so that the costs are left to the intuition of the decision-maker.   So doing will ensure that the decision-maker is logical, once he has intuited the costs, and this is by no means a minor achievement.

It will be useful to have a numerical example to follow throughout the argument.   We will suppose that a company must maintain inventories on three different items.   The relevant information concerning these items is

Item	D Yearly Demand	p Price
A	120,000	$3.00
B	80,000	2.00
C	600	96.00

These are actual data, rounded off, from an inventory problem in the petroleum industry.   The items were selected to provide some range in demand and price characteristics.   We will consider first the problem of determining the optimal order size.   We have already seen that this decision problem is solved by starting from the total-cost equation

$$TC = \frac{DC_1}{Z} + \frac{ZpC_2}{2}$$

and determining the minimum with regard to Z, the order size. The minimum total cost results when

$$Z = \sqrt{\frac{2DC_1}{pC_2}}$$

We cannot determine Z for the three items above without knowing the two costs, C_1 and C_2. Often, as discussed above, these costs can be approximated from cost-accounting data. However, it is also often the case that there are serious questions concerning the validity of the estimates. These questions arise mainly because of the difficulty of measuring opportunity costs which are involved in each of them. Thus, C_1 (ordering cost) will include a component based on the space occupied by the order department. But what is this space worth in terms of the other utilizations available to the company? What does it cost the company not to have available for other uses the manpower and money tied up in the order department? These questions and similar ones relating to C_2 (carrying cost) indicate that in some cases, at least, it may be very difficult to obtain valid estimates of C_1 and C_2. What can be done then?

Let us return to our equation. If we substitute the minimizing value of Z in the total-cost equation we get

$$TC = \sqrt{\frac{DC_1pC_2}{2}} + \sqrt{\frac{DC_1pC_2}{2}} = \sqrt{2DC_1pC_2} = \sqrt{2C_1C_2}\sqrt{Dp}$$

From this expression for the total cost it can be seen that, whatever the costs are, the total cost involved in maintaining an inventory for any particular item will be proportional to the square root of the product of yearly demand times price (yearly value used of the item in question). This will be true if the optimal order quantity has been determined by our equation for Z and it gives us means for determining optimal inventory policies when we don't know the costs but are given some restrictions on the solution.

We can use the three items above as an example of how we might proceed. Let us suppose that current policy is to order each of the three items every month. Then we can easily calculate the total number of orders and the total investment in inventory which will result.

ITEM	D	p	ORDERS PER YEAR	AVERAGE IN-VENTORY INVESTMENT: $Dp/24$
A	120,000	$3.00	12	$15,000
B	80,000	2.00	12	6,667
C	600	96.00	12	2,400
			36	$24,067

This policy will result in a total of 36 orders per year and an average inventory investment of \$24,067. But we know that any optimal policy will have the total cost for each item proportional to $\sqrt{Dp}$. For these items the square roots of yearly value of usage are

ITEM	D	p	$\sqrt{Dp}$
A	120,000	\$3.00	600
B	80,000	2.00	400
C	600	96.00	240
			1240

The sum of the square roots is 1240. Now, suppose that we do not know the costs (C_1 and C_2) but that we are told that 36 orders per year will be acceptable. What should be the policy in order to minimize the amount of inventory, granted that there will be 36 orders per year? This is now readily determinable. The final results, for 36 orders per year or any other number, must be proportional to the square roots of the yearly usage value of the items in question. We want to make the total number of orders equal to 36 while having the orders for each item proportional to the square root of its yearly usage values. In the general case this is accomplished by calculating *

$$\frac{\Sigma\sqrt{Dp}}{\text{Total orders desired}}$$

and multiplying $\sqrt{Dp}$ for each item by this factor to get the order size in dollars. This will give the ordering policy which produces the smallest possible total inventory for any given number of total orders. A little algebra is required to prove this and we will not give the proof here. In our specific case we want the optimal policy for 36 orders per year so we calculate $1240/36 = 34.44$. This must now be multiplied by each item's $\sqrt{Dp}$ to determine the optimal order size (in dollars). We calculate

ITEM	$\sqrt{Dp}$	ORDER SIZE, \$34.44 $\sqrt{Dp}$	QUANTITY ORDERED	NUMBER OF ORDERS PER YEAR	AVERAGE INVENTORY
A	600	\$20,664	6888	17.4	\$10,332
B	400	13,776	6888	11.6	6888
C	240	8266	86	7.0	4133
	1240			36.0	\$21,353

* The mathematical symbol Σ is convenient when we want to handle situations involving more than one item. It means simply "add" and it applies to whatever terms come after it. Here, for example, it means to add the $\sqrt{Dp}$ terms of each item.

Thus, an optimal policy based on 36 orders per year would require only $21,353 average investment in inventory as compared to the $24,067 investment required when each item is ordered the same number of times. The saving was accomplished by distributing the orders in accordance with the size of $\sqrt{Dp}$. The 11 per cent saving in inventory investment is a measure of the lack of rationality of the policy of ordering each item each month.

Alternatively, we could ask: How many orders per year would be required if an optimal policy were followed which required $24,067 (the amount under the original policy) average inventory investment? This is also easily accomplished. We want to divide the total inventory into amounts proportional to the items' square roots of yearly usage value. In the general case we do this by calculating

$$\frac{2\,(\text{total inventory desired})}{\Sigma\sqrt{Dp}}$$

where Σ means "add," and multiplying $\sqrt{Dp}$ for each item by this factor to get the order size in dollars. This will give the ordering policy which will minimize the total number of orders for any desired total inventory investment. In our case we want the optimal ordering policy for a total inventory investment of $24,067. We calculate $(2 \times 24,067) \div 1240 = 38.818$ and then

ITEM	$\sqrt{Dp}$	ORDER SIZE, $38.818 \sqrt{Dp}$	QUANTITY ORDERED	NUMBER OF ORDERS PER YEAR	AVERAGE INVENTORY
A	600	$23,291	7764	15.5	$11,645
B	400	15,527	7764	10.3	7764
C	240	9316	97	6.2	4658
				32.0	$24,067

An optimal policy constructed with the intention of having $24,067 in average inventory investment would require only 32 orders per year instead of 36. And, again, the saving of 4 orders per year is a measure of the lack of rationality in the policy of ordering each item each month.

In other words, we are able to use the information from our equations to improve existing inventory policies without knowledge of the true costs. If the decision-maker, for whatever reason, imposes a restriction on the number of orders per year or on the average inventory investment, then an optimal inventory policy can be determined subject to that restriction. The reason is that any such restriction implies a particular ratio between the two costs, C_1 and C_2. Thus,

from
$$Z = \sqrt{\frac{2DC_1}{pC_2}}$$

we can write
$$Z = \sqrt{\frac{C_1}{C_2}} \ \sqrt{\frac{2D}{p}}$$

or
$$\frac{C_1}{C_2} = \frac{Z^2 p}{2D}$$

This last equation explains why we can be certain that the original policy of ordering each item once each month was not optimal. Suppose that this policy is optimal. Then we can calculate for each item the imputed value of the cost ratio. We find

ITEM	ORDERS PER YEAR	QUANTITY ORDERED (Z)	C_1/C_2
A	12	10,000	1250
B	12	6667	556
C	12	50	200

Now, granting that these three items are similar with regard to carrying costs and that the order cost is the same for all items, there is no reason why these ratios should be different. The fact that they are different indicates that the inventory policy is not rational. When we fix the total number of orders per year at 36 we are fixing this cost ratio at 593, as can be calculated from any one of the items. And when we fix the average inventory investment at \$24,067 we are fixing this cost ratio at 753. Thus, suppose we knew that the carrying cost was \$0.12 per dollar inventory investment per year (C_2). If the decision-maker then fixes 36 orders per year as an objective of inventory policy he is, in fact, assigning or imputing a value of $593 \times 0.12 = \$71.16$ as the order cost (C_1). If, instead, he fixes the average inventory investment at \$24,067, then he is imputing a value of $753 \times 0.12 = \$90.36$ as the order cost. And, of course, we have already seen that establishing a policy of one order per month per item is simply illogical, and unnecessarily costly, because it imputes different order costs for each item.

We can use this same approach to develop an analysis of the inventory decision problem which permits the decision-maker to survey the whole range of possible optimal policies. We have developed above the optimal inventory policies which result from two specific assignments (even though implicit) of values to the ratio C_1/C_2. In fact, there is an optimal inventory policy for each and every ratio, C_1/C_2. In short, each ratio of C_1/C_2 determines an optimal number of orders per year and an optimal average inventory investment. A convenient way to present a picture of this whole set of optimal inventory policies is as follows. The number of orders per year (*not* the cost) in an optimal policy is given by substituting the expression for the optimal Z in D/Z (the number of orders per year for any Z whatsoever). This gives for any item

$$\text{Number of orders} = \frac{D}{\sqrt{\dfrac{2DC_1}{pC_2}}} = \sqrt{\frac{C_2}{C_1}}\ \sqrt{\frac{Dp}{2}}$$

Similarly, the average inventory investment (*not* the cost) for an optimal policy is given by substituting Z in $Zp/2$ (the average inventory investment for any Z whatsoever). This gives for any item

$$\text{average inventory investment} = \frac{p}{2}\sqrt{\frac{2DC_1}{pC_2}} = \sqrt{\frac{C_1}{C_2}}\ \sqrt{\frac{Dp}{2}}$$

These expressions hold for any optimal inventory policy for any item. If we multiply these two expressions together the terms involving C_1 and C_2 cancel out and we get

$$\text{Number of orders} \times \text{average inventory investment} = \frac{Dp}{2}$$

However, we want to handle situations involving more than one item. Using the symbol Σ we can write, for any number of items,

$$\text{Number of orders} \times \text{average inventory investment} = \tfrac{1}{2}(\Sigma\sqrt{Dp})^2$$

This is to be read, and calculated, by first taking the sum of the square roots of Dp for each item, squaring this sum, and then taking $\tfrac{1}{2}$ that total. For our three items we would proceed thus:

Number of orders $\times$ average inventory investment
$$= \tfrac{1}{2}(\Sigma\sqrt{Dp})^2 = \tfrac{1}{2}(600 + 400 + 200)^2$$
$$= \tfrac{1}{2}(1240)^2 = \tfrac{1}{2}(1,537,600)$$
$$= \$768,800$$

This relationship between the number of orders and the average inventory investment takes the form of a hyperbola. It can be conveniently graphed as in Figure 10.4. We already have determined two of the points on this curve in the two policies above. In the first we found 36 orders per year and an average inventory investment of \$21,353, and $36 \times 21{,}353 = \$769{,}000$ (rounded off), as it should. In the other policy we found 32 orders per year and an average inventory investment of \$24,067, and $32 \times 24{,}067 = \$770{,}000$ (rounded to the accuracy of the figures), again as it should. The equation, or curve, gives every possible optimal policy for these three items.

The advantage of this approach is that it permits the decision-maker to see the effects of his assumptions about limitations on the inventory policy. If, for example, he believes that the inventory investment must be held to no more than $15,000 then it follows directly that he must be prepared to handle 51.3 orders per year. If the order department cannot handle more than 20 orders per year then he must be prepared to

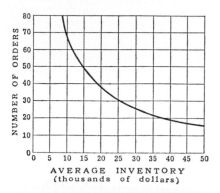

Figure 10.4. Optimal inventory policies.

have $38,440 average inventory investment. By use of this equation or the corresponding curve, the decision-maker can utilize directly his knowledge about the availability of capital for inventory investment and/or limitations on the capacity of the order department without having to attempt to get reliable estimates of the two associated costs. It must once again be emphasized, however, that the ratio of the costs, C_1/C_2, is tacitly involved in every solution represented by a point on this curve. Specifically, the cost ratio associated with any specific point on the curve is given by

$$\frac{C_1}{C_2} = \frac{\text{Average inventory investment}}{\text{Number of orders per year}}$$

Thus, holding the inventory investment to $15,000 is equivalent to assuming that

$$\frac{C_1}{C_2} = \frac{15,000}{51.3} = 292.4$$

or that the order cost is 292.4 times as large as the carrying cost. If the number of orders is held down to 20 per year, then the imputed cost ratio is

$$\frac{C_1}{C_2} = \frac{38,440}{20} = 1922$$

In other words, the change from 51 orders per year to 20 orders per year implies an increase in the estimate of order cost (C_1) by a factor of more than 6, as compared to the carrying cost.

In exactly the same way, out-of-stock costs are implied, or imputed, by any decision concerning reserve stocks. The decision-theory approach is to make these costs explicit, but they are always involved whether explicit or not. The demonstration of the way the out-of-stock cost is imputed by a reserve-stock decision would be longer and more complicated than that given above for carrying costs and ordering costs. Therefore we shall not give it here.

Instead, we will simply prove our statement that the out-of-stock cost is imputed by any reserve-stock decision. We know that a rational decision concerning reserve stocks would be achieved by balancing the out-of-stock costs against some opposing costs, such as carrying costs. We know that these costs exist, because if there were no out-of-stock costs there would be no need to have any reserve stock and if there were no opposing costs one would simply carry an enormous reserve stock. Now, any given amount of reserve stock implies a calculable probability of going out of stock, given the demand probability distribution. Suppose the out-of-stock cost were known. Then the out-of-stock cost associated with any reserve stock could be calculated. By the marginal principle the decision-maker would carry a reserve stock of such size that the last unit added to reserve decreased the out-of-stock cost by as much as it increased the carrying cost. But, by the same token, any given reserve stock, if it is to be considered the result of a rational policy, must be such that the last unit added equated these costs. Therefore, any reserve-stock decision establishes a ratio between the carrying cost and the out-of-stock cost even if the decision-maker does not explicitly know these costs. Generally, of course, the larger the reserve stock, the larger the imputed cost of out-of-stock.

88. NUMBER OF REPAIRMEN

A decision problem concerning the servicing of machines has some similarities to the inventory problems we have been considering. The elements of the problem are that some number of operating machines are subject to breakdown and repairmen are maintained on the payroll in order to restore the machines to operation. The decision problem is: How many repairmen should there be? The objective is to minimize costs. The strategies are the various numbers of repairmen who might be hired. The states of nature are the various rates at which the machines may break down. In short, all the usual components of a decision problem are easily found in this situation. The only step necessary in order to complete the payoff matrix is the evaluation of the payoff.

This problem has a striking similarity to the inventory problems we considered above. The close relationship between the two problems becomes apparent when we rephrase the repairmen problem: an inventory of repairmen's time must be maintained in order to meet future demand, which consists of the breakdown of machines. There is a cost which increases as the number of repairmen increases: the cost associated with their resulting idle time. And there is a cost which increases as the number of repairmen decreases: the cost of having machines out of operation because there is no repairman available to service them. These two costs correspond to the carrying costs and the out-of-stock costs, respectively, in the inventory decision problem. It might, therefore, seem as if the repairmen problem could be solved along exactly the same lines as the inventory problem. This is not the case, and the reason for the difference deserves emphasis.

In the inventory problem it is necessary to have information about the probability distribution of demand in order to determine the probability and, hence, the cost of out-of-stock associated with any specific level of reserve stock. Similarly, in the repairmen problem it will be necessary to have information concerning the demand, in this case the rate at which machines break down. But in the inventory problem any reserve stock is immediately available to meet the demand that occurs. Therefore, the out-of-stock cost associated with a specific level of reserve stock can be calculated fairly readily as some straightforward function of the excess of demand over the reserve stock. This is not true in the case of the repairmen. The reserve inventory in this case is the time of the repairmen, and this will only be avaiable to meet demand if one of the repairmen is unoccupied when a machine breaks down. If all the repairmen are occupied the machine must wait until one of them is free. This is not equivalent to being out of stock in an ordinary inventory problem because it can happen even when the total inventory of time is greater, over some interval of time, than the demand. The reason is, of course, that time cannot be stored. The repairmen's past idle time is not available when a number of machines suddenly break down. This difference from the inventory problem may seem small but it has some surprising consequences.

Let us take an example. Suppose that a machine shop has 30 machines and that the cost of one machine's being out of operation for one hour is estimated to be $40. Repairmen capable of repairing these machines are paid $5 per hour. As pointed out above, we need some information about the demand for repairmen's time, which results from the breakdown of machines. Information concerning this might be available in several forms, but a typical record might show the numbers of machines that broke down on each day. From such a record we can easily construct a frequency distribution and probability distribution.

Table 10.1

BREAKDOWNS PER DAY	NUMBER OF DAYS	PROBABILITY
0	99	0.495
1	70	0.350
2	24	0.120
3	6	0.030
4	1	0.005
	200	1.000

The probability has been determined as usual, by dividing each frequency (number of days) by the total frequency (total number of days). The form of the distribution which is given here is typical of that which is frequently found in data such as these—the Poisson distribution. It has many interesting properties, but we will merely note that it is always characterized by having a longer tail to the right than to the left. In the present case the mean of the distribution of machine breakdowns is 0.7 machines per day [readily calculated from $0(0.495) + 1(0.350) + 2(0.120) + 3(0.030) + 4(0.005) = 0.700$]. This means that, on the average, one machine breaks down every 1.429 days $(1/0.7 = 1.429)$.

Since the opposing cost in this decision problem is the cost of having machines out of operation we need some information concerning the length of time it takes to restore a machine to operation. Ordinarily, such information would be available from repairmen's time sheets. Suppose we find the following probability distribution.

Table 10.2

HOURS TO REPAIR	PROBABILITY
1	0.021
2	0.051
3	0.099
4	0.143
5	0.165
6	0.160
7	0.132
8	0.096
9	0.062
10	0.036
11	0.019
12	0.009
13	0.004
14	0.002
15	0.001
	1.000

It will often be found that these data, as here, will fall in a Poisson distribution. This is a reflection of the fact that many repair jobs will take some relatively small amount of time but that a few will take much longer times. In the present case the average repair time can be calculated to be 5.8 hours.

It might appear that there is really no decision problem here at all. On the basis of the information we have been given it seems that, on the average, a machine will break down every 1.429 days and that it will take a repairman, again on the average, 5.8 hours to fix it. Thus, one repairman can easily handle the necessary repairs and, in fact, will only work about 4 hours per day (5.8 hours every 1.429 days). It will cost 5.8 hours, or 5.8 × \$40 = \$232, in lost operating time for each machine which breaks down, but this is simply one of the facts of the situation. It would certainly seem that one repairman would be far more than sufficient. And, in deed, at this point the executive might well be wishing that labor wasn't so "lumpy." He would perhaps like to hire only half a repairman!

This conclusion, however, is too hasty because it overlooks the outstanding characteristic of this kind of problem. We have based the fallacious argument of the preceding paragraph on the assumption that, since it takes an average of 5.8 hours to repair a machine, we can calculate the cost of the machine's being out of operation by simply multiplying 5.8 by the cost per hour (\$40). The error in the reasoning lies in this assumption. Granted that it takes 5.8 hours to repair a machine—once the repairman is able to start work. But what about the times when he isn't able to start work on the machine because he is already working on another machine? In this event the machine will have to wait, and the time it has to wait costs \$40 per hour just as well as the actual repair time. It is this cost which we must investigate. This kind of situation has been studied extensively and a whole branch of probability theory has developed around it. Fittingly enough, it is called waiting-line, or queuing, theory.

Unfortunately, the mathematics involved in the analysis of waiting lines and waiting times is too complex for us to present here. We can, however, use Monte Carlo techniques to get some insight into the problem. The reader will remember that the idea behind Monte Carlo is to use random sampling to construct a simulated version of the process being analyzed. By this means we can actually see what happens rather than having to calculate it from mathematical equations. In the present case we want to see what happens if we have machines that break down in accordance with Table 10.1 and a repairman who repairs the machines in accordance with Table 10.2. We can readily do this with Monte Carlo by assigning blocks of three-digit numbers to the different possibilities in proportion to their probabilities. We will need the machine-breakdown data on an hourly basis in order to fit these data to the repair-time data. They can be obtained by a mathematical transformation of the data in Table 10.1 or directly from the original records. On an hourly basis the machine-breakdown data are

BREAKDOWNS PER HOUR	PROBABILITY
0	0.916
1	0.080
2	0.004
	1.000

These data are precisely equivalent to the data on a daily basis. Now we can assign three-digit numbers to each of these three possibilities in accordance with the given probabilities, and similarly for the repair times. For example,

BREAKDOWNS PER HOUR	PROBABILITY	NUMBERS ASSIGNED	REPAIR TIMES	PROBABILITY	NUMBERS ASSIGNED
0	0.916	000–915	1	0.021	000–020
1	0.080	916–995	2	0.051	021–071
2	0.004	996–999	3	0.099	072–170
			4	0.143	171–313
			5	0.165	314–478
			6	0.160	479–638
			7	0.132	639–770
			8	0.096	771–866
			9	0.062	867–928
			10	0.036	929–964
			11	0.019	965–983
			12	0.009	984–992
			13	0.004	993–996
			14	0.002	997–998
			15	0.001	999

Thus, for each of the two distributions we have assigned 1000 three-digit numbers. For example, 80 of them (916–995) will represent one breakdown in an hour. This is a probability of $80/1000 = 0.080$, exactly as it should be. Now we can use a table of random numbers (page 356) to obtain a sample of the behavior of our system. First we start reading three digit numbers from the table. Each number will represent one hour, consecutively, hour by hour. The specific three digit number shows, in accordance with our assignments of numbers to the possibilities, which possibility occurred in that hour. The first number we read was 573 and since this falls between 000 and 915 it means that there was no machine breakdown during the first hour. The second number is 608, again no breakdown. We continue reading numbers, one for each hour, until the ninth number we read is 919, meaning that a breakdown occurred in this hour. Proceeding similarly we can take a sample for any desired number of hours. In this case, a sample of 800 hours or 100 eight-hour days was taken. A record must, of course be kept of the specific hours in which the breakdown occurred. Having obtained the sample of breakdowns it is necessary to read a new random three digit number for each breakdown in order to determine the repair times. For example, for the first breakdown we read the number 257. Referring to the table of numbers assigned to the various repair times it will be seen that 257 designates a repair time of 4 hours. This, then, is the repair time for the first breakdown. When the repair time has been determined for each breakdown it is possible to calculate the waiting time for each breakdown. The hours in which the breakdowns occurred could be recorded in terms of days and hour of the day but it is easier for subsequent calculations to simply record them numerically, in this case from 1 to 800. Our data are recorded in Table 10.3.

These are our raw data and we must now calculate the waiting times of those breakdowns which had to wait for the repairman. This can be done quite simply by a routine procedure. The first step is to determine the hour at which each repair was terminated.

Let B_i designate the hour at which the ith breakdown occurred and let R_i designate the hours required for the repair of the ith breakdown. Finally, let T_i be the hour at which the repair of the ith breakdown was terminated. Then we have a simple rule:

$$T_i = T_{i-1} + R_i \quad \text{if} \quad B_i < T_{i-1}$$

or

$$T_i = B_i + R_i \quad \text{if} \quad B_i \geqq T_{i-1}$$

The first part of the rule says simply that if the ith breakdown occurs before the end of the repair of the $(i-1)$st breakdown then the repair of the ith breakdown will not start until T_{i-1} and, hence, will end at $T_{i-1} + R_i$. The second part of the rule says that if the ith breakdown occurs at or after the termination of the repair of the $(i-1)$st breakdown then the repair of the ith breakdown can start immediately. Using this rule we can quickly determine all the T_i for our sample (Table 10.4).

We can now determine the waiting times by finding $T_{i-1} - B_i$ for each breakdown for which this was positive. The $T_{i-1} - B_i$ (when positive) represent the waiting times since when $T_{i-1} > B_i$ then the ith breakdown

Table 10.3

Breakdown number (i)	Breakdown hour (B_i)	Repair time (R_i)	Breakdown number (i)	Breakdown hour (B_i)	Repair time (R_i)
1	9	4	37	355	4
2	26	4	38	375	5
3	35	4	39	401	2
4	59	2	40	413	3
5	62	6	41	430	8
6	75	8	42	435	2
7	94	6	43	436	6
8	104	3	44	440	3
9	110	4	45	450	5
10	111	6	46	452	15
11	111	7	47	467	5
12	135	6	48	483	6
13	153	8	49	504	7
14	156	2	50	505	7
15	157	5	51	509	7
16	171	1	52	533	6
17	173	5	53	534	6
18	187	4	54	538	6
19	189	8	55	582	9
20	223	9	56	612	4
21	224	4	57	624	3
22	226	3	58	631	3
23	232	8	59	634	7
24	241	4	60	640	10
25	244	4	61	647	4
26	245	4	62	663	6
27	250	5	63	678	10
28	260	4	64	694	9
29	298	5	65	702	4
30	299	3	66	743	5
31	307	6	67	746	4
32	309	7	68	756	6
33	313	6	69	763	9
34	316	4	70	764	10
35	318	7	71	796	13
36	320	5			

would have to wait until the conclusion of the repairs on the $(i-1)$st breakdown. The total waiting time for this sample with one repairman was 202 hours (Table 10.5).

Let us inspect the data we have obtained. Returning to the table showing the Monte Carlo sample it may be noted that we had two failures in one hour (111) even though the probability of this is only 0.004. We had one repair time of 15 hours (452) even though this probability is

Table 10.4

Breakdown hour (B_i)	Termination of repair (T_i)	Breakdown hour (B_i)	Termination of repair (T_i)
9	13	355	359
26	30	375	380
35	39	401	403
59	61	413	416
62	68	430	438
75	83	435	440
94	100	436	446
104	107	440	449
110	114	450	455
111	120	452	470
111	127	467	475
135	141	483	489
153	161	504	511
156	163	505	518
157	168	509	525
171	172	533	539
173	178	534	545
187	191	538	551
189	199	582	591
223	232	612	616
224	236	624	627
226	239	631	634
232	247	634	641
241	251	640	651
244	255	647	655
245	259	663	669
250	264	678	688
260	268	694	703
298	303	702	707
299	306	743	748
307	313	746	752
309	320	756	762
313	326	763	772
316	330	764	782
318	337	796	809
320	342		

only 0.001. But such are the ways of random samples—the seemingly unexpected is always happening, thus showing that it really shouldn't have been so unexpected. Since our sample covers 800 hours it is not surprising that some rare events occurred. How does the sample compare with the original data? A count shows that there were **71** breakdowns in the 100 days (800 hours). Since we know that the average number of breakdowns was 0.7 per day in the original data it follows

Table 10.5

Breakdown hour (B_i)	Waiting time $T_{i-1} - B_i$
111	3
111	9
156	5
157	6
189	2
224	8
226	10
232	7
241	6
244	7
245	10
250	9
260	4
299	4
309	4
313	7
316	10
318	12
320	17
435	3
436	4
440	6
452	3
467	3
505	6
509	9
534	5
538	7
640	1
647	4
702	1
746	2
764	8
	202

that the expected number of breakdowns in 100 days would be $100 \times 0.7 = 70$. Our sample, then, is very close to expected on number of breakdowns. Adding up all the repair times shows that it took 400 hours to repair these 71 breakdowns or an average of $400/71 = 5.63$ hours per breakdown. This compares well with the 5.8 hours average repair time of the original data. It appears that our sample is quite representative of the original data.

The total waiting time was 202 hours or an average of $202/71 = 2.845$ hours per breakdown. Alternatively, there were $202/100 = 2.02$ hours waiting time for each of the 100 days represented by the sample. At the stated cost of $40 per hour for a machine which is out of operation this amounts to $80.80 loss due to waiting time per day. Since an additional repairman would cost only $40 per day it appears worth investigating whether an additional repairman would save more than $40 in waiting time. We can use the same Monte Carlo sample for this purpose. Breakdown times and repair times remain the same but it is necessary to recalculate the termination of repairs for each breakdown. The rule to be followed is an obvious modification of the one we used for one repairman. Namely, a breakdown must wait for a repairman only if $B_i < T_{i-1}$ and $B_i < T_{i-2}$. In other words, a breakdown must wait for a repairman only if both repairmen are occupied with other breakdowns. We will not give the table showing the T_i here. The waiting times with two repairmen are:

BREAKDOWN	WAITING TIME
111	3
157	1
226	2
318	1
436	1
509	2
538	1
	—
	11

The total waiting time of 11 hours represents an average waiting time of 0.11 hours per day. At $40 per hour this is $4.40 per day. The additional repairman has decreased the average daily waiting time cost by $80.80 − 4.40 = $76.40. This saving has been achieved at the cost of one additional repairman's salary so the net saving is $76.40 − 40 = $36.40. The additional repairman should definitely be added.

This conclusion is surprising because of the seemingly large cost of idle time for the two repairmen. In this case almost 75 per cent of the total time of the two repairmen will be idle time. However, the conclusion of our analysis is correct and results from minimizing total costs, in accordance with the objective of this decision problem. The conflict between our conclusion and that which one expects is due to the fact that the obvious averages are not good measures of effectiveness in processes like these. On the average, 0.7 machines break down per day and, on the average, 5.8 hours are required to repair a machine so, on the average, the repairman will only work 4 hours per day so, on the average, why should we need another repairman? The fault in this reasoning is that it doesn't take account of a different kind of average: that, on the average, machines will not break down in intervals nicely spaced to meet the repairman's availability. Rather, the breakdowns will cluster in the way they do in our sample. This clustering of breakdowns accounts for the waiting time which is not considered in our on-the-average reasoning above.

89. THE ASSIGNMENT PROBLEM

Most of the decision problems we have considered in this chapter have involved decision-making under risk. It is a fact, however, that many important, and costly, decision problems are of the kind we have called decision-making under certainty. The idea that decision-making can be a problem when things are certain sometimes seems to involve a contradiction in terms. We have tried to show earlier that it is by no means a contradiction, but we will emphasize this fact once again. A few moments' thought about the game of chess will suffice to illustrate the genuine problems of decision-making under certainty. Everything is certain in chess in the sense that there are no secret moves and there is no chance element. Yet men have played chess for thousands of years with unflagging interest and there are no signs yet that the formidable decision problems involved are getting any easier despite all the certainty. The decision problem in chess results from the incredibly huge number of possibilities that exist. Each one of them is certain enough, but there are too many to think one's way through. Exactly similar problems arise in production and other areas of business. Fortunately, a variety of methods have been developed to help the executive find his best strategy, or strategies, from among the enormous number that may be possible. The remaining examples of this chapter will be devoted to this kind of problem: decision-making under certainty.

The first such example we will consider has the merit of being quite straightforward. A problem which arises in machine shops, in the paper manufacturing industry, in any multiplant operation, and in many other places, is that of assigning a group of jobs which must be done to a group of machines, plants, or processes, any one of which can do any one of the jobs. The jobs must be processed simultaneously and, typically, the machines, or processes, are of differing efficiencies in performing the various jobs. The reason may be that the machines are of differing ages or were designed for different kinds of jobs or simply that one machine is slower than another. Management usually has cost data available so that it knows the cost involved in having any specific machine do any specific job. The decision problem, then, is to assign the jobs to the machines in such fashion as to minimize the total costs of doing all the jobs.

Before we give some data we should meet a possible objection. We are calling this an example of decision-making under certainty. Yet one can object that everyone knows that cost data of this kind are not completely accurate and, indeed, can be quite unreliable. There is, then, no reason to assume that the costs are certain, even if everything else about the problem is. This objection is true—but not relevant. Management will assign the jobs on the basis of the cost data. We propose to accept the data as management does. We intend only to find means of ensuring that the decision based on these data will be the best one possible, granted the costs. In other words, the certainty in question is only there because management must accept the costs in reaching decisions. It does not imply that there is any eternal, or even temporary, truth in the cost figures.

Suppose, then, that a machine shop has five jobs to produce and five machines, any one of which can do any of the jobs, but at differing costs. The jobs must be assigned for simultaneous production, each job being assigned to one machine. The cost data are available and can be conveniently presented in a cost matrix.

| | MACHINE | | | | |
Job	1	2	3	4	5
A	$430	$440	$465	$480	$490
B	320	340	350	375	380
C	295	300	330	320	320
D	270	290	310	275	280
E	245	240	265	280	250

The entries in the matrix show the cost of having the given machine do the given job. Thus, it will cost $275 to have machine 4 do job D. The decision problem is: How assign the jobs to the machines in order to minimize the total cost of producing all five jobs?

The first thing to notice is that one cannot proceed by simply assigning job A to the machine which does it most cheaply, job B to the machine which does it most cheaply, and so on. It can happen that this procedure will give the lowest-cost assignment but usually, as in the present example, one machine can do several of the jobs more cheaply than any other machine can do them. Thus, in the present example, machine 1 can do jobs A, B, and C more cheaply than any other machine can do them. But only one of these jobs could, at most, be assigned to machine 1. Nor can one start by assigning job A to the machine which does it most cheaply (machine 1 here) and then assign job B either to the machine which does it most cheaply or, in case of conflict (as in the present example), to the second cheapest machine. In the present case this procedure would result, for the first two jobs only, in assigning job A to machine 1 and job B to machine 2 for a total cost of $\$430 + 340 = \$770$, but it is evident that assigning job A to machine 2 and job B to machine 1 would cost only $\$440 + 320 = \$760$. One might try the other approach: assign each machine to the job it does most cheaply. But this, too, will not generally work. In the present example four of the machines (1, 2, 3, and 5) do job E more cheaply than any other job. In short, none of these obvious attempts guarantees finding the minimum-cost assignment.

One infallible procedure for determining the minimum-cost assignment would be to try all possibilities, calculate the cost of each, and select the cheapest. Unfortunately, however, this procedure is frequently impracticable. In the present example there are only 120 different possible assignments. So it would be feasible to calculate the cost for each one of them—though it would be more arithmetic than most of us would prefer to do if we could avoid it. But the number of possible assignments increases very rapidly as the number of jobs and machines increases. The assignment of 10 jobs to 10 machines would require calculating more than 3.5 million possible assignments. And assigning 15 jobs to 15 machines involves 1.3 trillion (1,300,000,000,000) possible assignments. This is too many even for a computer! It is clear that we need some procedure other than the enumeration of possibilities. What we would like to have would be some simple algorithm (a mathematical term meaning a systematized procedure for finding a solution) which would enable us to quickly locate the optimal assignment.

Such a procedure (the desired algorithm) is available and is remarkably quick and easy to use. It is based squarely on an economic concept which we have already had occasion to discuss: opportunity cost. By opportunity cost we mean the hidden cost which results when we do not utilize our resources to the best possible advantage. The selection, and implementation, of any specific course of action relegates to the limbo of foregone possibilities all alternative courses of action. If the course of action (strategy) followed was not the best utilization of our resources then we have suffered a loss of the difference between what we actually achieve and that which we could have achieved. This loss is the opportunity cost of the strategy we followed and it is a real one even though it doesn't customarily show up on balance sheets. The only course of action which has zero opportunity cost is the best one.

So defined, the idea of opportunity cost is vague and fuzzy in outline. How can we measure opportunity cost unless we know the cost of the best strategy? To know this we would have to know the best strategy, and if we knew it we wouldn't need to introduce opportunity costs in the first place. The answer to this objection is that it is by defining the opportunity cost that we will be able to discover the strategy, or strategies, for which it is zero. It may appear somewhat like lifting oneself by one's shoelaces but it isn't really.

Instead of proceeding directly with our decision problem let us introduce some smaller examples which will serve better to illustrate the argument. Suppose we have the following cost matrix:

| | | MACHINE | |
| | 1 | 2 | 3 |
JOB			
X	100	150	170
Y	170	120	190
Z	180	220	150

Now, in this example, what is the opportunity cost associated with assigning a job to machine 1? There are two ways of defining it, depending on which alternatives one considers. As an example we can use the assignment of job Z to machine 1. The direct cost of this assignment is given in the cost matrix as $180. But there are, in addition, indirect costs which result from the fact that assigning job Z to machine 1 prevents us from assigning any other job to machine 1 and also prevents us from assigning job Z to any other machine. These assignments which are eliminated as possibilities by assigning job Z to machine 1 are the alternatives against which the opportunity costs are measured. Thus, first, an opportunity cost arises because a different job could be assigned to machine 1. The lowest-cost assignment of a job to machine 1 is job X, with a cost of $100. By comparison, then, we can say that the assignment of job Z to machine 1 involves an opportunity cost of $180 — $100 — $80. Similarly, and second, we can see that another opportunity cost arises because job Z could have been assigned to a different machine. Since the cheapest assignment of job Z would be to machine 3, at a cost of $150, it follows that this opportunity cost of assigning job Z to machine 1 would be $180 — $150 = $30. The first kind of opportunity cost arises because a different job could be assigned to the same machine; we will call it the *job opportunity* cost. The second kind arises because a different machine could be assigned to the same job. We will call this one the *machine opportunity* cost.

Both kinds are easy to determine. The matrix of job opportunity costs is obtained by subtracting the smallest cost in each column from every entry in that column. The matrix of machine opportunity costs is obtained by subtracting the smallest cost in each row from every entry in that row. For our example we have

	JOB OPPORTUNITY COST					MACHINE OPPORTUNITY COST			
	MACHINE						MACHINE		
	1	2	3				1	2	3
JOB	LOWEST COST				JOB	LOWEST COST			
	100	120	150						
X	0	30	20		X	100	0	50	70
Y	70	0	40		Y	120	50	0	70
Z	80	100	0		Z	150	30	70	0

It will be noted that the job-opportunity-cost matrix will always have at least one zero in each column and the machine-opportunity-cost matrix will always have at least one zero in each row.

In this example the three assignments with zero opportunity cost are identical in each matrix (X to 1, Y to 2, and Z to 3). When this happens the decision problem is solved, since we cannot do better than to have a zero opportunity cost and here we are able to assign each job to a machine so that every opportunity cost is zero. However, this is exceptional. In particular, it can only happen when there is no opportunity cost arising from the necessity to work the three jobs simultaneously. In the present case we would assign job X to machine 1 whether we had jobs Y and Z or not and similarly with the assignments of jobs Y and Z. In short, there is no conflict among the zero-opportunity-cost assignments. Let us take an example where there is conflict.

	DIRECT COSTS					JOB OPPORTUNITY COSTS					MACHINE OPPORTUNITY COSTS		
	MACHINE					MACHINE					MACHINE		
JOB	1	2	3		JOB	1	2	3		JOB	1	2	3
P	110	120	130		P	0	0	0		P	0	10	20
Q	115	140	140		Q	5	20	10		Q	0	25	25
R	125	145	165		R	15	25	35		R	0	20	40

Here there is no way to assign all jobs to machines which have zero opportunity cost. As a matter of fact, there is only one assignment of a job to a machine which has zero job opportunity cost and zero machine opportunity cost (job P to machine 1). Before we discuss what can be done about this situation we will introduce a simplification. It is awkward to have to use two matrices for the two kinds of opportunity costs. It would be much simpler if we could amalgamate both of them into one matrix of total opportunity costs. One method for doing this would be to simply add the two opportunity-cost matrices together to get a new matrix showing the total opportunity cost of each assignment. This method will work perfectly well, but it requires somewhat more arithmetic than an alternative procedure. The alternative is to calculate the machine opportunity costs on the basis of the job-opportunity-cost matrix rather than directly from the original cost matrix. Thus, in our example we will not have two opportunity-cost matrices. Rather, we will obtain one total-opportunity-cost matrix from the job-opportunity-cost matrix by subtracting the minimum cost in each row of the job-opportunity matrix from each entry in that row. This gives

OPPORTUNITY COSTS

JOB	MACHINE		
	1	2	3
P	0	0	0
Q	0	15	5
R	0	10	20

where, for example, row Q comes directly from row Q of the job-opportunity-cost matrix by subtracting 5 from each entry in that row, and similarly with the other rows. It is perhaps not intuitively obvious that this single matrix is equivalent to the total-opportunity-cost matrix referred to above, but it can be shown that it is.

In order to have an assignment of the jobs to the machines which has zero opportunity cost it is necessary that there should be three zeroes in the matrix such that no two of them occur in the same row or column. This is clearly not the case for our matrix. And the fact that it isn't the case means that we have not got the opportunity costs right. This statement is simply a matter of definition. Opportunity costs are defined in terms of the optimal assignment, which we don't know yet. The optimal assignment will have, by definition, zero opportunity cost. This means that there will be three zeroes in the matrix such that no two of them occur in the same row or column, once we have found the optimal assignment. Since the zeroes we have in this matrix do not fulfill this condition it follows automatically that some of them, at least, have a nonzero opportunity cost and, hence, are not correctly given as zeroes. It remains for us to find out how to change them to get the correct opportunity costs.

The procedure for changing the opportunity costs is simple once it is recognized why they are wrong. The reason is that we have not yet taken account of the fact that we cannot use two zeroes if they are in the same row or column. We can use at most one of them. But our opportunity-cost matrix has three zeroes in one row and three in one column. If we select any zero in row P, for example, we deny ourselves the opportunity to select any other zero in the same row. This fact, then, produces an opportunity cost of which we have not yet taken account. It should be noted that generally we will not have only zeroes in the rows or columns in which our zeroes fall, although that is the case in this little example. The same argument which applies to the zeroes would apply to any nonzero entry in the row or column with the zeroes. Let us show why this is so. Suppose the entry at $P1$ were 5 instead of 0. We know that this 5 would be the wrong opportunity cost for $P1$ because in evaluating the 5 we have not included any opportunity cost to reflect the fact that the selection of this assignment (job P to machine 1) would eliminate the possibility of selecting any zero in the same row or column.

We want, then, to change the opportunity costs of the entries in the rows and columns in which the zeroes occur. In which rows and columns do the zeroes occur? In our example it is obvious that they are row P and column 1 but usually there is some choice in selecting them. And even in this case one could say that there are zeroes in columns 1, 2, and 3 or in rows P, Q, and R and be perfectly correct. However, we follow the rule of always choosing the rows and columns which include zeroes so that the total number is the least possible. In other words, we select the least possible number of rows and/or columns which includes all the zeroes in the matrix. The number of rows and/or columns required to do this will always be less than the total number of rows (or columns, since the matrix is square) in the matrix. If the least number of rows and/or columns required to include all the zeroes equals the total number of rows then the decision problem is solved, because there must be a set of zeroes in the matrix which provides an assignment of jobs to machines with zero total opportunity cost. Consider a three-by-three matrix with zeroes as follows:

	1	2	3
G		0	
H	0		0
K		0	

All of these zeroes can be included in row H and column 2. This in itself shows that the problem is not yet solved. A matrix with zeroes

	1	2	3
G		0	
H	0		0
K		0	0

requires three rows or columns to include all the zeroes. And this one is solved by assigning G to 2, H to 1, and K to 3, with total opportunity cost of zero.

In those cases where there are various ways to choose the rows and/or columns which include all the zeroes it doesn't matter which one is selected. All selections will lead to a solution.

Why is this question of the selection of the rows and/or columns which include all the zeroes so important? Simply because the entries in these rows and columns have the wrong opportunity costs and we are going to change them. The simplest procedure for changing these costs is based on the following argument. At least one of the zeroes must be moved from the row or column in which it occurs. The smallest possible cost involved in such a move would be if it were moved to replace the smallest nonzero entry in the matrix which is *not* on one of the rows and/or columns containing the zeroes. In our example this is 5 at $Q3$. The least possible opportunity cost involved, then, in selecting any entry on row P (except $P1$) would be to move a zero to $Q3$, which would cost 5. Similarly, the least possible opportunity cost involved in selecting any entry in column 1 would be to force the move of a zero in that column to $Q3$, costing 5. Therefore, we will add this opportunity cost, 5, to every entry in row P and in column 1 (except for $P1$). Why the exception for $P1$? Because if we select $P1$ we will force the move of two zeroes, one in row P and one in column 1. This will cost at least twice the minimum entry in the general case, here $2 \times 5 = 10$. Actually it will cost more in the present case, but the assignment of an additional opportunity cost of $2 \times 5 = 10$ to $P1$ will work equally well and is simpler to do. These, then, are the changes: add 10 to $P1$, add 5 to every other entry in row P, and add 5 to every other entry in column 1. This gives

OPPORTUNITY COSTS

JOB	MACHINE		
	1	2	3
P	10	5	5
Q	5	15	5
R	5	10	20

We now repeat the procedure of subtracting the lowest opportunity cost in each column from each entry in the column. In the present case this step produces a zero in each row so for this example it is unnecessary to subtract the minimum entries from the rows which would otherwise be required. This gives

OPPORTUNITY COSTS

JOB	MACHINE		
	1	2	3
P	5	0	0
Q	0	10	0
R	0	5	15

and this matrix has three zeroes which meet our requirement, no two of which are on the same row or column. These are the zeroes at $P2$, $Q3$, and $R1$. The minimum-cost assignment is, therefore, job P to machine 2, job Q to machine 3, and job R to machine 1. Referring to the original cost matrix we see that the total cost of these assignments is $120 + 140 + 125 = 385. No other assignment of these three jobs to the three machines will cost less than this amount.

It may be noted that it is not necessary to go through the various steps of the above method. A little thought suffices to show that the whole procedure is equivalent to adding 5 to the entry at the intersection of the row and column, leaving the other entries in row P and column 1 unchanged, and subtracting 5 from each entry in the matrix which is not on row P or column 1. By following this rule we can quickly and easily make the necessary changes in opportunity costs in only one step.

The whole procedure can be boiled down to the following steps:

1. Determine the job-opportunity-cost matrix by subtracting the smallest entry in each column of the cost matrix from every entry in the column.

2. Determine the total-opportunity-cost matrix by subtracting the smallest entry in each row of the job-opportunity-cost matrix from each entry in the row.

3. Determine the smallest number of rows and/or columns which include all the zeroes in the total-opportunity-cost matrix. If this number equals the total number of rows the problem is solved and it is only necessary to select the assignments from among the zeroes.

4. If the problem is not solved in step 3 then find the smallest entry in the matrix which is not on one of the rows and/or columns containing zeroes. Add this entry to the entry at every intersection of a row and a column containing zeroes. Subtract it from every entry in the matrix which is not on one of the rows and/or columns containing zeroes.

5. Repeat the process until step 3 shows that a solution has been obtained.

In common with many other step-by-step procedures for finding a solution the verbal description is more difficult than the procedure, which is really very simple. Let us return to the original 5-by-5 matrix and demonstrate the method on it. Our first step is to determine the matrix of job opportunity costs by subtracting the smallest cost in each column from every entry in that column. This gives

Job	MACHINE				
	1	2	3	4	5
A	185	200	200	205	240
B	75	100	85	100	130
C	50	60	65	45	70
D	25	50	45	0	30
E	0	0	0	5	0

Next we determine the machine opportunity costs directly from this matrix by subtracting the smallest entry in each row from every entry in that row.   This gives

JOB	MACHINE				
	1	2	3	4	5
A	0	15	15	20	55
B	0	25	10	25	55
C	5	15	20	0	25
D	25	50	45	0	30
E	0	0	0	5	0

We are now at step 3.   We can include all these zeroes in columns 1 and 4 and row E.   The smallest entry not in columns 1 or 4 or in row E is 10 at $B3$.   Columns 1 and 4 intersect row E at $E1$ and $E4$ so we add 10 to these entries.   Then we subtract 10 from every entry not in columns 1 and 4 or in row E.   This gives

JOB	MACHINE				
	1	2	3	4	5
A	0	5	5	20	45
B	0	15	0	25	45
C	5	5	10	0	15
D	25	40	35	0	20
E	10	0	0	15	0

The repetition of steps 1 and 2 doesn't change this matrix because there is already a zero in every row and column.   We can include all these zeroes in four columns and rows: columns 1, 3, and 4, and row E.   The problem is, therefore, not yet solved.   The smallest entry not in one of these columns or in row E is 5, at $A2$ and $C2$.   The columns 1, 3, and 4 intersect row E at $E1$, $E3$, and $E4$ so we add 5 to these entries.   Then we subtract 5 from every entry in the matrix which is not on columns 1, 3, or 4 or row E.   This gives

JOB	MACHINE				
	1	2	3	4	5
A	0	0	5	20	40
B	0	10	0	25	40
C	5	0	10	0	10
D	25	35	35	0	15
E	15	0	5	20	0

A little experimenting suggests that we cannot include all these zeroes with less than five rows and/or columns.   We quickly find a solution to the decision problem: assign A to 1, C to 2, B to 3, D to 4, and E to 5.

These assignments have, of course, zero total opportunity cost. Referring to the original cost matrix we find that the total cost of producing the five jobs with these assignments is $430 + 300 + 350 + 275 + 250 = $1605. The fact that the total opportunity cost is zero guarantees that no other assignments could have a smaller total cost than this. In general it is possible that more than one assignment can have the same total cost, but our procedure ensures the selection of a strategy (assignment) at least as small in total cost as any other.

This procedure, with a little practice, is a remarkably quick way to solve this kind of decision problem. For large matrices, however, it is necessary to use computers as the hand computations are too onerous. Generally speaking, the potential savings resulting from the use of this solution to the decision problem are larger when the cost matrix is larger. For small matrices it will usually be true that the decision-maker has found semiquantitative, semi-intuitive methods which give nearly optimal assignments. However, as the dimensions of the matrix increase the strain on intuition becomes too great and strategies selected are likely to be far from optimal. In these cases the savings resulting from the use of this procedure can be considerable.

90. THE TRANSPORTATION PROBLEM

The next decision problem under certainty which we will consider will be one which arises in transportation. The major decision problem in transportation is the obvious one: How can we get the required amounts of materials or products to the right places with a minimum of cost? Transportation costs represent major expenditures in many businesses, and sizable savings can result from any lessening of them. This kind of decision problem is, therefore, an important one.

Many situations which involve transportation nonetheless do not have any difficult decision problems in transportation. For example, a single plant supplying its products nationally will have to ship to each of the warehouses carrying the products. Usually there will be a variety of alternative means of transportation to any specific warehouse and these will have differing costs. However, the single plant must ship to each warehouse because the plant is the only source of supply. Frequently there will be some time requirements on the shipments which will eliminate some of the alternatives. But from among the feasible alternatives for each specific warehouse it is only necessary to select the cheapest in order to minimize the total transportation costs. This statement is not meant to gainsay the fact that difficulties and niceties can arise. For example, the probability of loss in shipping a highly perishable product may be a function of the days in transit. The reader will recognize that this would be handled by calculating for each alternative an expected loss. The transportation cost plus the expected loss would then be known for each alternative, and the lowest such amount would be the minimum-cost means of transportation for each warehouse. One can also, if desired, include the extra loss in interest on the capital tied up in the goods in transit owing to additional time in transit. For example, this might be a very important factor for a bank shipping currency. Generally, however, such niceties are not important factors. In any event, such complications can all be handled for each warehouse separately and there is no additional complexity to the decision problem.

Entirely different is the common case where there are several possible origins of the goods to be transported and several possible destinations. A typical case would be one in which several plants located in different regions must supply a number of different warehouses. Here we have a decision problem which can be of considerable complexity owing to the fact that the various warehouses can be supplied by any one of the plants. As the number of warehouses and plants increases, the total number of possible different ways of transporting the required amounts to the various warehouses increases with such rapidity that it quickly becomes impossible to evaluate the total cost associated with each of them. The decision problem, then, is to select a strategy of shipping from the plants to the warehouses which meets the warehouse requirements and remains within the capacities of the plants. The objective is to minimize total transportation costs. Note that we assume that the kind of analysis discussed in the preceding paragraph has already been performed for each plant-warehouse combination. In other words, we assume that the transportation cost from each plant to each warehouse is already known. And, of course, we certainly know the requirements of each warehouse and the capacity of each plant. In short, all the relevant information is known with certainty and we are dealing with a decision problem under certainty.

The kind of data which is required can be conveniently presented in a matrix. Let us consider as an example a situation where three plants are supplying five warehouses. The transportation cost between each plant and each warehouse, the amount required by each warehouse, and the capacity of each plant are as follows:

| | PLANTS | | | |
| WAREHOUSE | 1 | 2 | 3 | WAREHOUSE REQUIREMENTS |
	TRANSPORTATION COST PER UNIT			
A	$4	$7	$5	400
B	6	5	4	700
C	5	8	6	300
D	4	5	7	500
E	6	6	5	500
PLANT CAPACITIES:	1000	800	600	2400

The transportation costs, given in the body of the table, differ because of different alternative means available and simply because of different distances involved. The decision problem is to meet the requirements of each warehouse while remaining within the capacity of each plant and to minimize the total costs of transportation.

Why can't we proceed by meeting the requirements of each warehouse from the plant with the lowest transportation cost to that warehouse? Simply because a plant may have the lowest transportation cost to several warehouses and be unable to meet the requirements of all of them. Thus, in our example plant 2 has lowest transportation costs to warehouses B and D. These two warehouses have total requirements of 1200 units and the capacity of plant 2 is only 800 units. Should we, therefore, ship 600 from plant 2 to warehouse B and 200 from plant 2 to warehouse D or ship 300 to B and 500 to D, or some other combination? The same problem arises with plant 1 with regard to warehouses A, and D. The problem, even with these few plants and warehouses, is too complicated to think one's way through unaided. Fortunately, we have available a relatively simple procedure which enables us to resolve all these questions simultaneously by discovering the method of shipping with the lowest total transportation cost.

The statement in the last paragraph of the difficulties of the obvious approach suggests a procedure to resolve them. The problem is that by shipping, for example, 600 units from plant 2 to warehouse B we have foregone the possibility of shipping more than 200 units from plant 2 to warehouse D. In short, there is an opportunity cost involved in this shipment and, indeed, in any specific shipment. For example, the shipment of 600 units from plant 2 to warehouse B has one opportunity cost owing to the fact that warehouse B now has 600 units which cannot be shipped to it from any other plant. We must take account of these opportunity costs in order to find the minimal-cost shipping strategy.

How can this be accomplished? Let us take the simplest possible case as an example. Suppose there are two plants and two warehouses with the relevant data as follows.

WAREHOUSE	PLANTS		WAREHOUSE
	1	2	REQUIREMENTS
X	$5	2	300
Y	4	3	700
PLANT CAPACITIES:	400	600	1000

A possible shipping strategy would be

WAREHOUSE	SHIPMENTS		WAREHOUSE REQUIREMENTS
	1	2	
X	300		300
Y	100	600	700
PLANT CAPACITIES:	400	600	

This strategy meets all the requirements and there is only one specific shipment (2 to X) which is not included in the strategy. First, let us note that the total transportation cost of the strategy is $300(5) + 100(4) + 600(3) = \$3700$. Now, how can the strategy be changed to include the shipment from plant 2 to warehouse X? The final result must still balance out to meet requirements and capacities, so compensating changes have to be introduced. To add one unit to $X2$ while leaving the total of X at the required 300 means that we must subtract 1 unit from $X1$. Similarly, to keep the total of plant 2 at 600 we would have to subtract one unit from $Y2$. Finally, to balance the two subtractions we would have to add one unit to $Y1$. These changes are all necessary in order to ship one unit from plant 2 to warehouse X. They amount to making the following changes in shipments:

	CHANGES				SHIPMENTS		
	1	2			1	2	
X	−1	1	giving	X	299	1	300
Y	1	−1		Y	101	599	700
					400	600	

The total cost of making these four changes of one unit would be simply $\$4 + 2 - 5 - 3 = -\$2$, since it costs $\$4$ to ship an extra unit from 1 to Y and $\$2$ to ship a unit from 2 to X while we save $\$5$ by not shipping a unit from 1 to X and another $\$3$ by not shipping a unit from 2 to Y. In short, we save $\$2$ for every unit shipped from 2 to X. The opportunity cost of our original strategy, then, is $\$2$ per unit in terms of the shipment from plant 2 to warehouse X. It will be seen that the opportunity cost is simply the amount saved by the changes $(\$5 + 3)$ minus the amount the changes cost $(\$4 + 2)$.

How will we change our shipping strategy? Since we save $\$2$ for each unit we ship from 2 to X we will want to ship the maximum possible amount. What is the maximum possible amount? The matrix of unit changes, above, shows that anything added to $X2$ must be subtracted from $X1$ and $Y2$. Since we cannot ship negative amounts it follows that we cannot ship more from 2 to X than we can subtract from the $X1$ and $Y2$ shipments. The minimum of these two therefore establishes an upper limit to the amount we can ship from 2 to X. In this case the limit is the 300 shipped from X to 1. We can, therefore, ship 300 units from 2 to X by making the necessary changes in the other shipments. Thus

	CHANGES				SHIPMENTS		
	1	2			1	2	
X	-300	300	gives	X		300	300
Y	300	-300		Y	400	300	700
					400	600	

This is the minimum-cost shipping strategy in this example. The total cost is $\$300\,(2) + 400\,(4) + 300\,(3) = \$3100$.

The question can be raised as to how we know that some combination of all four shipments isn't less costly than either our original strategy or the last one, which we said was the minimum-cost strategy. Both of these strategies involved only three shipments. The answer to this question is an important one. In our reasoning about the change to make in our initial strategy after we found its opportunity cost we said that since each unit shipped from 2 to X saved us $2 we would want to ship as many units as possible. Similarly, if a specific shipment cost us some amount extra we would want to ship as few units as possible. This reasoning can be generalized mathematically and it can be proved that an optimal shipping strategy need never include more different shipments than the number of plants plus the number of warehouses minus one. In our case this is $2 + 2 - 1 = 3$, so we know that the best strategy involving three shipments is at least as good as any strategy involving four shipments. In some cases the optimal strategy may involve less shipments than this number (three in our case). Such cases are said to be degenerate and require some slight modifications in the procedure we are developing here.

For our little two-by-two example, then, there was no difficulty and we could find the optimal strategy quickly. Basically, three steps are involved:

1. Start with a strategy meeting the requirements.

2. Evaluate the opportunity costs of the strategy in terms of the shipments not in the strategy.

3. If all opportunity costs are less than or equal to zero the problem is solved and the strategy is optimal. If one or more opportunity costs are greater than zero incorporate the relevant shipment in the strategy and repeat steps 2 and 3.

We must now find how to accomplish these three steps in larger matrices.

We will begin with step **2**. Our little example should have sufficed to show that the opportunity costs were determined solely from the costs of the shipments not in the strategy. The amounts of the shipments in the strategy were not used. Only the information that certain shipments are in the strategy is necessary in order to evaluate the opportunity costs. Suppose, then, that we were given our two-by-two matrix of costs in this form:

	1	2
X	5	?
Y	4	3

We are told that the three costs given are those of the three shipments used in our strategy. What can we say about the cost of $X2$, which we are assuming we don't know? We know that any change in our strategy to include a shipment of one unit from **2** to X must be of the form

	1	2
X	-1	1
Y	1	-1

Therefore, we know that the cost change which will result will be

$$X2 + Y1 - X1 - Y2 = X2 + 4 - 5 - 3 = X2 - 4$$

We can now state that if $X2$ is greater than 4 it will cost more to include this shipment, if $X2 = 4$ the cost will be the same whether we include this shipment or not, and if $X2$ is less than 4 we will save money by including the shipment from **2** to X. In fact, we know that this last case was true so we did include the $X2$ shipment in our strategy. Alternatively, the savings resulting from the changes will be $5 + 3 = 8$ and the additional costs will be $4 + X2$. Therefore, the opportunity cost of the strategy in terms of $X2$ is simply $8 - (4 + X2) = 4 - X2$. If this opportunity cost is positive (if 4 is greater than $X2$) we know we should include the shipment from **2** to X in our strategy.

Now let us take a larger matrix and try the same procedure. Suppose we are given, analogically to the last example:

	1	2	3
R		3	
S	6		4
T		5	2

It will be noted that we have included $3 + 3 - 1 = 5$ shipments in our strategy since this number is sufficient to get the optimal strategy and will be required unless we have a degenerate case. How can we evaluate the empty cells in this matrix? It appears as if we do not have sufficient information. We only know how to evaluate the opportunity cost for a two-by-two matrix with only one empty cell. But consider $R1$. First, it is in 4 two-by-two submatrices of this matrix.

	1	2			1	3			1	2			1	3
R		3		R				R		3		R		
S	6			S	6	4		T		5		T		2

Which one should we use to evaluate $R1$? Second, not one of the four submatrices including $R1$ has three cost entries in it. So how can we evaluate $R1$ from any of them? The answer to the first question is that all four submatrices will give the same opportunity-cost evaluation for $R1$. And the answer to the second question is that we can't start by evaluating $R1$ first. We must start with a two-by-two submatrix which does have three entries. Let us start with

	2	3
S		4
T	5	2

To include a shipment of one unit from 2 to S we need to make the following changes (in order to continue to meet the restrictions):

	2	3
S	1	−1
T	−1	1

This will give a total cost change of $S2 + 2 - 4 - 5 = S2 - 7$, or an opportunity cost of $7 - S2$. We therefore evaluate $S2$ as **7**, the value for which the opportunity cost is zero. Using this cost for $S2$ we can now evaluate $T1$ from

	1	2			1	2
S	6	7	with the changes	S	−1	1
T		5		T	1	−1

The cost change resulting from the inclusion in our strategy of one unit shipped from 1 to T will be $T1 + 7 - 6 - 5 = T1 - 4$. The opportunity cost of $T1$ is, therefore, $4 - T1$ and we evaluate $T1$ as 4. Similarly, we can calculate $R3$ from

$$
\left.\begin{array}{c|cc}
 & 2 & 3 \\
\hline
R & 3 & \\
S & 7 & 4
\end{array}\right\}
\quad \text{with the changes} \quad
\left\{\begin{array}{c|cc}
 & 2 & 3 \\
\hline
R & -1 & 1 \\
S & 1 & -1
\end{array}\right.
$$

The cost change resulting from the inclusion in our strategy of one unit shipped from 3 to R will be $R3 + 7 - 3 - 4 = R3 + 0 = R3$. The opportunity cost is $0 - R3$ and we therefore evaluate $R3$ as 0. This gives the following cost matrix:

$$
\begin{array}{c|ccc}
 & 1 & 2 & 3 \\
\hline
R & & ③ & 0 \\
S & ⑥ & 7 & ④ \\
T & 4 & ⑤ & ②
\end{array}
$$

where the circled numbers are the actual costs of the shipments in our strategy. We have left the evaluation of $R1$ till last in order to demonstrate the fact that all four submatrices given above lead to the same value for $R1$. We have

$$
\left.\begin{array}{c|cc}
 & 1 & 2 \\
\hline
R & & 3 \\
S & 6 & 7
\end{array}\right\}
\quad \text{gives} \quad R1 + 7 - 3 - 6 = R1 - 2
$$

$$
\left.\begin{array}{c|cc}
 & 1 & 3 \\
\hline
R & & 0 \\
S & 6 & 4
\end{array}\right\}
\quad \text{gives} \quad R1 + 4 - 0 - 6 = R1 - 2
$$

$$
\left.\begin{array}{c|cc}
 & 1 & 2 \\
\hline
R & & 3 \\
T & 4 & 5
\end{array}\right\}
\quad \text{gives} \quad R1 + 5 - 3 - 4 = R1 - 2
$$

$$
\left.\begin{array}{c|cc}
 & 1 & 3 \\
\hline
R & & 0 \\
T & 4 & 2
\end{array}\right\}
\quad \text{gives} \quad R1 + 2 - 0 - 4 = R1 - 2
$$

Every one of these evaluations gives a cost change of $(R1 - 2)$ or an opportunity cost of $(2 - R1)$ so $R1$ would be evaluated as 2. A comparison of the actual costs of these shipments with these calculated values would then suffice to decide whether any specific shipments should be in-

cluded in our strategy. For example, if the actual original cost matrix
were

	1	2	3
R	4	3	2
S	6	6	4
T	5	5	2

we would proceed by calculating, entry by entry, the quantity

$$\text{Calculated value} - \text{Actual cost} = \text{Opportunity cost}$$

We get

	OPPORTUNITY COSTS		
	1	2	3
R	−2	0	−2
S	0	1	0
T	−1	0	0

The only opportunity cost which is greater than 0 is that of $S2$ so we
would include $S2$ in our strategy.

This procedure isn't too difficult for our step 2 but it is a great deal
more laborious than we would like. Fortunately, we can accomplish the
same thing much more quickly. The algebraic proof of the equivalence
of this simpler method to the one that we have discussed above will not
be given here. Suffice it to say that it leads to precisely the same evaluation of the opportunity costs. The procedure is to ascribe costs to the
rows and columns of the matrix containing only the transportation costs
of the shipments in our strategy. These costs are so determined that the
transportation costs which are already in the matrix (those of the shipments in our strategy) are each equal to the sum of the cost ascribed to
the row and to the column in which it occurs. This can be done very
simply since we can arbitrarily assign a zero cost to any row or column
we choose. Consider our example. The matrix showing only the costs
for the shipments in our strategy was

	1	2	3
R		3	
S	6		4
T		5	2

Let us arbitrarily assign a zero cost to row R. Then, in order to have
$R2 = 3$ we must have column 2 with a cost of 3 (since row R plus column 2 must equal $R2$). But $T2 = 5$ so row T must have a cost of 2

(since row T plus column 2 must equal $T2$). But $T3 = 2$ so column 3 must have a cost of 0 (since row T plus column 3 must equal $T3$). But $S3 = 4$ so row S must have a cost of 4 (since row S plus column 3 must equal $S3$). And, finally, column 1 must equal 2 to have $S1 = 6$. Thus, the row and column costs are all determined. This gives

	1	2	3	Row COST
R		3		0
S	6		4	4
T		5	2	2
COLUMN COST:	2	3	0	

All of the entries in the matrix now equal the sum of the row and column costs as required. If the other entries are now filled in by taking for each entry the sum of the costs of its row and column we get

	1	2	3	Row COST
R	2	③	0	0
S	⑥	7	④	4
T	4	⑤	②	2
COLUMN COST:	2	3	0	

where the original entries are circled. It will be seen that this matrix is identical to the one we calculated before by the more lengthy procedure. Thus, this much shorter method can be used for step 2. This calculated matrix minus the original cost matrix gives the opportunity-cost matrix as before.

We now turn to step 3. If we have discovered a positive opportunity cost we know that it should be included in our strategy. How do we include it? Suppose the shipments for our 3-by-3 example are

	1	2	3	WAREHOUSE REQUIREMENT
R		200		200
S	300		400	700
T		500	100	600
PLANT CAPACITY:	300	700	500	

We determined above that the only shipment with a positive opportunity cost was $S2$. We therefore want to include $S2$ in our strategy. Furthermore, each unit shipped from 2 to S saves us \$1 so we want to ship the maximum number possible. How can we rearrange the shipments so all requirements are still met while we increase $S2$ to the maximum amount possible? The procedure is easy. We must simply find a path consisting of a series of right-angled steps which changes direction only at entries included in our strategy and which starts at $S2$ and ends at $S2$. Then we make compensating changes along this path. Thus, for $S2$ we can proceed as follows: $S2 \rightarrow S3 \rightarrow T3 \rightarrow T2 \rightarrow S2$. Pictorially,

	1	2	3
R		200	
S	300	□ $\longrightarrow$	400
		↑ ↓	
T		500 $\longleftarrow$	100

Now, we are going to add some amount to $S2$, so in order to balance row S we must subtract that amount from $S3$. Since we must balance column 3 we add that amount to $T3$. Then, in order to balance row T we have to subtract that amount from $T2$. And then, in order to balance column 2 we have to add that amount to $S2$, which is what we wanted to do and which completes the cycle. The general rule in such a cycle is: subtract from the termination of every horizontal step and add to the termination of every vertical step. The subtractions constitute the limitation since we cannot have a negative shipment. Here, we are subtracting from $S3$ and from $T2$ and the smaller of these is 400. So 400 can be added to $S2$ and all the indicated changes are made: add 400 to $T3$, subtract 400 from $S3$ and $T2$. This gives our new strategy:

	1	2	3
R		200	
S	300	400	
T		100	500

Now, of course, steps 2 and 3 would be repeated to see whether any further improvement is possible.

Let us illustrate the procedure with the other cells of the matrix even though their opportunity costs are negative. For $R1$ we have the path:

	1	2	3
R	□ $\longrightarrow$	200	
	↑		
S	300 $\longleftarrow$		400
		↓ ↑	
T		500 $\longrightarrow$	100

The smallest entry at the end of a horizontal step is $T3 = 100$. Therefore 100 is the largest amount which can be shipped from 1 to R. Making the necessary changes gives

	1	2	3
R	100	100	
S	200		500
T		600	

For $T1$ we have the path:

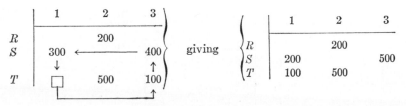

and for $R3$ we have

	1	2	3
R		200 ← □ ←	
S	300	↓	400
T		500 → 100 ┘	

giving

	1	2	3
R		100	100
S	300		400
T		600	

Such a path can always be found unless we have a degenerate case. This, then, is the procedure for step 3.

The method for accomplishing step 1 is very easy and can be demonstrated on our original decision problem, to which we now return. We want a strategy which meets the warehouse requirements and is within the plant capacities. To get one we start in the northwest corner of the matrix ($A1$) and work down the column, completely meeting the requirements of each warehouse until the capacity of plant 1 is exhausted. Then we complete the requirements of the warehouse in which we stopped from plant 2 and continue similarly until we end up in the southeast corner ($E3$). In our case this gives

	First strategy 1	2	3	Warehouse requirements
A	400			400
B	600	100		700
C		300		300
D		400	100	500
E			500	500
Plant capacities:	1000	800	600	

It will be seen that this procedure automatically gives a strategy meeting all requirements. In our case we have $3 + 5 - 1 = 7$ entries as we should. If there are less than this number (rows + columns $- 1$) it is a degenerate case and must be handled by variants of our procedure which we will not give here. If there are more than this number, an arithmetical mistake has been made. The cost of this strategy is \$13,300.

Now we are ready for step 2. First, we determine the row and column costs so that each of the unit costs of the shipments we have used in our strategy equals the sum of its row and column costs.

	1	2	3	Row COST
A	4			0
B	6	5		2
C		8		5
D		5	7	2
E			5	0
COLUMN COST:	4	3	5	

Then we calculate the values of the other entries by summing the row and column costs for each entry.

	1	2	3	Row COST
A	④	3	5	0
B	⑥	⑤	7	2
C	9	⑧	10	5
D	6	⑤	⑦	2
E	4	3	⑤	0
COLUMN COST:	4	3	5	

Subtracting the original cost matrix from this, entry by entry, gives the opportunity-cost matrix.

	1	2	3
A	0	-4	0
B	0	0	3
C	4	0	4
D	2	0	0
E	-2	-3	0

There are several positive opportunity costs and we can put any one of the corresponding shipments into our strategy. It is quickest to use the largest ones first. Let us, therefore put $C1$ in our strategy. The path to be used in changing is

	1	2	3
A	400		
B	600 ←— 100		
	↓ ↑		
C	□ —→ 300		
D	400	100	
E	500		

The smallest termination of a horizontal step is 300 so we can ship 300 units from 1 to C by making the indicated changes. Repeating step 2 we get

SECOND STRATEGY

	1	2	3		1	2	3	Row COST		1	2	3	Row COST			1	2	3
A	400			A	4			0	A	④	3	5	0	A		0	−4	0
B	300	400		B	6	5		2	B	⑥	⑤	7	2	B		0	0	3
C	300			C	5			1	C	⑤	4	6	1	C		0	−4	0
D		400	100	D		5	7	2	D	6	⑤	⑦	2	D		2	0	0
E			500	E			5	0	E	4	3	⑤	0	E		−2	−3	0

COLUMN COST: 4 3 5   COLUMN COST: 4 3 5   (OPPORTUNITY COST 1 2 3)

The cost of the second strategy was $12,100. Again we have positive opportunity costs and again we select the largest, $B3$, to include in our next strategy. The path to be used in including $B3$ is

	1	2	3
A	400		
B	300	400 ←— □	
C	300	↓ ↑	
D		400 —→ 100	
E		500	

The smallest termination of a horizontal step is 100, so this is the amount we ship from 3 to B. Making the indicated changes and repeating step 2 gives

THIRD STRATEGY

	1	2	3		1	2	3	Row COST		1	2	3	Row COST			1	2	3
A	400			A	4			0	A	④	3	2	0	A		0	−4	−3
B	300	300	100	B	6	5	4	2	B	⑥	⑤	④	2	B		0	0	0
C	300			C	5			1	C	⑤	4	3	1	C		0	−4	−3
D		500		D		5		2	D	6	⑤	4	2	D		2	0	−3
E			500	E			5	3	E	7	6	⑤	3	E		1	0	0

COLUMN COST: 4 3 2   COLUMN COST: 4 3 2   (OPPORTUNITY COST 1 2 3)

The cost of the third strategy was \$11,800. Some opportunity costs are still positive so we select $D1$ for inclusion in our strategy. The path to be used in making the necessary changes is

	1	2	3
A	400		
B	┌─300 ← 300	100	
C	│ 300	↑	
D	└→ □ ──→ 500		
E		500	

The most we can ship from 1 to D is 300 units. Making the indicated changes and repeating step 2 gives

FOURTH STRATEGY

	1	2	3
A	400		
B		600	100
C	300		
D	300	200	
E			500

	1	2	3	Row COST
A	4		0	
B		5	4	0
C	5			1
D	4	5		0
E			5	1

COLUMN COST: 4 5 4

	1	2	3	Row COST
A	4	5	4	0
B	4	5	4	0
C	5	6	5	1
D	4	5	4	0
E	5	6	5	1

COLUMN COST: 4 5 4

OPPORTUNITY COST

	1	2	3
A	0	−2	−1
B	−2	0	0
C	0	−2	−1
D	0	0	−3
E	−1	0	0

The cost of this fourth strategy is \$11,200. Since no opportunity cost is greater than zero we cannot do better than this strategy. Therefore, this strategy is the solution to our decision problem.

Familiarity with the relatively simple steps of this procedure permits it to be done with pencil and paper quite rapidly. However, this kind of decision problem is very often so large that it requires a computer to perform the computations.

91. ALLOCATION OF PRODUCTIVE FACILITIES

A major production decision problem arises in connection with the allocation of the productive facilities. This kind of problem arises frequently and can involve very large savings resulting from the determination of the optimal strategy. Some of the most spectacular results of operations research have been obtained through analyses of this class of decision problem.

It will be convenient to take a simple example around which we can develop our discussion. Consider a small plant which has two departments, grinding and plating. This plant makes two products, each of which requires processing in each of the two departments. The capacities of the two departments are different for the two products and the profit per item is also different for the two products. The relevant data can be summarized in a table.

| | CAPACITIES (PER DAY) | | |
PRODUCTS	DEPT. I, GRINDING	DEPT. II, PLATING	PROFIT PER UNIT
A	400	250	$1.00
B	200	400	1.25

Granted these data, the decision problem is: How many units of each product should be produced? The objective is to achieve the maximum profit. We have referred to this as a decision problem in the allocation of the productive facilities because we can phrase the decision problem alternatively: How much of the capacity of each department should be allocated to each product?

First, let us examine the decision problem: Is it a real one or is the solution obvious? We could produce nothing but product A. In that case we are limited by Dept. II to a total production of 250 units and a profit of $250. We will have excess capacity in Dept. I since we will have only used $250/400 = 62.5$ per cent of its capacity, but there is no advantage in using this capacity to produce B because there is no capacity left in Dept. II. Similarly, we could produce nothing but B. In this case we are limited by Dept. I to 200 units and a profit of $200 \times \$1.25 = \$250$. Dept. II would have 50 per cent of its capacity unused but the Dept. I bottleneck would prevent its utilization. In either case we made the same profit, $250. Is this, then, the best that can be done? The fact that each of these two possibilities leaves unused capacity is sufficient to make us at least wonder whether we can find a combination of productions of A and B which would use some of this capacity and, hence, return a larger profit. How can we find it?

In decision-theory terms the problem is clear. The available strategies are all possible combinations of amounts of A and B which are within the capacities of the two departments. The profits and capacity restrictions are known and for any given amounts of A and B the outcome is certain, a calculable amount of profit. In short, this is a decision problem under certainty. The difficulty is the usual one in this kind of decision-making. The number of possible strategies is very large. How can we find the optimal one?

The first thing to be emphasized is the meaning of the capacities. Dept. I can produce either 400 units of A or 200 units of B, not both. Of course, combinations of amounts of A and B can be produced providing the total capacity is not exceeded. How can we tell what combinations are permissible? Fortunately, this is easy to answer; it is only necessary to determine the percentages of capacity of the two departments which are used up by the production of one unit of each product. One unit of A uses up $1/400 = 0.25$ per cent of the capacity of Dept. I and $1/250 = 0.4$ per cent of the capacity of Dept. II. One unit of B uses up $1/200 = 0.5$ per cent of the capacity of Dept. I and $1/400 = 0.25$ per cent of the capacity of Dept. II. These data can be presented in tabular form.

PERCENTAGE OF CAPACITY,
REPRESENTED BY ONE UNIT

	DEPT. I	DEPT. II
A	0.25%	0.4%
B	0.5%	0.25%

It should be noted that this conversion to percentages of capacity is based on a hidden assumption. We have assumed a linear relationship between capacity and amount produced. In simpler words, we have assumed that the production of twice as much A will take twice as much capacity. This is a reasonable assumption—and a crucial one. If it is not true the analysis of this kind of decision problem becomes much more difficult. Fortunately, it is very often true or at least so nearly true that the discrepancy does not seriously affect the analysis.

Once these percentages have been calculated it is easy to determine what combinations of amounts of A and B are within the capacity limitations of each department. Any combination is possible which doesn't exceed 100 per cent of capacity. Thus, for Dept. I we could have such combinations as the following:

DEPT. I

A		B		TOTAL
UNITS	PERCENTAGES	UNITS	PERCENTAGES	PERCENTAGE
400	100	0	0	100
300	75	50	25	100
200	50	100	50	100
100	25	150	75	100
0	0	200	100	100

We can summarize all possible combinations for Dept. I with an inequation:

$$\text{Dept. I:} \quad 0.25X_A + 0.5X_B \leq 100.0$$

where X_A and X_B are the amounts of A and B respectively. The reader will remember that the sign, $\leq$, between the two sides of the inequality is read "less than or equal to" and that we usually refer to expressions containing this symbol as inequations. It is the symbolic representation of the fact that there is no requirement that we use up the full 100 per cent of capacity of Dept. I. We can certainly produce any amounts requiring less than 100 per cent capacity if we want to.

For Dept. II we could have such combinations as

DEPT. II

A		B		TOTAL
UNITS	PERCENTAGES	UNITS	PERCENTAGES	PERCENTAGE
250	100	0	0	100
200	80	80	20	100
150	60	160	40	100
100	40	240	60	100
50	20	320	80	100
0	0	400	100	100

and we can summarize all possible combinations for Dept. II with a similar inequation:

$$\text{Dept. II:} \quad 0.4X_A + 0.25X_B \leqq 100.0$$

where X_A, X_B, and $\leqq$ have the same meaning as above.

The particular combinations of amounts of A and B produced which are given in the above two tables only represent a few examples from the total number of possibilities for each department. Some of the possibilities given in each table are impossible in the other table. For example, in Dept. I we could produce 200 units of A and 100 units of B, but the table for Dept. II shows that if we produce 200 units of A we can only produce 80 units of B. This shows that not all the solutions of the Dept. I inequation are possible strategies. Nor, of course, are all solutions of the Dept. II inequation. Some of the combinations in each table are, however, possible in the other table. For the example discussed above the combination 200–80 is possible. As another example, in Dept. I we could produce 100 units of A and 150 units of B and the table for Dept. II shows us that with 100 units of A we could produce as much as 240 units of B. The smaller of the two is always limiting, but at least we know that it is possible to produce 100 units of A and 150 units of B. This is, in short, a possible strategy.

We have, then, two problems. First, we must determine what the possible strategies are. It may be noted that in the mathematical theory which underlies our analysis the possible strategies would be called the *feasible solutions* of the two equations above. Second, we must locate that particular strategy which will give the largest profit. One could try to proceed by determining the possible strategies, calculating the profit resulting from each, and then selecting the strategy with the largest profit. This would generally be prohibitively time-consuming, if not impossible, so it is necessary to find more expeditious means.

Such means are available in the form of a procedure which requires only some repeated simple algebraic manipulations. The idea behind the procedure is to start with any possible strategy (feasible solution, in the mathematician's terms) and to determine the profit which would result from that strategy. Then a criterion is applied to determine whether it is possible to increase the profit by switching to a different strategy. If it is possible to increase the profit another criterion tells us how to find a strategy which does increase profit. Then the procedure is repeated. When the profit cannot be increased by switching to any other strategy we know that we have found the optimal strategy.

The first thing we need in order to accomplish this outlined procedure is a quick means of calculating the profit from any specific strategy. This is easy to do in terms of the symbols we have already introduced. If X_A and X_B are the amounts of A and B which are produced in any specific strategy we have

$$\text{Profit} = 0.1X_A + 1.25X_B$$

since the profit for each unit of A produced is \$1 and the profit for each unit of B produced is \$1.25. For example, 100 units of A and 150 units of B would produce a profit of $1(100) + 1.25(150) = \$287.50$.

The next thing we must do is include symbols for all the possible components of our strategies. It is obvious that our strategies consist of the possible amounts of A and B which we might produce. For any specific combination of amounts we might find that some of the capacity of Dept. I and/or Dept. II was unused. But mathematics is like accounting: things have to balance out. So we must include symbols to represent the fact that our strategies may include leaving some of the capacity of one or both of the departments not utilized. This is easy to do. We have already obtained inequations expressing the capacity restrictions of Depts. I and II. These expressions are inequations precisely because of the fact that they include allowance for the fact that some part of capacity may not be utilized. By introducing symbols for unused capacity we will simply convert these inequations to equations. Thus, let X_1 represent unused capacity in Dept. I. Then we can change our inequation for Dept. I

$$0.25X_A + 0.5X_B \leqq 100.0$$

to an equation

$$0.25X_A + 0.5X_B + X_1 = 100.0$$

This equation now automatically expresses the amount of unused capacity in Dept. I for any specific strategy. Thus, the strategy of producing 250 units of A and zero units of B results in

$$0.25(250) + 0.5(0) + X_1 = 100.0$$

or
$$X_1 = 100 - 0.25(250) = 37.5$$

This means that this strategy results in $X_1 = 37.5$ or 37.5 per cent unused capacity in Dept. I. Similarly, we put X_2 equal to the unused capacity in Dept. II and convert the inequation for Dept. II

$$0.4X_A + 0.25X_B \leq 100.0$$

to the equation

$$0.4X_A + 0.25X_B + X_2 = 100.0$$

The variables, X_1 and X_2, are often called *slack variables* because they serve to take up the slack in the inequations.

All of the necessary preliminary work is now done and we have a simple mathematical model of our decision problem. Our objective is to maximize profits, and we have to do this subject to the capacity limitations of the two departments. In our mathematical model we have an objective function.

$$\text{Profit} = 1X_A + 1.25X_B$$

which we wish to maximize subject to the restrictions

$$0.25X_A + 0.5X_B + X_1 = 100.0$$

and
$$0.4X_A + 0.25X_B + X_2 = 100.0$$

We are now ready to find the optimal strategy. Our outline of the procedure suggested the following steps:

1. Start with a possible strategy.
2. Determine the profit from that strategy.
3. Use a criterion to see whether profit could be increased by using some other strategy.
4. If profit can be increased use some criterion to discover a strategy which will increase it.
5. Repeat the process until step 3 shows that no other strategy will increase profit. The optimal strategy has, then, been found.

We will follow these steps in finding the optimal strategy for our example.

In choosing a strategy with which to start the search for the optimal strategy there is one major requirement. It can be shown mathematically that the optimal strategy will not include more components than the number of restrictions. In our case we have four variables which may be components of the optimal strategy: X_A, X_B, X_1, and X_2. But since we have only two restrictions (the two equations expressing the department capacity limitations) we know that the optimal strategy will contain at most two of them. The other two will be zero. The requirement on the strategy with which we start our search is, then, that it should contain only two of the variables at nonzero levels. This restricts us somewhat but still leaves a number of possible starting points. Expressed mathematically, we must start with two of the four variables chosen so that the two equations can be satisfied when the other two variables are zero. For example, we can start with X_1 and X_2, since $X_1 = 100$ and $X_2 = 100$ satisfy the equations when X_A and X_B are both equal to zero. This starting strategy would be the strategy of not producing anything. Or we could start with X_A and X_1, since $X_A = 250$ and $X_1 = 37.5$ satisfy the equations when X_B and X_2 are both equal to zero. This would be the strategy of producing only A, and we have already seen that this leaves 37.5 per cent ($X_1 = 37.5$) of the capacity of Dept. I unutilized. Or we could start with X_B and X_2, since $X_B = 200$ and $X_2 = 50$ satisfy the equations with X_A and X_1 both equal to zero. This is the strategy of producing nothing but B, and we saw above that this strategy left 50 per cent ($X_2 = 50$) of the capacity of Dept. II unutilized.

We will start with X_1 and X_2 because it is always possible to start with the slack variables in problems of this kind. This starting strategy is equivalent to the strategy of producing nothing. The next step is to determine the profit which results from the strategy. In this case there is no profit because the strategy involves only X_1 and X_2—we are producing nothing. The third step is to discover whether some other strategy would produce a larger profit. The criterion for doing this is extremely simple. It is based on the fact that none of the variables in our equations (X_A, X_B, X_1, and X_2) can be negative. It is obviously meaningless to have a negative amount produced or a negative amount of capacity. This being the case, we look at our objective function (which will change in form as we proceed)

$$\text{Profit} = 0.1X_A + 1.25X_B$$

If any one of the variables occurs in this equation with a positive coefficient it follows, since the variables cannot be negative, that the objective, profit, can be increased by increasing that variable. In the present case both X_A and X_B have positive coefficients, so we know that profit can be increased by increasing either X_A or X_B.

The fourth step is to find a strategy which will, in fact, increase profit. We know that only two of the four variables can occur at nonzero levels in the optimal strategy. Therefore, the only way we can increase X_A or X_B is by replacing either X_1 or X_2 by X_A or X_B. To decide which to replace we rewrite our two equations with only X_1 on the lefthand side of the first one and only X_2 on the lefthand side of the second one. Thus:

$$X_1 = 100 - 0.25X_A - 0.5X_B$$
$$X_2 = 100 - 0.4X_A - 0.25X_B$$

We can increase profit by increasing either X_A or X_B but we only make one change at a time. Since we may as well make that change first which produces the greatest increase in profit we choose the variable with the largest positive coefficient in the objective equation. In this case it is X_B, with a coefficient of 1.25. We propose, therefore, to replace either X_1 or X_2 by X_B to get a new, more profitable strategy. Which shall it be? We want to make X_B as large as possible because the larger it is the more profit will be made. But neither X_1 nor X_2 can be negative, and this places a restriction on how large we can make X_B. According to the first equation X_B cannot be larger than $100/0.5 = 200$ because if it were larger than this X_1 would have to be negative. According to the second equation X_B cannot be larger than $100/0.25 = 400$, because if it were larger than this X_2 would have to be negative. The limit to the size of X_B is, therefore, the smaller of these two limits, 200, which results from X_1. We shall, therefore replace X_1 by X_B to obtain a new, more profitable strategy.

To do this we solve the first equation for X_B and substitute the expression for X_B in the other equation and in the objective function. Thus, from

$$X_1 = 100 - 0.25X_A - 0.5X_B$$

we get

$$0.5X_B = 100 - 0.25X_A - X_1$$

or

$$X_B = 200 - 0.5X_A - 2X_1$$

Substituting this expression for X_B in the other equation gives

$$\begin{aligned}
X_2 &= 100 - 0.4X_A - 0.25(200 - 0.5X_A - 2X_1) \\
&= 100 - 0.4X_A - 50 + 0.125X_A + 0.5X_1 \\
&= 50 - 0.275X_A + 0.5X_1
\end{aligned}$$

and substituting the expression for X_B in the objective function gives

$$\begin{aligned}
\text{Profit} &= 1X_A + 1.25(200 - 0.5X_A - 2X_1) \\
&= 1X_A + 250 - 0.625X_A - 2.5X_1 \\
&= 250 + 0.375X_A - 2.5X_1
\end{aligned}$$

Our calculations have accomplished steps 1 and 2 of the next cycle of our search already. Our new strategy involves only X_B and X_2. If we were to use this strategy, X_A and X_1 would both be zero, so our equations tell us exactly what the values of X_B and X_2 are and also the resulting profit. This strategy has $X_B = 200$ (produce 200 units of B) and $X_2 = 50$ (leave 50 per cent of the capacity of Dept. II unutilized). The resulting profit is \$250. We had already calculated this particular strategy above, and we might have used it as our starting strategy. But our procedure has produced it automatically. Let us continue.

We now need to apply step 3 again. Our objective function now is

$$\text{Profit} = 250 + 0.375X_4 - 2.5X_1$$

Can we increase profit by some other strategy? Since the coefficient of X_4 is positive we see that profit can be increased by increasing X_4. Note that we cannot increase profit by increasing X_1. An increase in X_1 would decrease profit. We want, therefore, to find a new strategy which will increase X_4. This can only be done by replacing either X_B or X_2 by X_4. The two restricting equations show the limits to the amount to which X_4 can be increased. From the equation for X_B we see that X_4 cannot be larger than $200/0.5 = 400$ since, otherwise, X_B would have to be negative. From the equation for X_2 we see that X_4 cannot be larger than $50/0.275 = 181.8$. The limit on the size of X_4 is, therefore, X_2, and we shall replace X_2 by X_4 in our next strategy.

This is done in the same way as before. First, solve the X_2 equation for X_4.

$$X_2 = 50 - 0.275X_4 + 0.5X_1$$

gives $\quad\quad\quad 0.275X_4 = 50 - X_2 + 0.5X_1$

or $\quad\quad\quad X_4 = 181.8 - 3.636X_2 + 1.818X_1$

Then substitute this expression for X_4 in the X_B equation and the objective equation.

$$\begin{aligned}
X_B &= 200 - 0.5(181.8 - 3.636X_2 + 1.818X_1) - 2X_1 \\
&= 200 - 90.9 + 1.818X_2 - 0.909X_1 - 2X_1 \\
&= 109.1 + 1.818X_2 - 2.909X_1
\end{aligned}$$

and

$$\begin{aligned}
\text{Profit} &= 250 + 0.375(181.8 - 3.636X_2 + 1.818X_1) - 2.5X_1 \\
&= 250 + 68.18 - 1.364X_2 + 0.6818X_1 - 2.5X_1 \\
&= 318.18 - 1.364X_2 - 1.8182X_1
\end{aligned}$$

Again, steps 1 and 2 have been accomplished by our calculations. This strategy is to produce 109.1 units of B and 181.8 units of A with a total profit of \$318.18. (To get these values simply set $X_1 = 0$ and $X_2 = 0$ in the two equations and the objective equation.) In repeating step 3 we see that profit cannot be increased any more because both X_1 and X_2 occur in the objective equation with negative coefficients. The optimal strategy is, therefore, the one we have just stated. No other strategy can produce a larger profit. It will be noted that the optimal strategy in this example leaves no unused capacity in either department (X_1 and X_2 both equal zero). This is, of course, by no means always the case. Optimal strategies often include leaving some capacity unused.

Decision problems of this kind occur frequently in production. Our example had only two products and two departments, but precisely the same procedure would be followed if there were more products and/or more departments. And, of course, the decision problem does not have to refer to departments at all. The same kind of problem might arise with machines instead of departments or, for a multiplant company, with plants instead of departments. Other restrictions than those imposed by capacity limitations can easily be introduced. An example would be a requirement that at least some minimum amount of a specific product must be produced. Exactly the same procedure we have followed will suffice to determine the optimal strategy in any of these variants of this basic decision problem. Of course, as the number of equations increases it quickly becomes impractical to perform the necessary computations by hand. Fortunately, computers are available to handle the computations in these cases.

PROBLEMS

1. (a) In our repairmen problem we used Monte Carlo to obtain a sample of the behavior of the system. We used random numbers to find the times of breakdowns and then used a different selection of random numbers to find lengths of time of the repairs required. Why couldn't we use the same random numbers to do both of these things simultaneously?
   (b) In the repairmen problem we didn't analyze what would happen if there were three repairmen. Was this an oversight?

2. Four business-school students who are fatigued by their studies decide to interrupt their labors and to spend an evening with some young ladies. Since they do not know any they call a neighboring girls' school and, after some negotiations, succeed in finding four girls who are willing to make a collective "blind date." After introductions are made, and while the girls are getting their coats, the young men decide that since they are business students they should try to maximize their total utility. They quickly use the standard-gamble technique, or some other system, to express their utilities for each of the girls:

BUSINESS STUDENTS	GIRLS			
	BLONDE	BRUNETTE	REDHEAD	?
A	0.50	0.85	1.00	0
B	0.75	1.00	0.90	0
C	0.50	0.90	1.00	0
D	0.40	0.80	1.00	0

Note that this decision problem requires maximization of the total utility whereas the technique we used in this chapter for this kind of problem was designed for minimization. This difference causes no difficulties. Simply calculate the disutilities by subtracting each entry from 1. The minimization of the disutility matrix is equivalent to the maximization of the utility matrix.

(a) Determine the set of four "twosomes" which maximizes total utility.

(b) In the solution it will be found that it is necessary to have *A* match coins with one of the other students to see who will get the date with the redhead and who will get "?." *A* lost and then protested bitterly. He maintained that he had been forced to take a gamble with expected utility of $0.5 = [\frac{1}{2}(1.00) + \frac{1}{2}(0)]$ whereas he would have very much preferred to have the certainty of a date with the blonde, with the same utility. He asserted that this would have meant the same total utility and would therefore not have affected the maximization. He further asserted that he had a strong aversion to gambling and if he had known that he would have to gamble he would have changed his utilities. Comment on his argument.

   Postscript. In the actual case it developed that the young ladies had had a brief discussion and had agreed on an allocation of the young men which in no way corresponded to the solution found above. This, of course, they easily accomplished. The moral of this is that decision-problem solutions are of no avail if there is no control over implementation—a subject which will be treated in the last chapter.

   Furthermore, it may be noted that the student who got "?" found her to be quite the most delightful girl he had ever met.

3. A well-known book on operations research has a problem dealing with inventories of spare parts for generators. Each spare part is built uniquely for the specific generator and may not be used on any other generator. If the part is ordered with the generator the cost is $500. If a part is needed and is not available the cost of having it made plus the cost of the time the generator is out of operation will be $10,000. The probability distribution for failures of the parts is

NUMBER OF SPARE PARTS NEEDED	PROBABILITY
0	0.90
1	0.05
2	0.02
3	0.01
4	0.01
5	0.01
	———
	1.00

(a) The authors of the book in question solve the problem in a way which in our terms would produce the following decision payoff matrix:

STRATEGIES: NUMBER OF SPARE PARTS	STATES OF NATURE DEMAND					
	0	1	2	3	4	5
0	$0	10000	20000	30000	40000	50000
1	500	0	10000	20000	30000	40000
2	1000	500	0	10000	20000	30000
3	1500	1000	500	0	10000	20000
4	2000	1500	1000	500	0	10000
5	2500	2000	1500	1000	500	0

This payoff matrix is wrong. Try to state exactly why it is wrong and deduce the fault in the reasoning which led to the error. Note that it could have been avoided by precisely stating the objective.

(b) Solve the decision problem correctly.

4. A company maintains an inventory on three items for which we have the following information:

ITEM	PRICE	YEARLY DEMAND
A	$4.00	10,000
B	2.00	30,000
C	1.00	10,000

The company estimates carrying costs at 12 per cent per year and ordering cost at $10 per order. Current policy is to order each item once each month.

(a) What are the total carrying and ordering costs per year with the present policy?

(b) What is the optimal ordering policy which has the same total number of orders? What is the total cost per year?

(c) What is the optimal ordering policy which has the same total inventory? What is the total cost per year?

(d) What is the optimal ordering policy and what is its total cost per year?

(e) Find and graph the curve showing the total inventory and the total number of orders which result from the optimal policy for every ratio of ordering cost to carrying cost.

(f) What ratio of ordering cost to carrying cost is implied by (b)? by (c)?

5. A company must ship from 3 factories to 7 warehouses. The transportation cost per unit from each factory to each warehouse, the requirements of each warehouse, and the capacity of each factory are:

WAREHOUSES	FACTORIES			WAREHOUSE REQUIREMENTS
	1	2	3	
A	$6	11	8	100
B	7	3	5	200
C	5	4	3	450
D	4	5	6	400
E	8	4	5	200
F	6	3	8	350
G	5	2	4	300
FACTORY CAPACITY:	600	400	1000	2000

(a) Find the minimum-cost transportation schedule.

(b) Suppose warehouse B goes out of business. This means that there is now excess capacity of 200 units. Find the minimum-cost transportation schedule.

    Hint: Leave B in as a dummy warehouse with the same requirement of 200 units. Change the transportation costs to B from each factory to zero. A shipment to B now corresponds to leaving 200 units of capacity unused, which has zero transportation cost. Now solve as before.

(c) How would you handle the case where total warehouse requirements exceed total factory capacity?

6. Earlier in the book we mentioned that one particular kind of maximization problem involved a simultaneous minimization. The example of the allocation of productive resources illustrates this. The procedure used in maximizing profit in this example is known as linear programming, and it is a mathematical fact that to every such maximization problem there is an equivalent minimization problem, called the *dual*. For our example the dual is

Minimize $\qquad\qquad\qquad Z = 100W_1 + 100W_2$

with $\qquad\qquad\qquad\qquad 0.25W_1 + 0.4W_2 \geqslant 1$

$\qquad\qquad\qquad\qquad\qquad 0.5W_1 + 0.25W_2 \geqslant 1.25$

This is minimized by $W_1 = 1.818$ and $W_2 = 1.364$.

(a) Carefully compare the formulation of the dual with the original formulation. All the numbers are the same but they are arranged differently. Can you express in words what is being minimized and what restrictions the inequations represent?

(b) Calculate Z from the equation, using the given values of W_1 and W_2. Compare Z with the final profit obtained in the original problem. Try dimensional analysis to determine in what units W_1 and W_2 are expressed. W_1 and W_2 have an important economic significance which will be discussed in Chapter 13.

7. A factory with three departments makes three products. The maximum capacity of each department for each product, assuming it makes nothing else, and the profit for each unit of each product are:

| PRODUCT | DEPARTMENT | | | PROFIT |
	I	II	III	PER UNIT
A	333	286	500	\$4.00
B	500	1000	1000	1.50
C	1000	667	500	2.00

(a) Determine the maximum possible profit and the amounts of each product which must be produced to obtain it.

(b) Try to set up the dual to this maximization problem.

(c) Suppose that it is decided not to produce product B. Find the amounts of the other two products which must be produced to obtain maximum profits.

Chapter eleven

Of Administration

Marketing and production are line activities. Together they form the backbone of the majority of business organizations. Supporting these line activities are the great variety of staff functions which deal with information, personnel, money, policy, and major decisions. By "administration" we mean all of these functions and any others which cannot be properly assigned to marketing and production. As a result of this classification many different kinds of decision problems are subsumed under administration; simply because of space limitations we could not hope to present examples of all the major types. But there are additional reasons for limiting the number of examples. First, some administrative areas have not yet been studied to any significant degree in terms of the approach to decision problems which we are using. Second, some administrative decision problems which have been analyzed are of such complexity that they cannot be realistically simplified for presentation here. Third, some administrative decision problems which have been analyzed and which are not too complex require mathematical methods beyond the scope of this book.

Some of the complexities of administrative decision problems result from the fact that these problems are especially likely to involve multiple objectives. Further, many of the objectives are of the sort that is difficult to quantify, and relevant costs are often difficult to estimate. Nonetheless, the framework which decision theory provides for the analysis of decision problems is just as applicable in administration as it is in marketing and production. Our selection of examples in this chapter is intended to illustrate this fact, but, for the reasons given above, we have had to pass over some of the major areas within administration.

92. *MAINTENANCE SCHEDULING*

Maintenance is typically an administrative problem. Models describing the amount of maintenance which should, or must, be done can be formulated in a variety of ways. Different maintenance strategies, including the degree to which preventive maintenance is used, the scheduling of maintenance crews, the replacement of old and worn equipment, and so on, produce different payoffs over the long run. States of nature which affect deterioration, breakage, and failures of various sorts are difficult to detect and can require a great deal of careful observation before any reasonable predictions can be made. The study of failure rates as states of nature is of particular importance in the maintenance field. The reader will recall how the Monte Carlo technique was used to determine the failure characteristics of a unit for which the failure characteristics of the component were known. Based on even limited knowledge of the states of nature optimal replacement policies for machines, light bulbs, tool bits, and so on can sometimes be determined by analytical methods. It is interesting to observe that in this area many techniques have been suggested and partially developed but generalized problem-solving techniques are rarely found. The mathematical representation of replacement strategies is complex. Similarly, sequencing and routing models have not yet been solved for enough general cases, and purely mathematical solutions are available only for special cases. In this area the selection of optimal maintenance strategies is largely a matter of intuition and hard work.

We do not mean to imply that either replacement problems or sequencing problems are solely in the province of maintenance. At certain levels, replacement problems are more nearly financial problems, and sequencing problems exist in almost every area of business. They are of particular importance in scheduling production facilities and routing a variety of jobs through a factory. This same general type of problem appears in routing salesmen through a company's territory in such a way as to minimize the distance covered, or the time and money required. Although many interesting aspects of this problem have been uncovered, a general solution is lacking.

Bearing in mind the above remarks, we will now proceed to develop several examples of routing models which can be solved. There are other possible examples, but these will serve to illustrate the kinds of solutions which have been obtained. They will also demonstrate the advantages to be gained by using formal problem-solving methods whenever possible. The first example requires scheduling factory maintenance crews in such a way as to minimize their idle time. The company, we will assume, has eight large machines which receive preventive maintenance. The maintenance team is divided into two crews, A and B. Crew A takes the machine down and replaces parts according to the number of hours of use the machine has accumulated up to the time of servicing. The second crew resets the machine and puts it back into operation. Different training and different abilities are required by each crew. The machines are not alike and, therefore, the servicing times are not the same for each machine. The specific servicing times are given in hours, as follows:

| | MACHINE | | | | | | | |
	a	b	c	d	e	f	g	h
Crew A	5	4	22	16	15	11	9	4
Crew B	6	10	12	8	20	7	2	12

The method for minimizing idle time of the maintenance crews requires a few simple rules. The rules can be developed in mathematical terms, but there is no practical advantage in this approach since the formulae must be interpreted in the following manner:

1. Choose the single smallest value that appears in the two rows.

2. If it is in the second row (which is always reserved for the second operation in the two-step servicing sequence), then that machine will be serviced last by crew A.

3. If it is in the first row (the first operation in the two-step sequence), then that machine will be serviced first by crew A.

4. Cross out the column of the machine which has been assigned.

5. In general, from the remaining numbers choose the single smallest value which appears in the two rows. If the number is in the second row, then that machine is assigned to be serviced last by crew A—if no previous assignment to the last place has been made. If a previous assignment has been made to the last place, then the machine goes into the next to the last place. If two previous assignments, to the last and next to last place, have been made, then the machine is placed into the next to the next to the last place. Cross out the column and proceed until all possible assignments have been made.

6. If the smallest value remaining is in the first row, then the machine is assigned to be serviced first, second, third, or whatever, depending upon how many previous assignments have been made. After an assignment, cross out the column and proceed until all possible assignments have been made.

7. If a tie exists for the smallest value remaining, choose either one. Cross out the column chosen and proceed until all possible assignments have been made.

Let us apply our rules to the example above. If a machine is to be serviced last by crew A we will use the number 8 to denote this fact, since there are only eight machines. The number 7 will indicate the next to the last assignment. The number 2 will denote an assignment to second place, and so forth.

Then, our minimum number in the table is 2. It appears in the second row. Therefore we make the assignment $g8$, which means that machine g will be serviced last (or eighth) by crew A. The next minimum number is 4 and it appears twice. We choose either one—let us pick machine b. We get $b1$. It has been assigned first place since it appears in the first row. This leaves the other 4 as a minimum number, so we get $h2$. Proceeding in this fashion, we derive the sequence

$$g8, b1, h2, a3, f7, d6, c5, e4$$

We can arrange these in order, and put down the servicing times for crews A and B.

	Crew A	Crew B
1b	4	10
2h	4	12
3a	5	6
4e	15	20
5c	22	12
6d	16	8
7f	11	7
8g	9	2

This order of servicing the machines is the optimal sequence. We can represent it on a chart as shown in Figure 11.1. The sold black areas are the idle time of crew B. The result has given us 11 hours of idle time for crew B. The method can be applied to any number of machines, but

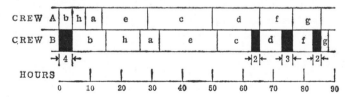

Figure 11.1 Sequencing machine maintenance with two crews and eight machines.

the number of maintenance operations is limited to two. However, the technique can be extended to three maintenance operations by means of a few additional steps which were developed by S. M. Johnson.*

---

* Johnson, S. M., "Optimal Two- and Three-Stage Production Schedules with Setup Times Included," Nav. Res. Log. Quart., 1, Nr. 1, 61–8 (March, 1954).

We are going to transform the problem to a different maintenance situation (it will be left to the reader to apply the necessary modifications to the machine example). For this second example, we will consider the problem of an oil company with eight refineries located in different parts of the country. Each refinery has its own maintenance crew to do the necessary routine work. However, once a year each refinery undergoes a complete overhaul. For this work the company hires outside maintenance crews which specialize in the required kind of maintenance work. Because these crews are very expensive the company would like to minimize their idle time. We will assume that the yearly overhaul (or turnaround) procedure involves three distinct steps, A, B, and C. Furthermore, we will suppose that phase B is handled by the local refinery maintenance group while phase A is handled by crew A of the outside team and phase C is taken care of by crew C of the outside team. Then, the problem can be set down in the following form, where the entries are the number of hours required by each crew to complete its phase of the work.

	$R1$	$R2$	$R3$	$R4$	$R5$	$R6$	$R7$	$R8$
Crew A	5	4	22	16	15	11	9	4
Crew B	4	3	2	4	3	4	2	3
Crew C	6	10	12	8	20	7	2	12

The approach which is used requires adding the time required by crews A and B for each refinery and thereby forming a new row: crew A + crew B. The same procedure is used for the time required by crews C and B for each refinery and in this manner we obtain a second row: crew C + crew B. Thus,

	$R1$	$R2$	$R3$	$R4$	$R5$	$R6$	$R7$	$R8$
Crew A + Crew B	5 + 4	4 + 3	22 + 2	16 + 4	15 + 3	11 + 4	9 + 2	4 + 3
Crew C + Crew B	6 + 4	10 + 3	12 + 2	8 + 4	20 + 3	7 + 4	2 + 2	12 + 3

which is

	$R1$	$R2$	$R3$	$R4$	$R5$	$R6$	$R7$	$R8$
Crew A + Crew B	9	7	24	20	18	15	11	7
Crew C + Crew B	10	13	14	12	23	11	4	15

We apply the previously developed rules in exactly the same way. The smallest value is 4, appearing in the second row. Therefore, we assign $R7$ to the last operation of crew A, and so forth. The result is:

	CREW A	CREW B	CREW C
1 $R2$	4	3	10
2 $R8$	4	3	12
3 $R1$	5	4	6
4 $R5$	15	3	20
5 $R3$	22	2	12
6 $R4$	16	4	8
7 $R6$	11	4	7
8 $R7$	9	2	2

Figure 11.2 graphically depicts this optimal sequence. In this case, we find 13 hours of idle time for crew C. There is one important limitation of this method which restricts its usefulness. Crew B, which is in the middle of the servicing sequence A–B–C, cannot have any servicing times which are greater than the minimum servicing times of both A and C.

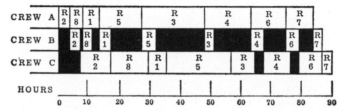

Figure 11.2   Sequencing refinery turnaround with three crews and eight re-fineries.

In other words, the minimum servicing time in the first row (crew A) is 4. The minimum servicing time in the third row (crew C) is 2. The maximum servicing time in the second row (crew B) is 4. Since this last value is not greater than both the minimums of the other two rows, the method can be used in the manner we have shown. However, if the maximum servicing time in the second row had been 5, this method could not have been employed.

Minimizing the idle time of the maintenance crews is most certainly an important objective. However, if we suppose that once turnaround has begun the refinery must be either entirely or partially shut down—which is quite generally the case—then the objective of minimizing the idle time of the maintenance crews becomes of secondary importance. The major objective of the oil company is to minimize down-time of the refineries. Lost production time is the bane of this and other process industries. Therefore, the administrator of the maintenance function would reject the solution which we have just found. The same consideration might well apply to the machine problem which was the first sequencing example that we used. If once maintenance starts on a machine that machine cannot be used until the servicing is completed, then the first objective would be to get that machine back into use as soon as possible. This would be particularly true when an expensive machine is involved since the cost of machine down-time would be high in relation to the cost of the maintenance crews.

To handle this objective, we will now examine a method which insures that each refinery will be put back into operation as soon as possible. Subject to this condition, we will minimize the idle time of the maintenance crews. For this example, two maintenance crews, A and B, will service the eight refineries. The sequencing methods which we have explained are composed of components which provide service and elements which require service. As the reader will have noticed, the method can be used for any number of elements which *require* service. As yet, there is no general solution available for more than two components which *provide* service. Our second sequencing example involved three components which provided service (crews A, B, and C). However, as we subsequently explained, the solution only applies when the intermediate servicing step has no value greater than the minimums of both of the other two servicing steps. Consequently, we do not even have a general model to cover three components which provide service. The same limitation applies to the model we are about to explain. For this reason, the example consists of only two crews and eight refineries. It is convenient to use the same data as were previously used in the machine-servicing problem as the reader can refer to Figure 11.1 to derive the values which are shown below.

Once again, crew A must precede crew B. However, in this case, as soon as crew A begins to work at any one refinery we will assume that the refinery must be shut down. On this basis, the following table of information can be prepared.

	R1	R2	R3	R4	R5	R6	R7	R8
Servicing time Crew A (in hours)	5	4	22	16	15	11	9	4
Servicing time Crew B (in hours)	6	10	12	8	20	7	2	12
Total servicing time for each refinery	11	14	34	24	35	18	11	16
Unnecessary down-time for each refinery	13	0	2	0	4	0	0	6

We can see that the total, unnecessary down-time derived by our first method is 25 hours. We know from our previous results that 11 hours of idle time had resulted for crew B under the optimal condition. Even if we assumed that 100 men composed crew B and that these men were paid $5.00 per hour, the idle-time cost would be $5500. Compared to the

25 hours of lost refinery production, the idle-time cost would be relatively insignificant.

For this reason, the administrator would be prepared to increase the amount of idle time in exchange for no unnecessary down-time of the refineries. In order to obtain no unnecessary down-time, each refinery must be serviced in the manner shown in Figure 11.3.

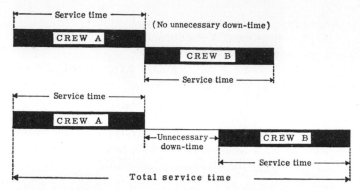

Figure 11.3 *Illustrating the requirement for no unnecessary down-time.*

Our problem consists of finding the optimal sequence of refineries when the condition for no unnecessary down-time is enforced. Looking back to Figure 11.1, we observe the gaps between the servicing periods of crews A and B for h, a, e, and c. (These are equivalent to our refineries $R8$, $R1$, $R5$, and $R3$.) In order to get rid of these gaps, we can compare the idle time for sequential pairs of refineries. Figure 11.4 illustrates several pairs of refineries: $R1$–$R2$, $R1$–$R4$, $R7$–$R4$.

For every possible combination of pairs of refineries we determine the idle time enclosed by two consecutive servicing operations of either crew. Sometimes the idle time occurs for crew A and sometimes for crew B. We do not include any idle time which might arise at the lead or end of the sequence. From Figure 11.4 we find that $R1$–$R2$ has **2** hours of idle time, $R1$–$R4$ has **10** hours of idle time, and $R7$–$R4$ has **14** hours of idle time. It isn't necessary to draw pictures for every possible sequence in order to determine the enclosed idle time. Using the original table of data we obtain the absolute value for

$$| Ri(B) - Rj(A) |$$

where $i =$ any one of the refineries which is serviced first, and
$\quad\quad j =$ all of the other refineries which are serviced second.

Thus, for $i = 1$, then $j = 2, 3, 4, 5, 6, 7,$ and 8, we get

$$| R1(B) - R2(A) | = | 6 - 4 | = 2$$
$$| R1(B) - R3(A) | = | 6 - 22 | = 16 \quad\quad \text{(and so on)}$$

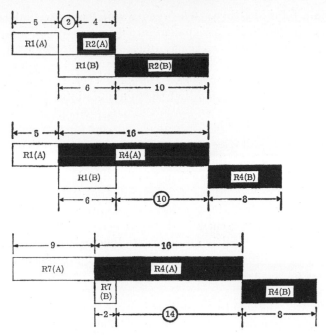

Figure 11.4 Determination of idle time for sequences with no unnecessary down-time.

For $|R1(B) - R1(A)|$ we obtain no value since a refinery cannot follow itself.

Proceeding in this manner we can determine the idle time for any sequence of two refineries. The idle times can be presented in a matrix as follows:

				FIRST				
SECOND	R1	R2	R3	R4	R5	R6	R7	R8
R1	x	5	7	3	15	2	3	7
R2	2	x	8	4	16	3	2	8
R3	16	12	x	14	2	15	20	10
R4	10	6	4	x	4	9	14	4
R5	9	5	3	7	x	8	13	3
R6	5	1	1	3	9	x	9	1
R7	3	1	3	1	11	2	x	3
R8	2	6	8	4	16	3	2	x

This table shows the idle time for any sequence of two refineries where the first is given in the column heading and the second by the row. Thus, refinery $R4$ followed by refinery $R7$ results in idle time of 1 hour. We would like to find the total sequence, including all refineries, which has the minimum total idle time. The reader will recognize that this problem is very similar to the assignment problem treated in the preceding chapter. However, there is a crucial difference. In the assignment problem it was sufficient to find the minimum-cost assignment and any machine could be assigned to any job. Here, however, there are additional restrictions. Suppose we found that the minimum total idle time resulted from a sequence containing $(R4–R1) \ldots (R1–R8) \ldots (R8–R4)$. This sequence would be impossible since it would call for servicing $R4$ twice. Such a sequence is called a *cycle*, and the additional restriction on sequencing problems is that there should be no cycles in the final sequence. The restriction makes this problem similar to the famous travelling-salesman problem. A salesman, for example, must start from Washington, D.C., and travel to each of the 50 state capitols and return to Washington. How should we schedule the sequence of state capitols so that his total distance travelled is minimized? There is no general solution to this problem and there is none to our sequencing problem. However, this does not mean that there is nothing that can be done with the problem.

One thing we can do is to solve it as if it were an assignment problem. If the solution has no cycles we have solved the sequencing problem. If it does have cycles we cannot use the sequence, but at least it represents the minimum sequence as a starting point from which to make changes. Therefore, we will solve the assignment problem for our matrix. The reader will remember that the method we use here is based on opportunity costs, but he may want to review the method as given in the last chapter since we will not repeat the argument here. Subtracting the minimum entry in each column from each element in the column and then doing the same thing by rows in the resulting matrix gives (we assume the x's are of very great magnitude and ignore them):

	$R1$	$R2$	$R3$	$R4$	$R5$	$R6$	$R7$	$R8$
$R1$	x	4	6	2	13	0	1	6
$R2$	0	x	7	3	14	1	0	7
$R3$	14	11	x	13	0	13	18	9
$R4$	6	3	1	x	0	5	10	1
$R5$	5	2	0	4	x	4	9	0
$R6$	3	0	0	2	7	x	7	0
$R7$	1	0	2	0	9	0	x	2
$R8$	0	5	7	3	14	1	0	x

All the zeroes in this matrix can be included in seven rows and columns: rows $R2$, $R5$, $R6$, $R7$, $R8$ and columns $R5$ and $R6$. Therefore, since this is less than eight, we know the problem is not yet solved. The minimum entry in the matrix, if these rows and columns are excluded from it, is one and we now subtract one from every entry not in one of the seven rows and columns, add it to every entry at the intersection of any of the seven rows and columns, and leave the other entries unchanged. This gives

	$R1$	$R2$	$R3$	$R4$	$R5$	$R6$	$R7$	$R8$
$R1$	x	3	5	1	13	0	0	5
$R2$	0	x	7	3	15	2	0	7
$R3$	13	10	x	12	0	13	17	8
$R4$	5	2	0	x	0	5	9	0
$R5$	5	2	0	4	x	5	9	0
$R6$	3	0	0	2	8	x	7	0
$R7$	1	0	2	0	10	1	x	2
$R8$	0	5	7	3	15	2	0	x

The zeroes in this matrix cannot be included with less than eight rows and columns, so we know the assignment problem is solved. Actually, there are several solutions in this matrix; this is a good thing for our purposes because we hope to find one with no cycles. We can begin by finding the rows and columns with only one zero, as such a zero must be in the solution. Columns $R4$ and $R6$ have only one zero so we know that $(R6–R1)$ and $(R4–R7)$ must be in the solution. Row $R3$ has only one zero so $(R5–R3)$ is in the solution. There are two zeroes in column $R2$ but one of them is in row $R7$, and $(R2–R7)$ is impossible because we already have $(R4–R7)$. Therefore, $(R2–R6)$ must be in the solution. There are no further eliminations possible from the standpoint of the assignment problem. However, there are two zeroes in column $R1$. $(R1–R2)$ is impossible for our problem because we already have $(R2–R6)$ and $(R6–R1)$. Therefore, we must have $(R1–R8)$. But this makes $(R7–R8)$ impossible, so we must have $(R7–R2)$. Since we already have $(R5–R3)$ we cannot have $(R3–R5)$, so we must have $(R3–R4)$. This, in turn, requires that we have $(R8–R5)$ which completes the solution. Putting these together we get

$$R6–R1–R8–R5–R3–R4–R7–R2–R6$$

Since there is no cycle (other than the complete one) we have the sequence which has minimum idle time. If we had found a cycle we would have had to use trial-and-error methods, starting with the solution to the assignment problem. Returning to the original table we see that the idle time is the sum of the entries indicated by the optimal sequence. That is,

$(R6–R1)$ 2
$(R1–R8)$ 2
$(R8–R5)$ 3
$(R5–R3)$ 2
$(R3–R4)$ 4
$(R4–R7)$ 1
$(R7–R2)$ 2
$(R2–R6)$ 1
———
$17 =$ Total idle time (hours)

We can see the way in which the 17 hours of idle time arise by referring to Figure 11.5. We observe that there is no unnecessary down-time. The saving in down-time is accomplished at the expense of six additional hours of idle time. Using our previous example of 100 men paid $5.00

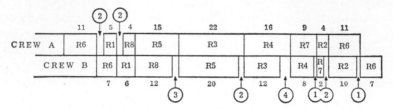

Figure 11.5 *Optimal sequence for eight refineries with no unnecessary downtime.*

per hour, we find that the administrator in this case is paying an additional $3000 to idle maintenance crews in return for a saving of 25 hours of refinery production. It is quite certain that the management of the oil company would gladly accept this trade. For other types of maintenance problems, the choice might not be so easily made. Assuming that the company faced with this problem is able to estimate the cost of lost production, a balancing of these two objectives which can usually be expressed in terms of the same scale, dollars, could be accomplished. An additional aspect of the problem might require analysis of the costs of transporting maintenance crews between refineries or plants in such a sequence as to minimize transportation costs. In this case a third objective, which can usually be expressed on a dollar scale, is evident. However, the direct minimization of any one of the three kinds of outcomes will usually result in a less than optimal value for the remaining outcomes. It should be noted that the cost of transporting maintenance crews between refineries could be entered in the matrix. Idle time can be converted from hours into the appropriate dollar value, which would then be summed with the transportation cost.

93. DIVIDEND PROBLEM

One of the major objectives of management groups is to satisfy the stockholders for whom they work. At first glance, this would seem like an easy objective to fulfill. As long as the company is making a sufficient profit, the company can pay a regular dividend at the average rate for the industry—or better—and thereby satisfy the stockholders. But stockholders are not uniformly satisfied with this policy. Many times, they will sell their holdings in a company which is paying a regular dividend and buy ownership, instead, in a company which is paying no dividend at all. Why? Both stockholders and management are interested in maximizing dividends. Maximization of dividends may be achieved by a company which does not pay any dividend whatever and uses this money to reinvest in company expansion. Of course, this process is not expected to go on indefinitely. An alert management will take advantage of a period which is particularly favorable for the company to expand. The average stockholder who is alert to the opportunities in his company's industry will concur wholeheartedly with management's decision to skip a dividend in order to maximize, in the long run, the stockholder's dividend.

The question of how much money management should pay out as a dividend and how much they should put back into the expansion of the company is very complex. A great variety of factors must be considered. As we shall explain, analytical methods can be used to obtain an approximate answer. The reason that the result is approximate and not exact is simply that it isn't feasible to include all of the factors which affect the solution. Furthermore, predictions are required which are difficult to make—particularly as these predictions move further into the future. But the solution does give some basic notions to the decision-maker. The objective of management is to maximize the dividend payout over a period of N years. Management has a great number of strategies which it can use to attempt to achieve the objective. But this is a case where the number of possible strategies is not so great that we cannot consider a reasonable number of them. Our payoffs will be the total dividend which can be paid to the stockholders at the end of N years. Normally, a variety of states of nature could occur. For example, the income of the company could vary each year depending upon many conditions outside of the control of the company. Returns on additional investments could be treated as a probability distribution rather than as the expected value which we have used. Dividends to be paid in the future could be discounted to their present value. Market growth, new competitors, technological breakthroughs, rapidly changing economic conditions, and many other factors influence the decisions which must be made at each dividend period. In the same way, a number of strategic variations exist. The company could pay a stock dividend, or a combination of stock and monetary dividends could be used. The company might decide to raise additional capital for investment in expansion by means of a bond issue or through other stock issues. All of the possibilities we have mentioned could conceivably be included in the approach which we are about to explain. However, the number and complexity of computations which are required by this method when the problem is viewed in its expanded form would prove unsuitable for any example, and difficult for any real problem. For this reason we have included only the basic elements which underlie the problem. The method we will use is based upon the principles of dynamic programming which were developed by Richard Bellman.[*]

A company has only A_0 dollars available at the beginning of a year. It can use all of this money for dividends, or it can use part of it for dividends and part for reinvestment, or it can use all of it for reinvestment. We will assume that the company pays a dividend only once a year since this assumption will further reduce the amount of computation which must be shown, without affecting the method. The company will pay out X_0 dollars as dividends at this initial time. The remainder of the A_0 dollars, which is an amount $(A_0 - X_0)$, will be used for the expansion of the company's facilities. We will assume that A_0 equals $500,000$. However, all numbers will be given in thousands of dollars. Therefore, $A_0 = \$500$. Now, a year elapses. The company has earned another $500. In addition, it has earned a return on the amount $(A_0 - X_0)$ which it had reinvested. This means that at the end of the first year, $N = 1$, the company has an amount $A_1 = A_0 + (A_0 - X_0)R$. The return on reinvested money, R, decreases as the size of the reinvestment increases. In this way, we take account of the diminishing return on investments. Our assumption is that the return on reinvested money continues at the same rate over time and that the rate of return is reasonably constant over a period of years. As previously explained it is mostly for computational convenience that we have made assumptions of this kind. Figure 11.6 shows the return rate, R, as a function of reinvested money, $(A_i - X_i)$. We can either use Figure 11.6 to provide us with all of the necessary return rates or else the following table.

$(A_i - X_i)$ AMOUNT REINVESTED	(R) RATE OF RETURN
$ 0–99	0.60
100–199	0.55
200–299	0.50
300–399	0.45
400–499	0.40
500–	0.35

The way in which we will proceed is to examine what outcome results if we follow the strategy of paying no dividend, $X_0 = 0$; what outcome results if we pay out in dividends $100, $200, $300, $400, and $500. The required result is A_1: the amount of money on hand at the end of the first year. Thus, at $N = 1$:

X_0	$A_0 + (A_0 - X_0)R = A_1$	
0	$500 + (500)0.35$	$= 675$
100	$500 + (400)0.40$	$= 660$
200	$500 + (300)0.45$	$= 635$
300	$500 + (200)0.50$	$= 600$
400	$500 + (100)0.55$	$= 555$
500	$500 + (0)0.60$	$= 500$

[*] Bellman, Richard, *Dynamic Programming*, Princeton University Press, Princeton, N. J., 1957.

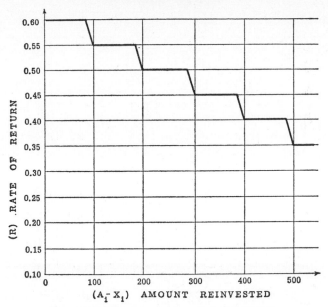

Figure 11.6   Rate of return on reinvested capital.

Now, if the company's objective is to maximize dividend payout for a one-year period, the policy that should be followed is to pay out $500 at each of the two dividend periods.   We can see that result by looking at the table below.

If first dividend X_0 is	0	100	200	300	400	500
and total capital earned, A_1, is paid out as a dividend, X_1	675	660	635	600	555	500
then total paid to stockholders is . . .	675	760	835	900	955	1000

Since the last column represents the largest payout, that is the strategy which should be followed for a one-year objective.   But let us suppose that the company wants to maximize the dividend payout over a two-year period.   The amount earned at the end of the second year is A_2, and $A_2 = A_1 + (A_1 - X_1)R$.   The second dividend paid is X_1, and R has the same meaning as before.   Then we can compute the A_2 value for all possible values of X_0 and X_1 as follows:

	$X_0 = 0$				$X_0 = 100$	
	$A_1 = 675$				$A_1 = 660$	
X_1	$A_1 + (A_1 - X_1)R = A_2$			X_1	$A_1 + (A_1 - X_1)R = A_2$	
0	$675 + (675)0.35$	$= 911$		0	$660 + (660)0.35$	$= 891$
100	$675 + (575)0.35$	$= 876$		100	$660 + (560)0.35$	$= 856$
200	$675 + (475)0.40$	$= 865$		200	$660 + (460)0.40$	$= 844$
300	$675 + (375)0.45$	$= 844$		300	$660 + (360)0.45$	$= 822$
400	$675 + (275)0.50$	$= 813$		400	$660 + (260)0.50$	$= 790$
500	$675 + (175)0.55$	$= 771$		500	$660 + (160)0.55$	$= 748$
600	$675 + (\ 75)0.60$	$= 720$		600	$660 + (\ 60)0.60$	$= 696$

Similar computations have been made for $X_0 = 200, 300, 400,$ and 500. These results are compiled in the Table 11.1 which shows the resulting A_2 values for all possible combinations of X_0 and X_1. The diagonals

Table 11.1 Matrix of A_2.

A_1

	675	660	635	600	555	500	
			X_0				
X_1	0	100	200	300	400	500	500
0	911	891	857	810	749	675	600
100	876	856	822	775	737	660	700
200	865	844	809	760	715	635	800
300	844	822	786	735	683	600	900
400	813	790	753	700	640	555	1000
500	771	748	709	655	588	500	
600	720	696	656	600			

each represent those combinations of X_0 and X_1, which sum to a particular value. In other words, the \$400 diagonal results from $X_0 = 0$, $X_1 = 400$; $X_0 = 100$, $X_1 = 300$; $X_0 = 200$, $X_1 = 200$; and so on. The greatest value on each diagonal is marked with a dot.* That is the only value which needs to be considered. The reason that no other value is important can be understood if we assume we are stockholders for the moment. Let us consider the \$400 diagonal. As stockholders we would have received \$400 in some combination of payments, but our company would have more money left to work with if they had used the combination of payments $X_0 = 100$ and $X_1 = 300$. Therefore, that is the combination of dividend payments which is optimal for a total payout of \$400. Any additional dividend X_2 will be added to \$400, so it will not matter what combination was used. The company cannot possibly be better off by having less money. For this reason, we take only the dotted values from the matrix. If there is a tie for the maximum diagonal value it does not matter. It is the same value, in either case, which is taken from the matrix.

Now, if we assume the objective is to maximize dividend payout over a two-year period, $N = 2$, we find

$X_0 + X_1$	0	100	200	300	400	500	600	700	800	900	1000
Max A_2	911	891	865	844	822	790	753	709	656	600	500
Total	911	991	1065	1144	1222	1290	1353	1409	1456	1500	1500

* The method is suggested by Andrew Vazsonyi, *Scientific Programming in Business and Industry,* John Wiley & Sons, N. Y., 1958; p. 219–254.

The optimal strategy yielding the largest payout is either the 900 or the 1000 column. When $X_0 + X_1$ equals 900, A_2 equals 600. When $X_0 + X_1$ equals 1000, A_2 equals 500. Both strategies produce a total of 1500. We now go back to Table 11.1 and we find that the 600 value resulted when X_0 equals 300 and X_1 equals 600. In the same table we see that 500 resulted when X_0 equals 500 as before and X_1 equals 500. Therefore, we observe that the optimal strategy for a two year period does not necessarily begin in the same way as an optimal strategy for a one year period.

We will go one step further. Our next set of computations are of the same type as our former ones. That is,

$$X_0 + X_1 = 0$$
$$A_2 = 911$$

X_2	$A_2 + (A_2 - X_2)R = A_3$	
0	$911 + (911)0.35$	$= 1230$
100	$911 + (811)0.35$	$= 1195$
200	$911 + (711)0.35$	$= 1160$

$$X_0 + X_1 = 100$$
$$A_2 = 891$$

X_2	$A_2 + (A_2 - X_2)R = A_3$	
0	$891 + (891)0.35$	$= 1203$
100	$891 + (791)0.35$	$= 1168$
200	$891 + (691)0.35$	$= 1133$

Similar computations are carried out for all combinations of X_2 and $(X_0 + X_1)$. Table 11.2 is the result. Again, we see that the maximum value on each diagonal is dotted. And again, the same reasoning applies. We have now reached the end of the third year in our computations. We could continue indefinitely in the same fashion. Automatic

Table 11.2 Matrix of A_3.

	A_2										
	911	891	865	844	822	790	753	709	656	600	500
	$(X_0 + X_1)$										
X_2	0	100	200	300	400	500	600	700	800	900	1000
0	1230	1203	1168	1139	1110	1067	1017	957	886	810	675
100	1195	1168	1133	1104	1075	1032	982	922	851	775	660
200	1160	1133	1098	1069	1040	997	947	887	838	760	635
300	1125	1098	1063	1034	1005	986	934	873	816	735	600
400	1090	1087	1051	1021	991	966	912	848	784	700	555
500	1075	1067	1029	999	967	935	880	814	742	655	500
600	1051	1037	998	966	933	895	837	769	690	600	
700	1017	996	956	923	889	844	785	714			
800	972	946	904	870	835						
900	918										

computing equipment would do the same job with less wear and tear and in much less time once an appropriate program was fashioned.

Let us examine the result at the end of the third year, $N = 3$. This time the stockholder is going to be paid the A_i value since the objective is to maximize dividend payout for the end of the third year. Then,

$X_0 + X_1 + X_2$	0	100	200	300	400	500	600	700
A_3	1230	1203	1168	1139	1110	1087	1067	1037
TOTAL	1230	1303	1368	1439	1510	1587	1667	1737

$X_0 + X_1 + X_2$	800	900	1000	1100	1200	1300	1400	1500
A_3	999	967	935	895	844	785	714	600
TOTAL	1799	1867	1935	1995	2044	2085	2114	2100

The maximum total payout at the end of three years can be achieved by the combination, $X_0 + X_1 + X_2 = 1400$. Because of our three year objective, $X_3 = A_3$. In other words, our fourth dividend, paid at the end of the third year is a complete payout of the available capital of the company. $(A_3 - X_3) = 0$, and no money is going to be reinvested for expansion. Looking back at Table 11.2, we see that when $X_0 + X_1 + X_2 = 1400$, then for the dotted value on the diagonal, $X_2 = 700$ and $X_0 + X_1 = 700$. We then return to Table 11.1 where we find that for the diagonal $X_0 + X_1 = 700$, the dotted value resulted when $X_0 = 200$ and $X_1 = 500$. This is the final solution of the problem.

$$X_0 = 200$$
$$X_1 = 500$$
$$X_2 = 700$$
$$A_3 = 714$$

TOTAL PAYOUT: 2114

Once again, we observe that the optimal dividend payout policy has been changed by the fact that an additional year has been included in the objective. As the rate of return increases, the optimal policy tends to shift from immediate payout to delayed payout so that advantage can be taken of the opportunities for reinvestment. Exercise number 8, at the end of this chapter, is intended to demonstrate this effect.

94. SIZE OF WORK FORCE

A very frequently occurring decision problem concerns the number of men who should be maintained on the payroll full-time in order to meet a variable work load. Examples are such operations as a post office, a bank, clearing houses, freight handling. In cases such as these the amount of work which has to be processed is subject to a variety of cyclical and random variations. Generally in such cases some maximum processing time is an upper limit to the time that the work can be held. Therefore, when variations cause the work load to be greater than can be handled by the available work force it becomes necessary either to hire temporary employees or to have the regular work force work overtime in order to get the work processed. On the other hand, when the work load falls below the amount which could be processed by the regular work force the employees are idle. The decision problem is to determine the number of employees which will minimize the total cost of processing the work.

The similarity of this problem to some of the inventory problems we have already discussed is apparent. The variable work load is the demand and the inventory is the number of employees available to meet the demand. The states of nature are the possible levels of demand (amount of work load). In the general case there are a great many strategies available: offer inducements to customers in order to smooth out the variability in demand, hire and fire men in accord with the variations, take on temporary or part-time workers, and others. We will simplify the problem by considering a typical case where the only acceptable strategies are those which specify how many full-time employees to maintain on the payroll. In this case all work exceeding the capacity of the employees in their regular time will be processed by having them work overtime.

The analogy to the inventory problem suggests that there must be opposing costs in this situation. Of course there are and they can be found very quickly. A given number of men can handle a given amount of work in their regular hours. If demand is less than this amount the company pays wages for idle time. If demand is greater than this amount the company must pay extra wages in the form of overtime rates. These costs are the opposing costs, for as the number of men increases the cost of idle time will increase and the cost of overtime will decrease. Total costs will be the sum of these two components; the objective is to minimize the total costs. It should be noted that we are assuming there is no cost—in the form of loss of customer goodwill or in any other form—resulting from the delay involved in having to process some of the work in an overtime period.

Let us take an example. A large mail-order house has found (through depth interviews of customers) that customer complaint letters should be promptly answered by a personal letter. For this purpose the firm employs a number of college-graduate women who do nothing but answer these letters. These women are paid $2.00 per hour for regular time and $3.00 per hour for overtime. All incoming letters are answered on the same day even if it means overtime work. The average production of letters per hour per woman is 5, or 40 per 8-hour day. Records of the number of incoming letters per day show that the probability distribution of complaint letters per day is as follows:

COMPLAINT LETTERS	PROBABILITY
120–139	0.06
140–159	0.13
160–179	0.09
180–199	0.21
200–219	0.17
220–239	0.12
240–259	0.08
260–279	0.14
	1.00

This distribution gives the necessary information about the probabilities of the various states of nature. The strategies are the possible numbers of women who might be maintained on the payroll. We have all of the cost information necessary to evaluate the payoffs in each cell of the payoff matrix, so our decision problem is completely defined.

The payoff measure is total cost and is easy to evaluate. Suppose there are 5 employees. For any number of complaint letters up to 200 these 5 employees can handle the answers in their regular time. Further, it will cost the same amount, $5 \times \$16 = \$80$, whether there are 120 letters or any number up to 200 letters. If there are more than 200 letters overtime will be required. Thus, if there are 240 letters the total cost will be $\$80 + 8(\$3) = \$104$, since 8 hours of overtime would be required to answer the additional 40 letters. Any cell in the matrix can be evaluated similarly. For example, the strategy of having 6 employees and the state of nature of a demand of 260 letters would cost $6(\$16) + 4(\$3) = \$108$ since 6 employees could answer 240 letters in their regular time and 4 hours of overtime would be required for the additional 20 letters. Proceeding in this way we could evaluate the entire payoff matrix. However, our subsequent calculations will require the use of the probabilities, which are given only for a class of incoming letters. Therefore, we do not need every individual payoff for each specific number of incoming letters, and it will be sufficient to calculate the payoff for each class as if the number of incoming letters were the midpoint of the class. We do not have to calculate endlessly since we know that the best strategy could not be to have less than 3 employees (120/40) since this would mean that the company would always be paying overtime. Similarly, the best strategy could not be to have more than 7 employees (280/40) since this would mean that the company would always be paying for idle time. States of nature can be identified by the midpoint of the class given in the probability distribution of incoming letters. Thus, the midpoint of the class 180–199 is 189.5 and this value is used in the payoff calculations for this class. The complete payoff matrix, then, is:

STATES OF NATURE

COMPLAINTS		129.5	149.5	169.5	189.5	209.5	229.5	249.5	269.5	EXPECTED TOTAL COST
PROBABILITY		0.06	0.13	0.09	0.21	0.17	0.12	0.08	0.14	
STRATEGIES										
G	3	$53.70	65.70	77.70	89.70	101.70	113.70	125.70	137.70	$97.86
I	4	64.00	64.00	69.70	81.70	93.70	105.70	117.70	129.70	91.78
R	5	80.00	80.00	80.00	80.00	85.70	97.70	109.70	121.70	91.31
L	6	96.00	96.00	96.00	96.00	96.00	96.00	101.70	113.70	98.93
S	7	112.00	112.00	112.00	112.00	112.00	112.00	112.00	112.00	112.00

Since this is an example of decision-making under risk we obtain the expected value of total costs which are calculated in the usual way. For example, for the strategy of having 4 employees we have

$$\text{Expected total cost} = 0.06(64) + 0.13(64) + 0.09(69.70) + \ldots + 0.08(117.70) + 0.14(129.70) = \$91.78$$

The expected total costs are given in the righthand column. The strategy with the smallest expected cost is that of having 5 employees, with an expected total cost of $91.31. This, then, is the optimal strategy.

We can easily calculate that the average number of complaint letters per day is 203.1 If it were possible to have exactly the necessary number of hours to handle this amount of letters it would cost $2(203.1/5) = $81.24, on regular time. For a given strategy the actual expected total cost varies from this amount owing to the costs of idle time, overtime, or both. All of the costs are included in the expected total cost, but it is worth noting how the two component additional costs vary with the strategies. We can calculate the component costs separately by determining for each strategy the cost of idle time and overtime separately. This is easy to do by finding the opportunity cost of each strategy for each state of nature. This is equivalent to the Savage measure of regret, except that we use the exact cost of handling the given number of incoming letters rather than the lowest cost in each column of the matrix. The exact costs are:

STATE OF NATURE

COMPLAINTS	129.5	149.5	169.5	189.5	209.5	229.5	249.5	269.5	EXPECTED COST
PROBABILITIES	0.06	0.13	0.09	0.21	0.17	0.12	0.08	0.14	
COST	$51.80	59.80	67.80	75.80	83.80	91.80	99.80	107.80	$81.24

These costs are determined by dividing the number of letters by 5 to get the number of hours required and then multiplying by $2 to get the cost. We now subtract each of these costs from each entry in the corresponding column of the payoff matrix to get the opportunity cost.

COMPLAINTS	129.5	149.5	169.5	189.5	209.5	229.5	249.5	269.5	EXPECTED COSTS	
									IDLE TIME	OVER-TIME
PROBABILITY	0.06	0.13	0.09	0.21	0.17	0.12	0.08	0.14		
STRATEGIES										
3	$1.90	5.90	9.90	13.90	17.90	21.90	25.90	29.90	$0	$16.62
4	12.20	4.20	1.90	5.90	9.90	13.90	17.90	21.90	1.28	9.26
5	28.20	20.20	12.20	4.20	1.90	5.90	9.90	13.90	6.30	3.77
6	44.20	36.20	28.20	20.20	12.20	4.20	1.90	5.90	16.71	0.98
7	60.20	52.20	44.20	36.20	28.20	20.20	12.20	4.20	30.76	0

All of the entries above the heavy line are the extra costs owing to overtime, calculated at the $1 per hour extra cost as compared to regular time, and all of the entries below the line are the costs of idle time. The expected costs of idle time and of overtime are calculated in the usual way. Thus, the idle-time cost of the strategy of having 5 employees is

$$0.06(28.20) + 0.13(20.20) + 0.09(12.20) + 0.21(4.20) = \$6.30$$

and, of course, the expected total cost for each strategy equals $81.24 plus the expected idle-time cost and the expected overtime cost for the strategy. The two costs behave as expected: idle-time costs increase and overtime costs decrease as the number of employees increases. This breakdown shows, furthermore, that we have been employing the idea of equating marginal costs. Adding a fourth employee saves $7.36 in overtime and costs $1.28 in idle time for a net saving of $6.08. Adding a fifth employee saves $5.49 in overtime and costs $5.02 in idle time for a net saving of $.47. And the sixth employee would save only $2.79 while costing $10.41, a loss of $7.62. Therefore we stop at five employees.

The amount of saving in this problem is relatively small, but this merely serves to emphasize that the returns to be derived from a rational approach to a decision problem are relative to the amount of resources involved in the problem situation. Exactly the same technique could be applied to situations with a much larger work force or to situations involving expensive office machines. In either of these cases considerable amounts of money could be involved and, hence, returns from the solution could be large.

95. WORK POOLS

In the preceding example the problem was to determine the optimal number of employees to handle a varying volume of work. The converse situation is also a frequently recurring decision problem. Here the amount of work is fixed but the number of employees varies because of absenteeism. In a great many kinds of operations, where the work that must be done is not too specialized, it is possible to deal with this problem by maintaining a work pool of employees who function as replacements for any absent workers. This immediately raises the decision problem of determining the optimal number of employees to maintain in the work pool. The similarity with inventory problems is obvious. The work pool is an inventory of workers and the demand is the number of absentees. It is distinguished from other inventory problems because the inventory creates demand since the work-pool employees can also be absent. In common with all inventory problems there are two opposing costs. As the number of employees in the work pool increases the amount of idle time increases, since not all of the work-pool employees will be needed on each day. As the size of the work pool decreases, however, the probability, and the expected cost, of being short of workers increases. The objective will usually be the minimization of the total costs, which will require a balancing of these opposing costs.

Let us take as an example a machine shop which has 100 punch presses. The men who operate the presses are paid on a piece-work basis, but a press operator who is in the work pool and idle must be paid $2.50 per hour. The company estimates the cost of having a press idle for a day at $100. In order to solve the decision problem we need information about the demand for workers from the work pool. The company's records of the 100 regular press operators are analyzed to determine the probability that a given number of them will be absent on the same day. The following distribution is obtained:

NUMBER OF ABSENT EMPLOYEES	PROBABILITY
0	0.007
1	0.034
2	0.084
3	0.141
4	0.175
5	0.175
6	0.146
7	0.105
8	0.065
9	0.036
10	0.018
11	0.008
12	0.004
13	0.002
	1.000

The states of nature are the numbers of absent employees, and this distribution gives the probabilities. The strategies are the possible numbers of employees in the work pool. We know the objective, so all that is needed to complete the analysis of the decision problem is the determination of the payoff (total costs) for each state of nature and strategy, and then the calculation of the expected total cost for each strategy. However, the payoff matrix is too big to write out explicitly and we would like to cut down on the amount of calculation. This can be done since we know that the expected total costs are high for small numbers of employees in the work pool and high again for large numbers of work-pool employees. Therefore, we need only calculate the expected total cost for two adjoining strategies somewhere in the middle of the reasonable strategies and see which way the expected total cost is moving. If it is smaller for the larger number of employees then we continue in the same direction until the minimum expected total cost is found. If it is higher then we work in the other direction to find the minimum expected total cost.

The calculation of the payoffs for each cell of the matrix is simple. Consider, as an example, the strategy of having five employees in the work pool. If there are no absentees this will cost 5($20) = $100. If there is one absentee the company pays the work pool replacement on a piece rate basis, instead of the absent worker and so the single replacement costs nothing. The other four in the work pool are idle and cost $80. For five absentees the cost is zero. For six absentees the cost is $100 for one machine out of operation, and so on. We start our calculations of expected total costs with the strategy of having five employees in the work pool.

STATES OF NATURE

ABSENTEES:	0	1	2	3	4	5	6	7
PROBABILITY:	0.007	0.034	0.084	0.141	0.175	0.175	0.146	0.105
STRATEGIES								
5	$100	80	60	40	20	0	100	200
6	120	100	80	60	40	20	0	100
7	140	120	100	80	60	40	20	0
8	160	140	120	100	80	60	40	20

ABSENTEES:	8	9	10	11	12	13	EXPECTED TOTAL COST
PROBABILITY:	0.065	0.036	0.018	0.008	0.004	0.002	
STRATEGIES							
5	$300	400	500	600	700	800	$105.30
6	200	300	400	500	600	700	79.22
7	100	200	300	400	500	600	70.66
8	0	100	200	300	400	500	74.70

The expected total costs are calculated in the usual way. Since the expected total cost for maintaining six men in the work pool is less than that for maintaining five men in the work pool we continue our calculations in the same direction until the expected total cost begins to get larger. This occurs at the strategy of maintaining eight workers in the pool, so we know that the strategy of maintaining seven workers in the pool is the optimal strategy. We know this because the expected total costs of more than eight or less than five workers in the pool would be still larger.

The minimum-total-cost strategy, then, would seem to be to have seven workers in the pool. However, this may not be the optimal strategy, and the expected total costs are certainly wrong. The reason is that we have based our calculations on the probabilities of given numbers of absentees from 100 employees, whereas if we add seven employees in the work pool we will actually have 107. In short, we have not taken account of the fact, mentioned earlier, that in this problem the inventory itself increases demand because the work-pool employees may also be absent. This additional complexity can be handled mathematically, but we will use iterations of the above method in order to avoid introducing mathematical analysis which is beyond the general level we have been using.

The first thing we need is the probability distribution of the number of absentees for various total numbers of employees, including those in the work pool. This is easy to get by Monte Carlo methods or mathematically. The original distribution was obtained by taking a period of time, say one year, and then taking each of the 100 workers' employment records and marking his absences on the given days during the year. When this was completed, a straightforward count of the total absences each day gave our original distribution. Dividing the total number of absences by the total number of man-days gives the probability that a specific worker would be absent on a given day. In our case this probability is 0.05, or one day absent in twenty working days. It is now possible to add any desired number of workers to the original distribution by Monte Carloing each additional worker's absence or presence on each day, with the absence having a probability of 0.05. This procedure gives in our case the following probability distributions of number of absentees.

| | TOTAL NUMBER OF EMPLOYEES | | | |
| | 107 | 108 | 109 | 110 |
NUMBER OF ABSENT EMPLOYEES	PROBABILITIES			
0	0.005	0.005	0.004	0.004
1	0.025	0.024	0.024	0.022
2	0.068	0.066	0.064	0.062
3	0.121	0.119	0.116	0.113
4	0.162	0.160	0.158	0.156

	TOTAL NUMBER OF EMPLOYEES			
NUMBER OF	107	108	109	110
ABSENT EMPLOYEES	PROBABILITIES			
5	0.174	0.173	0.172	0.171
6	0.155	0.155	0.156	0.157
7	0.118	0.120	0.122	0.123
8	0.079	0.081	0.083	0.085
9	0.047	0.049	0.050	0.052
10	0.025	0.026	0.027	0.029
11	0.012	0.013	0.013	0.014
12	0.006	0.006	0.006	0.007
13	0.002	0.002	0.003	0.003
14	0.001	0.001	0.001	0.001
15			0.001	0.001
	1.000	1.000	1.000	1.000

With these probability distributions of the number of absent employees we can now solve the decision problem. First let us see what effect the inclusion of the seven work-pool employees in the absent-employees distribution has on our previous calculation. The calculation of the payoffs is exactly the same as before. The only thing that has changed is our estimation of the probabilities of the various states of nature. We have

STATES OF NATURE

ABSENT EMPLOYEES	0	1	2	3	4	5	6	7
PROBABILITY	0.005	0.025	0.068	0.121	0.162	0.174	0.155	0.118
STRATEGY 7:	$140	120	100	80	60	40	20	0

ABSENT EMPLOYEES	8	9	10	11	12	13	14	EXPECTED TOTAL COST
PROBABILITY	0.079	0.047	0.025	0.012	0.006	0.002	0.001	
STRATEGY 7:	$100	200	300	400	500	600	700	$74.46

As might be anticipated, the expected total cost has increased. This would be anticipated because the change in the probabilities takes the form of a decrease in the probabilities of a small number of absences and an increase in the probabilities of larger numbers of absences. We cannot use these same probabilities to calculate the expected total cost of maintaining eight employees in the work pool for the reason given before. Instead, we must use the probabilities for 108 employees. This gives

STATES OF NATURE

ABSENT EMPLOYEES	0	1	2	3	4	5	6	7
PROBABILITY	0.005	0.024	0.066	0.119	0.160	0.173	0.155	0.120
STRATEGY 8:	$160	140	120	100	80	60	40	20

ABSENT EMPLOYEES	8	9	10	11	12	13	14	TOTAL EXPECTED COST
PROBABILITY	0.081	0.049	0.026	0.013	0.006	0.002	0.001	
STRATEGY 8:	$0	100	200	300	400	500	600	$73.76

Since the expected total cost has decreased we must calculate the expected total cost for the strategy of mintaining nine workers in the work pool. We must, of course, use the probability distribution for 109 employees.

STATES OF NATURE

ABSENT EMPLOYEES	0	1	2	3	4	5	6	7
PROBABILITY	0.004	0.024	0.064	0.116	0.158	0.172	0.156	0.122
STRATEGY 9:	$180	160	140	120	100	80	60	40

ABSENT EMPLOYEES	8	9	10	11	12	13	14	15	EXPECTED TOTAL COST
PROBABILITY	0.083	0.050	0.027	0.013	0.006	0.003	0.001	0.001	
STRATEGY 9:	$20	0	100	200	300	400	500	600	$82.30

The expected total cost for this strategy increases, so we know that the optimal strategy is to maintain eight workers in the work pool. This strategy has an expected total cost of $73.76.

The change to take account of absences among the work-pool employees has changed the optimal strategy from the previous (and incorrect) seven to eight employees in the work pool. The original calculation, however, was not wasted since it enabled us to approximately locate the optimal strategy and thus spare ourselves unnecessary work in determining the probability distributions.

Finally, it may be noted that this decision problem is an example of a situation where the selection of a strategy affects the probabilities of the states of nature.

96. ABSENTEEISM

The company of the preceding example has an absentee problem which is costing it considerable sums of money. Its optimal strategy is to maintain eight employees in the work pool. This policy will cost the company $73.76 per day, $368.80 per week, or about $18,000 per year. Assuming a rather high discount factor of 20 per cent per year, the solution of the absentee problem would have a present worth of about $108,-000. This would require the complete elimination of absenteeism, which is obviously impossible, but the size of the amounts involved would indicate that the company could well afford to undertake some kind of remedial action. In this section we will discuss the kinds of information an executive would need in order to evaluate the decision problem of what, if anything, to do about absenteeism. We do not propose to solve the decision problem itself since a solution would depend upon the special circumstances of the company to a great degree. Besides which, the problem is too hard!

The first thing the executive would want to know would be what a specific degree of improvement would be worth to the company. The present rate of absence is 1 every 20 days. What would the company gain if it could be cut to 1 every 22 days, or 1 every 25 days? This information can be readily supplied, at the cost of some calculations. The first thing needed is the probability distribution of absences per day at different absence rates. This can be accomplished most easily by mathematical manipulations of the original, and actual, distribution. However, it can also be done by Monte Carlo methods. We will not present the details of the procedure here since we are not trying to solve a decision problem in this section. Once these distributions are available it is possible to use the procedure of the preceding section to determine the optimal strategy for any one of them. We calculate the following:

| | OPTIMAL STRATEGY: | | |
ABSENCE RATE	NUMBER IN POOL	COST PER DAY	COST PER YEAR
0.01	2	$32.70	$8,175
0.02	3	47.24	11,810
0.03	5	56.42	14,105
0.04	6	65.32	16,330
0.05	8	73.76	18,440

A graph of the costs per year is given in Figure 11.7. It will be noted that the points fall almost on a straight line from an absence rate of 0.02 (1 in 50 days) to a rate of 0.05 (1 in 20 days). We can summarize this interval by saying that a decrease in the absence rate of 0.001 will decrease the company's yearly expected cost by $221. The denominator of the absence ratio varies from about 27,000 man-days at 0.05 to about 25,750 man-days at 0.02 because of the differing numbers of employees in the work pool. However, to a sufficient approximation we can say that over this range a change of 0.001 in the ratio equals about 26 absences. Therefore, we conclude that in this range one absence costs the company about $8.50 ($221/26).

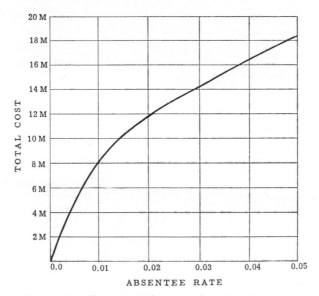

Figure 11.7 The cost of the optimal work pool strategy.

The important point about this cost of $8.50 per absence is the considerable difference between it and the common-sense cost per absence. "Common sense" would suggest that there are an average of 5.4 absences per day at a cost of $73.76 and that, therefore, the average cost per absence is $73.76/5.4 = $13.66. The reason that common sense fails is that a disproportionate amount of the total cost of absences occurs in the interval from 0 to 0.02 absences per working day. The common-sense cost would be correct if all absences could be eliminated, but this is obviously impossible. Therefore, the true value to the company must be that of eliminating *some* absences, and this value is given by our calculations. The error which could result from using the incorrect value for evaluating the economics of possible solutions is considerable.

The other major information the executive would need would be a distribution showing how the absences were distributed among the employees. A frequency distribution showing the number of employees with a given number of days' absence in a given time, say 250 working days, can easily be obtained from the employees' records. This distribution can be converted to a probability distribution and might look like this:

Days absence	Probability
0–4	0.26
5–9	0.21
10–14	0.16
15–19	0.15
20–24	0.09
25–29	0.06
30–34	0.04
35–39	0.02
40–44	0.01
	———
	1.00

The general shape of this distribution is quite likely to be found in data on absenteeism. It provides the framework within which a solution to the problem must operate. The worst 7 per cent of the employees account for 19.5 per cent of the absences, the worst 13 per cent account for 32.5 per cent of the absences, and the worst 22 per cent of the employees account for 48.3 per cent of the absences.

An obvious attempt to ameliorate the situation would be to offer a bonus for a good employment record with few absences. The difficulty is that such a bonus cannot be offered only to the workers with many absences. Besides being unjust this would have the effect of tempting some employees to increase their number of absences so they could subsequently qualify for the bonus. Therefore, it would have to be offered to all employees. Further, a bonus fails of its purpose if it sets a goal which most employees view as unattainable. Therefore it must set a reasonable goal. Suppose, for example, that the company offered a $50 bonus for every employee with 9 or fewer absences per year. They would immediately have to pay 47 employees $2350 with no improvement from the company's point of view, since that many employees are already below the stated limit. Now, what improvement may they expect? The bonus of $50 equals approximately 2½ days' wages. It is assumed that the workers could avoid being absent so much if they wanted to do so, else there would be no point in offering the bonus. This being so, the question must be asked as to how many voluntary absent days a worker will give up in order to get an additional 2½ days pay. Suppose he will give up 10 days of absence for the bonus. If all of the workers with between 10 and 19 days' absence move down to the 5–9 class the company will pay another 31 × $50 = $1550, or a total of $3900 in bonuses. In exchange it will cut the average number of days absent by $0.15(17 - 7) + 0.16 \cdot (12 - 7) = 2.30$ for a total saving of $2.30 \times 100 \times \$8.50 = \$1955$ and a net loss of $1945. Note that there is no reason to assume that the other workers will improve since they will view the bonus as either unattainable or undesirable. Obviously, one could make other assumptions about the classes of workers who would be tempted by the bonus, but in this example there is no need to consider them. If all the workers with more than 9 days' absence responded to the offer of the bonus by cutting their absences to 9 days the company would pay $5000 in bonuses and the average number of absences would be cut to $2(0.26) + 7(0.21) + 9(0.53) = 6.76$. The company would then save $(12.50 - 6.76) \times 100 \times \$8.50 = \$4879$, which is still a loss. The evident answer to this situation is to lower the amount of the bonus or require a smaller number of absences to get the bonus or both. But either of these steps will lower the inducement and, hence, the improvement. We conclude that there are serious difficulties in the way of this solution.

An alternative possible solution would be to utilize group pressure on the workers with large numbers of absences. This might be accomplished by organizing a competition among subgroups of workers for the lowest total absences with a bonus going to each month's winning group. If the plant is already divided into subgroups this approach immediately suggests itself. Some quantitative considerations are relevant here. The effectiveness of such a competition will depend on the degree to which the groups try to win and use group pressure on the workers with larger numbers of absences. This, in turn, will depend on the probability that the group could win if it tried. If the company can set up the groups especially for this competition it could ensure that every group started with the same average number of absences. But in this case the workers assigned to a group would not constitute, in a sociological sense, a real group, and would probably not function as one, to the detriment of the competition. Therefore, the company will ordinarily have to utilize whatever natural groupings may already exist, and this implies that the groups will be at relative advantages and disadvantages when the competition starts. Suppose, for example, that there are ten natural groups of ten workers each. We may assume that the workers are distributed at random among the groups with respect to number of absences. Then a typical grouping, obtained by Monte Carlo, would be

Group	Average absences
1	7.0
2	7.0
3	9.5
4	11.5
5	12.0
6	13.5
7	15.5
8	16.0
9	16.5
10	16.5

It may be noted parenthetically that this distribution shows the dangers of comparisons between extreme subgroups of one population. It would be easy for management to conclude that morale must be very bad in groups 9 and 10, as compared to groups 1 and 2. However, they are all from the same population, and the differences are due solely to sampling fluctuations. Our point here is that the same kinds of questions must be asked as in the case of individual bonuses. We will not repeat the line of reasoning again, but it is easy to evaluate the possible gains to the company on the basis of plausible assumptions about the group behavior with regard to the chance of winning the bonus. The possible advantage of the group incentive plan as compared to the individual incentive plan is that when a sufficient number of members of the group consider the incentive worthwhile the others who do not consider it to be worthwhile will nevertheless be obliged to work toward the common goal. In addition some group members with good absence records will try to improve them further. Thus, for example, if the majority of each group considers that one day off per year with pay is sufficient incentive to maintain the group's average number of absences at 9 or less, then the company would pay $2000 in incentives in order to save $4879 which is a total saving of $2879. A knowledge of group behavior would be required to formulate a successful group incentive plan.

Finally, we will mention one more of the many possible solutions to this difficult problem. It may have already occurred to the reader that one solution would be to fire all employees with more than some given number of absences. At least three difficulties may exist with regard to this solution:

1. Other workers may not be obtainable because of a generally high level of employment or because of a small labor market.

2. The absenteeism problem may be brought about by sociological factors such that the replacements will be just as bad.

3. The workers' union may prevent it.

Of these we can consider only the simplest one: the third difficulty. If this were the problem the company could try to negotiate with the union in order to have the right to fire all employees with more than 29 days' absence in one calendar year, to take one of the many possibilities as an example. Usually the company would have to trade something in exchange. From our table we see that if all the stated employees were fired and replaced by employees as good as the remainder there would be an average of 10.82 absences per man per year, $(1/0.93)(12.50) - 32(.04) - 37(0.02) - 42(0.01)$. The company would save $(12.50 - 10.82) \times 100 \times \$8.50 = \$1428$.

ws that the company cannot afford to trade a wage increase
$0.01 per hour for $40 \times 50 \times 100 = 200,000$ man-hours would
Perhaps some fringe benefit of importance to the union can
d which might make the trade an economical one. In any
clear that there are sharp economic limits to any such negotia-

solution to this decision problem has been suggested. Our purpose
in this section has been only to illustrate how calculations based on available information can be used to evaluate possible solutions to decision
problems. We have taken this excursion into an uncharted decision
problem in order to try and illustrate how some quantitative considerations can be applied in almost a qualitative way in evaluating possible
solutions. This difficult problem should have abundantly demonstrated
that not all decision problems can be easily fitted into a payoff matrix.
But we hope it has also shown that some guideposts can be found even
in such a case as this.

97. HOTEL RESERVATIONS

Hotels, in common with other organizations which offer advance reservations, have a problem involving the so-called no-shows. These are the
people who neither arrive to take their reservations nor notify the hotel
of cancellation. Organizations which have received an advance deposit
can inflict a penalty on the no-shows—airlines are a case in point—but
hotels do not customarily receive any advance deposits. Hotels attempt
to protect themselves against this behavior by only holding reservations
until some stated hour, but this procedure has its difficulties. The hotel
must hold the reservations long enough to afford sufficient convenience to
its customers and, by the same token, this is often too long to permit the
hotel to rent the rooms of the cancelled reservations. The difficulty only
arises during the busy season, when the hotel could otherwise fill all of
its rooms, but this is precisely the season which accounts for most of the
year's income so hotels would like to find a solution to this problem.

One possible approach would be to accept more reservations than there
are available rooms. The intention behind this strategy is obvious.
Ideally, the hotel would like to have just enough reservations so that the
rooms are all filled after the no-show reservations are deducted. It is
evident that this is a kind of inventory problem, but with a difference.
The hotel maintains an inventory of reservations which represent the potential customers for its rooms. In other words, the hotel is maintaining
an inventory of demand for its fixed supply of rooms. The actual demand which materializes will depend on the percentage of no-shows. In

common with all other inventory problems there are opposing costs connected with the size of inventory. If the inventory is too small there will be vacant rooms, with a corresponding loss of revenue. If the inventory is too large there will be a cost associated with some intensely dissatisfied customers who have been turned away despite their reservations. The strategies in the decision problem are evidently the various numbers of reservations which can be taken, and the states of nature are the various numbers of customers who may arrive. To solve the decision problem we need the costs, the payoffs, and the probabilities of the various states of nature.

Let us first consider the costs. Suppose that an average customer stays for nine days (determined from hotel records) at $30 per day. This is $270, and the hotel's net profit is $27 or a rate of 10 per cent. The hotel records show that a guest in any one year has a probability of 0.60 of returning to the hotel in the subsequent year. This means that the probability that the guest will return for i years is $(0.60)^i$. From this information we can calculate the expected lifetime income from a customer. The first time he arrives he will contribute profit of $27. He has a probability of 0.60 of returning a second time so his expected contribution to profit for the second time will be $0.60($27) = 16.20. This continues indefinitely, thus:

$$\text{Lifetime value} = \$27 + 0.60\,(27) + 0.36\,(27) + 0.216\,(27)$$

$$+ \ldots + (0.60)^i\,(27) + \ldots = \frac{\$27}{0.4} = \$67.50$$

However, this lifetime value is not worth $67.50 to the hotel, because if the hotel had to buy this income stream now it would pay less than $67.50 in order to take account of the fact that it can earn 10 per cent per year on its capital. We must, in short, discount the lifetime value by 10 per cent per year in order to find its present worth to the hotel. This gives

$$\text{Present worth: } \$27 + \frac{0.60\,(27)}{1.10} + \frac{0.36\,(27)}{1.21} + \ldots$$

$$+ \frac{(0.60)^i\,(27)}{(1.10)^i} + \ldots = \frac{\$27}{0.444} = \$60.81$$

This, then, is the present worth of the lifetime value of a customer. Now, the hotel will undoubtedly lose the entire amount for any customer who is turned away despite his reservation. He will be so indignant that it is most unlikely he will ever return. But will the hotel lose still more because an irate customer will warn others not to come? The hotel management thinks not. Most of their customers are gained by advertising rather than by personal recommendations. In any event, they intend to be so apologetic in such circumstances and to make such efforts to find the customer a room in another hotel that they hope to assuage his indignation to some extent. The loss of $60.81, then, represents the overstock inventory cost. The other cost is easier to evaluate. Since the overwhelming majority of expenses are fixed with reference to any one room, the cost of a vacant room owing to a no-show is assumed to be simply $30. These are the two opposing costs.

The probabilities of the states of nature depend on the demand distribution, as in every inventory problem. In this case demand depends on the probability of a no-show and, of course, on the total number of reservations. Hotel records indicate that 20 per cent of their reservations are no-shows. This means that if we are given the total number of reservations we can use the binomial probability distribution to calculate the probabilities of the various possible numbers of no-shows. Suppose the hotel has 12 rooms which will be vacant on a subsequent night. The decision problem is to determine how many reservations to accept for these 12 rooms. We know that the hotel will accept at least 12 since otherwise it would always have vacant rooms. How many more than 12 should it accept? First, let us determine the probabilities of the various numbers of no-shows for various numbers of total reservations. For R reservations we use the binomial probability distribution as follows:

Probability of i no-shows $=$

$$\frac{R(R-1)(R-2)\ldots(R-i+1)}{i(i-1)(i-2)\ldots(2)(1)}(0.20)^{i}(0.80)^{R-i}$$

This expression looks more complicated than it really is, and it is a very useful means of calculating probabilities of states of nature in various kinds of inventory, and other, decision problems. Let us illustrate its use. Consider $R = 13$ reservations. We have

$$\text{Probability of 1 no-show} = \frac{13}{1}(0.20)^{1}(0.80)^{12} = 0.17867$$

$$\text{Probability of 2 no-shows} = \frac{13 \times 12}{2 \times 1}(0.20)^{2}(0.80)^{11} = 0.26801$$

Proceeding in this way we can calculate the following probability distributions which we will need in our subsequent calculations. [Note that in the binomial distribution the probability of zero no-shows is always simply $(0.80)^{R}$.]

No-shows	PROBABILITY			
	$R = 13$	$R = 14$	$R = 15$	$R = 16$
0	0.055	0.044	0.035	0.028
1	0.179	0.155	0.133	0.113
2	0.268	0.250	0.231	0.211
3	0.246	0.250	0.250	0.246
4	0.153	0.172	0.187	0.200
5	0.069	0.086	0.103	0.120
6	0.023	0.032	0.043	0.055
7	0.006	0.009	0.014	0.020
8	0.001	0.002	0.003	0.006
9			0.001	0.001
	1.000	1.000	1.000	1.000

We have rounded the probabilities off to three places for convenience. These are the probabilities of the various states of nature. The costs were determined above and it is easy to calculate the payoffs. Consider $R = 13$ reservations. If there are zero no-shows there is one reservation too many and the hotel loses \$60.81. If there is one no-show there is no loss. If there are two no-shows the hotel has one vacant room and loses \$30. Proceeding similarly we have the following for strategies $R = 13$, $R = 14$, $R = 15$:

STATES OF NATURE

No-shows:	0	1	2	3	4	5	6	7	8	9	Ex-PECTED COST
PROBABILITY:	0.055	0.179	0.268	0.246	0.153	0.069	0.023	0.006	0.001		
STRATEGY: $R = 13$	\$60.81	0	30	60	90	120	150	180	210		\$52.93
PROBABILITY:	0.044	0.155	0.250	0.250	0.172	0.086	0.032	0.009	0.002		
STRATEGY: $R = 14$	\$121.62	60.81	0	30	60	90	120	150	180		\$45.89
PROBABILITY:	0.035	0.133	0.231	0.250	0.187	0.103	0.043	0.014	0.003	0.001	
STRATEGY: $R = 15$	\$182.43	121.62	60.81	0	30	60	90	120	150	180	\$54.59

Since this expected cost is larger than that for $R = 14$ we know that the minimum expected cost is that of the strategy of accepting 14 reservations for the 12 rooms. The expected cost of this strategy is \$45.89.

These calculations would be much too onerous if the number of rooms was much larger than we used in this example. Fortunately, mathematical methods can be used to handle such cases quickly and without much work, though these methods are beyond the scope of this book.

PROBLEMS

1. In our work-pool example we calculated the payoffs for each cell in a straight-forward manner. But it is easy to make mistakes in payoffs.
   (a) What would happen to the payoff if the workers were paid salaries?
   (b) Compare the payoffs here to problem 3 of Chapter 10 (p. 314). What is the difference?

2. In the hotel-reservation problem:
   (a) Calculate the expected cost of the strategy of accepting 12 reservations for the 12 rooms. (*Note:* you do not have to calculate the probability distribution of states of nature in order to do this.)
   (b) If the strategy of accepting 12 reservations is used we can presume that the hotel is ascribing a value of more than $60.81 to the cost of losing a customer. What is the minimum such value which it could use which would make the strategy $R = 12$ the optimal one?
   (c) Calculate the expected cost for $R = 16$. (The necessary probability distribution is given in the table in the text.)

3. Many companies have stenographic pools to handle all dictation and typing required by their executives. On the one hand this saves money by cutting down the total number of typists and/or stenographers required. On the other hand this eliminates all, or the majority, of private secretaries for the executives. Since a private secretary is often considered to be a major symbol of a certain degree of status many executives intensely dislike such pools. How would you analyze the decision problem "To pool or not to pool"?
   (a) How would you get rough estimates of the money savings?
   (b) How does size of the company affect the problem?
   (c) Could executives be split into two classes: those using the pool and those having private secretaries? How would you draw the line?

4. The idea of status seems simple but it is difficult to define satisfactorily. We will assume that status is *solely* a function of position in the organizational hierarchy. Suppose an organization has seven top executives, and consider the following three structures:

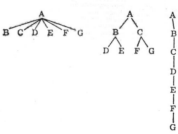

   (a) How would you define status? (Try to assign some kind of numerical measure.)
   (b) Which structure has the greatest total status (for all executives)?
   (c) Is the status of A different in the three cases?
   (d) Let us assume that executives of the second level hope to get increases in status during their professional life. Assume that a vacancy at the top level has a probability of $\frac{1}{4}$ of being filled outside the organization and that the remaining $\frac{3}{4}$ is divided equally among the subordinates of the immediately lower level. What structure gives the largest expected status for an executive of the second level?

(e) Suppose the company has a total amount of $210,000 which it can pay these executives. How would you set the salary limitations for the various positions in the three structures? Are the salaries you assigned related to status as you defined it? If so, which is the cause and which is the effect or what is the relationship, if not causal?

5. In our work-pool example we used a mathematical method for determining the probabilities of the states of nature for different numbers of employees in the work pool. This method depends on the fact that the probability that a given number of employees is absent is often given by the Poisson probability distribution. Let N be the total number of employees and let r be the absence rate per day; then the probability that K employees are absent on one day is given by $(e^{-Nr})(Nr)^K/K!$, where $e = 2.7183$ is a mathematical constant and $(K!) = K(K-1)(K-2) \ldots (2)(1)$. By using this equation we can calculate the probabilities of the various states of nature for different numbers of employees in the work pool. Suppose that a company has 50 machines and an absence rate of $r = 0.04$. The employees are paid $2.50 per hour and the company estimates the cost of one machine's being idle for one day at $60. Determine the optimal work-pool strategy.

[For convenience here are some relevant values of e^{-Nr}:

$e^{-2} = 0.13534$ $e^{-2.12} = 0.12003$ $e^{-2.24} = 0.10646$

$e^{-2.04} = 0.13003$ $e^{-2.16} = 0.11533$ $e^{-2.28} = 0.10228$

$e^{-2.08} = 0.12493$ $e^{-2.20} = 0.11080$ $e^{-2.32} = 0.09827$

Note that $(0!) = 1$, by definition.]

6. The example of sequencing machine maintenance with two crews and eight machines resulted in an optimal sequence with 11 idle hours for crew B. Assume that there are five men in crew B and that they receive $3.50 per hour.
   (a) If the previous sequence followed was: a, b, c, d, e, f, g, h, how much was saved by the sequencing study?
   (b) Assuming that each man does an equal share of the work, what result occurs if an additional man is added to group B?

7. A company has four departments which are to be modernized during the plant's annual summer-vacation shutdown. The work is to proceed in three stages: A, install new lighting fixtures and other equipment; B, plaster walls and make carpentry repairs; C, paint walls, ceilings, machines, and so on. The necessary sequence of the operations is A–B–C. The superintendent of maintenance decides on the size of the crews and schedules them as follows:

> First to be serviced: Department 2
> Second to be serviced: Department 3
> Third to be serviced: Department 4
> Fourth to be serviced: Department 1
> Size of crew A: 8 men
> Size of crew B: 6 men
> Size of crew C: 12 men

For the stated crew sizes, the hours required for servicing are given by the chart below.

	DEPARTMENT				TOTAL CREW TIME
	1	2	3	4	
Crew A	20	25	45	25	115 hours
Crew B	10	15	5	15	45 hours
Crew C	30	20	35	30	115 hours

The plant is shut down for a two-week period which allows 128 hours, including the use of Saturdays, to complete the job.

(a) If the superintendent's schedule is followed will the job be completed in time?

(b) How much idle time results from the superintendent's schedule?

(c) Is there a better schedule which can be followed?

(d) What happens to the optimal schedule if each of the crews is doubled in size?

(e) What happens if crew B is halved in size?

8. The company which we discussed in the dividend example in this chapter begins to experience the effects of a rapidly expanding market. As a result, the rate of return on its investment for expansion shifts upward. The following table gives the new rate-of-return schedule.

AMOUNT REINVESTED	RATE OF RETURN
$0–99	0.80
100–199	0.75
200–299	0.70
300–399	0.65
400–499	0.60
500–	0.55

Using the amount, $A_0 = 500$, as before, determine the optimum dividend policy for $N = 1$ and $N = 2$.

TABLE OF RANDOM NUMBERS

96268	11860	83699	38631	90045	69696	48572	05917	51905	10052
03550	59144	59468	37984	77892	89766	86489	46619	50263	91136
22188	81205	99699	84260	19693	36701	43233	62719	53117	71153
63759	61429	14043	49095	84746	22018	19014	76781	61086	90216
55006	17765	15013	77707	54317	48862	53823	52905	70754	68212
81972	45644	12600	01951	72166	52682	97598	11955	73018	23528
06344	50136	33122	31794	86423	58037	36065	32190	31367	96007
92363	99784	94169	03652	80824	33407	40837	97749	18364	72666
96083	16943	89916	55159	62184	86208	09764	20244	88388	98675
92993	10747	08985	44999	36785	65035	65933	77378	92339	96454
95083	70292	50394	61044	65591	09774	16216	63561	59751	78771
77308	60721	96057	86031	83148	34970	30892	53489	44999	18021
11913	49624	28510	27311	61586	28576	43092	69971	44220	80410
70648	47484	05095	92335	55299	27161	64486	71307	85883	69610
92771	99203	37786	81142	44271	36433	31726	74879	89348	76886
78816	20975	13043	55921	82774	62745	48338	88348	61211	88074
79934	35392	56097	87613	94627	63622	08110	16611	88599	02890
64698	83376	87524	36897	17215	74339	69856	43622	22567	11518
44212	12995	03581	37618	94851	63020	65348	55857	91742	79508
82292	00204	00579	70630	37136	50922	83387	15014	51838	81760
08692	87237	87879	01629	72184	33853	95144	67943	19345	03469
67927	76855	50702	78555	97442	78809	40575	79714	06201	34576
62167	94213	52971	85974	68067	78814	40103	70759	92129	46716
45828	45441	74220	84157	23241	49332	23646	09390	13032	51569
01164	35307	26526	80335	58090	85871	07205	31749	40571	51755
29283	31581	04359	45538	41435	61103	32428	94042	39971	63678
19868	49978	81699	84904	50163	22625	07845	71308	00859	87984
14294	93587	55960	23149	07370	65065	06580	46285	07884	83928
77410	52195	29459	23032	83242	89938	40510	27252	55565	64714
36580	06921	35675	81645	60479	71035	99380	59759	42161	93440
07780	18093	31258	78156	07871	20369	53947	08534	39433	57216
07548	08454	36674	46255	80541	42903	37366	21164	97516	66181
22023	60448	69344	44260	90570	01632	21002	24413	04671	05665
20827	37210	57797	34660	32510	71558	78228	42304	77197	79168
47802	79270	48805	59480	88092	11441	96016	76091	51823	94442
76730	86591	18978	25479	77684	88439	35112	26052	57112	91653
26439	02903	20935	76297	15290	84688	74002	09467	41111	19194
32927	83426	07848	59327	44422	53372	27823	25417	27150	21750
51484	05286	77103	47284	05578	88774	15293	50740	07932	87633
45142	96804	92834	26886	70002	96643	36008	02239	93563	66429
12760	96106	89348	76127	17058	37181	74001	43869	28377	80923
15564	38648	02147	03894	97787	35234	44302	41672	12408	90168
71051	34941	55384	70709	11646	30269	60154	28276	48153	23122
42742	08817	82579	19505	26344	94116	86230	49139	32644	36545
59474	97752	77124	79579	65448	87700	54002	81411	57988	57437
12581	18211	61713	73962	87212	55624	85675	33961	63272	17587
00278	75089	20673	37438	92361	47941	62056	94104	45502	79159
59317	31861	62559	30925	23055	70922	47195	29827	68065	95409
59220	42448	70881	33687	53575	54599	69525	76424	98778	10459
00670	32157	15877	87120	13857	23979	38922	62421	03043	19602

PART 4

THE EXECUTIVE
AND OPERATIONS RESEARCH

Chapter twelve

Evaluation of the Problem

The basic plan of this book is indicated by the titles of the four parts. Our first part dealt with executives and decisions and tried to show some of the major features of the host of decision problems with which the executive must cope if he is to successfully fulfill his function. Our second part dealt with decisions and operations research. Here we tried to present an over-all view of the way in which operations research could contribute to the clarification or resolution of decision problems. The third part was devoted to actual decision problems of some degree of generality. We tried to show how one can work one's way through to a solution of some of these decision problems by careful analysis of their various features. In other cases one can only gain some additional insights into the decision problem. But it has been our thesis that the decision-maker will always profit from a rational approach to his decision problems.

These three parts have set the stage for the concluding part of the book: the executive and operations research. Several questions remain to be discussed. First, granted the general usefulness of operations research in decision problems, it still does not by any means follow that the executive should call in operations research on every one of his decision problems. When, then, should he? This is the subject of Chapter 12. Chapter 12 will demonstrate the executive's need for a kind of broad-gauge understanding of the methods and approaches of operations research which he is unlikely to have received from the earlier parts of the book. So, and second, it is the purpose of Chapter 13 to provide this overview of operations research. Finally, and third, certain problems involving the implementation and control of operations-research solutions merit the executive's attention. Chapter 14 provides a brief discussion of these problems.

98. WHAT IS A PROBLEM?

We have no intention of trying to completely define what a problem is. The depth of that question is too great for us to attempt to sound it. We will be content to mention only some aspects of the question which are relevant to our future argument.

There is considerable agreement among people on some of the general characteristics of problems. Very often a problem results from, or can be phrased in terms of, some of the obvious questions.—Why should this be done? Why should this be done that way? How can this be done? How should this be done? When should this be done? Who should do this?—These questions, and hundreds of others like them, are problem-pointers. They indicate the possible existence of a problem. But by no means do they demonstrate the real existence of a problem, because we usually use the word *problem* when someone is coming to grips with one or more of these questions and is endeavoring to answer the question, or solve the problem. Generally, we recognize that the same questions can be asked simply from "idle curiosity" and we reserve the word *problem* for cases of "busy curiosity."

Frequently we refer to problems when the person involved is not aware there is any problem at all. For example, most businessmen would maintain that the president of a company that was steadily losing its share of the market had a problem. And they would maintain this even though the president might not know that the problem existed because a rising total market gave his company increasing sales. Of course, they would wonder how he could not know it—but that, for us, is another problem. Similarly, most accountants would hold that a small restaurant owner had a problem if the ratio of his liquid assets to his current liabilities was less than 10 per cent—even if the restaurant owner had never heard of this particular ratio. But in any such use of *problem* it is clear that somebody must recognize the problem even if not the person involved. Perhaps we can say that this use of *problem* implies that the person involved *should* be coming to grips with it.

One cannot come to grips with a problem until he is aware of it as a problem. This awareness of a problem, then, is the first prerequisite to dealing with it.

How does one become aware of a problem? There are obviously a multitude of ways, and we do not propose to catalogue them all. But it will be worth mentioning a few of the more common ways.

First, sometimes we become aware of a problem because reality is so obstreperous that it literally hits us head-on with the problem and there is no conceivable way that we could avoid being aware of it. Examples of this kind of awareness are, unfortunately, particularly numerous in terms of national problems. Thus, only the erosion of millions of acres of farmland leads to an awareness of the problem of soil conservation. Or the devastation of a hurricane is required before we become aware of the problem of an adequate storm warning system. There are also many examples in business problems. The executive who is not aware of the problem posed by a new competitive product until his sales slump to the vanishing point is one example. But we do not mean to imply that all such problems are so catastrophic in their effects. An executive might not become aware of the problems attendant upon an increasing size of organization until he is in the middle of them, but the effect of the executive's obtuseness may only be unnecessary inefficiency and wastage. When the consequences are serious, however, becoming aware of a problem in this way can be extremely costly. The attempts to cope with the problem must be on an emergency basis and there is no time for careful analysis. Such a situation can only result in a heightening of all the difficulties that surround the efforts to solve a problem even in calmer circumstances.

Second, some kinds of problems are highlighted by our way of looking at reality and we are always watching for them. We have called our ways of looking at reality our "models" of reality; we are now saying that our models of reality generally put some kinds of problems into bold relief. An outstanding example is the business executive's accounting model of his business. The accounting model is likely to call the executive's attention quickly to problems signaled by sales drops, unit cost increases, higher inventory investments, and a host of similar problems. And this problem-pointing characteristic of models deserves to be emphasized. The layman can be hard put to distinguish between costs and expenses. As a result he is unlikely to notice (become aware of) many problems which anyone familiar with the accounting model would be watching for. But there is a converse to this advantage of models which also deserves emphasis. This is that too great use of any one model is likely to lead to that philosophical error we called hypostatization—the confusion of our model with reality. A microscope is an excellent device for looking at bacteria but useless for seeing stars. A telescope is fine for the stars but not suitable for seeing bacteria. And neither is it any good for reading books. For adequately seeing the universe we need all three: microscopes, telescopes, and good vision. A person who looked at everything through a microscope would get a rather distorted picture of the universe.

It is precisely the same with our models: they can function as blinders instead of as aids to better vision. This is one of the greatest ills that minds are heir to. Classical economic theory is a good example. The classical economists had a model of the economic activities of society which included only market-place phenomena. They were so delighted with this model that they resolutely refused to admit the relevance to economics of social problems that were a direct consequence of economic policies. The indefatigable persistence with which some of the classical economists adhered to this position can only be marveled at. Fortunately, the labor of subsequent economists has resulted in economic models that more adequately reflect reality. In the business world the same kind of thing can happen. It will be useful to consider the accounting model in this regard. Inventory carrying charges are highlighted, but there is no entry for lost profit because of lost sales nor is there an entry for the loss of customer goodwill because of out-of-stocks. All kinds of direct costs are emphasized, but there is no place for opportunity costs. Such examples can be multiplied easily. We are not criticizing the accounting model for not doing something it is not intended to do. Rather, we want to point out that an executive who leaned too exclusively on this one model would miss problems that he should be aware of. What would happen? His organization would continue along its path until reality brought him to a sharp realization of the problems— our first method. At that time it might be too late for satisfactory remedial action. The executive must always remember that any model should serve as a problem-pointer, not a problem-blinder.

Third, the awareness of a problem can result from the fact that someone has become aware of the problem and presents his discovery with such irresistible logic that others become aware through his efforts. Such contributions to our awareness of problems frequently require creative genius of a high order. As an example, we can cite Frederick W. Taylor's discovery of the problems of production. The success with which he promulgated his discovery is well known. Sometimes it is a question of converting "idle curiosity" into "busy curiosity"—changing a problem-pointing question into a problem. And in this conversion the state occasionally takes a hand by means of legislation. Thus, a state may make employer contributions to unemployment insurance depend on the amount of use of the insurance by the employees. This is a pointed, and effective, way of making the employer treat the variability in his employment as a problem rather than simply considering it to be an unfortunate accident of his line of business.

Fourth, and last, one can become so problem-oriented that when no problems can be discovered by any other means one goes looking for them. Such a search is usually predicated on the proposition that "things can't be perfect." While history provides ample evidence that this proposition is true, it is not necessarily a basis for problem-searching. The belief that such a search will uncover problems is, in the case of organizations, only too often justified by the fact that the searching process creates problems which are then discovered. Such self-justifying processes provide continual reasons for their own existence without necessarily contributing to the organizational well-being. A number of our subsequent remarks will be relevant to the question of when one can reasonably initiate a search for problems.

Such, then, are some of the major ways in which one can become aware of problems. But it is obvious that not all persons view the same things as problems even when they are faced with the same kinds of situations. Some persons will come to grips with the problem and attempt to solve it. In other words, they will treat it as a problem. Other persons will not make any effort to solve the problem. For them there is only a problem-pointing question, not a problem in our sense of the word. We must now consider the reasons for this difference.

99. PROBLEMS AND OBJECTIVES

Let us consider a particular kind of situation which arises in a variety of circumstances. A bank manager observes the formation of long waiting lines in front of the open teller windows; the manager of a government tax office observes long waiting lines of citizens desiring assistance in preparing their tax statements; a doctor observes his waiting room filled with prospective patients. Now, the reactions of the three observers of this phenomenon are likely to be quite different. The bank manager will probably order additional windows to be opened, if any are available. If there are none available and the situation is repeated he will probably recognize it as a problem and treat it as such. In this event he will consider possible strategies such as redesigning the bank to get more teller windows, expanding, opening a branch office, relocating. In short, he will probably treat this situation as a genuine decision problem and take some suitable action to resolve it.

The manager of the tax office is much less likely to view the same situation as a problem. He will certainly take any available steps equivalent to opening additional teller windows, but he is not likely to view the repetition of the situation as indicating a problem with which he must deal. Instead, he might well view the queues as legitimate punishment for the dilatory citizens who waited till the last minute to fill out their forms. And the citizens themselves probably accept it as such.

The doctor will probably not have the equivalent of any additional windows to open, and he is unlikely to view the situation as a problem at all. On the contrary, he is likely to view the waiting line as highly desirable. He can reason that the waiting line is proof to every patient that he is a good doctor and confirmation of the patient's choice in coming to him. Furthermore, the patients themselves may well view the waiting line in this way.

From the standpoint of queuing theory we can say that the doctor and the manager of the tax office are placing extremely high values on their own time and very low value on the time of the people waiting. The bank manager, however, puts a high value on the time of his customers. Wherein is the difference? The bank manager could use precisely the same arguments as the other two. Like the manager of the tax office he could say that the waiting lines are a form of punishment for those customers who insist on coming to the bank from 12:00 to 1:00. If they would distribute themselves over the whole day they wouldn't have to wait. And like the doctor he could say that the waiting lines prove to his customers that it is a good bank and confirm the wisdom of selecting that bank. But he uses neither of these arguments. Instead, he views the situation as a problem to be solved. Why?

Clearly the answer to this question is that the objectives are different in the three cases. There are other differences, but this appears to be the most important reason for the differing responses to the same situation. The doctor will not view the waiting line as a problem but rather its absence would be a problem. The doctor's objective is to have a sufficient number of patients, and by his argument the waiting line can contribute to his achievement of his objective. His argument may be wrong but he has considerable empirical data which indicate that the waiting line is no impediment to his achievement of his objective. Therefore, he can, and does, ignore it as a problem. The tax-office manager has a variety of objectives which have no reference to the waiting line. One of his objectives is, of course, to provide assistance to the taxpayer but this is of the nature of a free service. If the citizen will not come early and if the citizen wants this free service rather than paying for the advice of a tax consultant, then he must wait. Therefore, the waiting line is not a problem. The objective of the tax-office manager is, so to speak. a reasonable availability of advice for reasonable citizens. There is no objective for "unreasonable" citizens. The bank manager, like the doctor, has an objective of getting the maximum number of customers. He has many competitors who will be delighted to have his customers, and he thinks that long waiting lines is one of the quickest ways to give his customers to them. Faced with the doctor's argument he would reply that the patients' payoff from having a superb doctor as compared to having a good doctor is large so the patient will wait, since the waiting confirms the quality of the doctor. But the bank customer has no such large payoff from one bank as compared to another so he will not wait—particularly since, if anything, the waiting is a sign of a poor bank rather than a good one. Therefore, the bank manager views waiting lines as impinging directly on his objective and he treats the situation as a problem.

This latter kind of attitude is generally involved in our selection of the problems with which we try to cope. First and foremost are those problems which have a direct effect on our objectives. We usually become aware of them first and act on them first. This is natural because we are objective-oriented. The models we find most congenial and most useful, and the ones we use the most, are those which help to point out the problems that have the greatest and the most direct effect on our major objectives. Problems that have a smaller or more indirect effect on our primary objectives are not noticed so quickly and are not acted upon until priority has been given to problems with a more direct or larger effect.

To say that a starving, dirty man will concern himself with his hunger before he worries about his cleanliness is not to say very much. But this is not what we are saying here. The hungry man has two objectives, food and soap, and he is simply giving precedence to his more basic objective. We are not here discussing the question of multiple objectives, which we covered earlier in the book. Rather, we are considering *problems*, which may have an immediate, direct effect on our objectives or which may have an indirect effect.

No sharp line of demarcation can be drawn between "indirect" and "smaller." However, "smaller" effect on our objectives does not seem to convey all that we mean by an "indirect" effect. For example, the entry of a local competitive product in one of our sales regions will have a smaller effect on our objective (maximum sales, maximum profit, and so on) than will the entry of a nationally distributed competitive product in all of our sales regions. But both of these effects are direct ones. On the other hand, an increasing labor turnover in our plant will have a more indirect effect on the objective of maximizing share of the market, although it could conceivably have a larger effect. This same problem of increasing labor turnover would have a direct effect on the objective of maximizing profit. A problem relating to financial structure would have an indirect effect on most objectives but, perhaps, a direct effect on the objective of paying a given, or maximum dividend to stockholders.

As one would expect, the directness or indirectness of the effect of a problem on an objective depends on the objective as well as the problem. The difficulty involved in distinguishing between direct and indirect effects is illustrated by a problem in product quality. A slight decrease in product quality would probably have only an indirect effect on most objectives but a large decrease would undoubtedly have a direct effect.

However, it is not necessary for us to attempt to define precisely the difference between direct and indirect effects. It is evident that there is some difference, even if only one of degree. We want simply to point out that awareness of problems depends on their relatedness to the objectives. Generally, problems with a direct effect on objectives will be noted and acted upon before problems with an indirect effect. And, of course, problems with a larger effect are likely to be observed and acted upon before problems with a smaller effect.

Granting that this is the case, we can observe in the business world that there are differences in the procedures followed by different companies in dealing with problems. And this remains true even when the problems have similar kinds and sizes of effects on the various companies' objectives. We must next consider why this is so.

100. PROBLEMS AND SIZE OF COMPANIES

The question we want to consider in this section can be typified by an example. Company A produces electronic equipment for a local market. It is small and profitable. The company has a problem situation in the form of too high turnover in the plant labor force. Having become aware of the problem the plant manager calls a meeting of his foremen and discusses the problem with them for an hour. Finding no answers, he closes the meeting by ordering the installation of a suggestion box. Then he returns hastily to other, more pressing problems. Company B produces electronic equipment for the national market. It is large and profitable and it, too, has a problem in the form of too high turnover in the plant labor force. Having become aware of the problem the vice-president in charge of production calls in a team of consultants which includes industrial psychologists, sociologists, and an applied anthropologist. After a reasonably lengthy investigation they will probably make some good recommendations as to how the problem can be resolved. The responses of the two companies to the same problem are totally different. Now, the kind of situation typified by this example is so common that similar examples are probably familiar to anyone with more than a nodding acquaintance with the business world. Our question is: Why is there this difference in response to identical problems?

The answer to the question is fairly obvious. Speaking generally, it is that the returns that result from solving a problem tend to be proportional to the income, sales, or profit of the company, while the cost of solving the problem tends to be a fixed amount. We want first to justify this answer and then to discuss how it affects company attitudes towards problems.

The first part of the answer is that the returns that result from solving a problem tend to be proportional to some measure of the company involvement in the area of the problem. Such measures are income, sales, operating costs, profit, and the like. This requires little demonstration since it is reasonably apparent. A company with extra labor costs of $100,000 per year owing to high turnover may save $25,000 or $50,000 from cutting the amount of turnover. But they certainly can't save more than $100,000. Another company with an extra labor cost of $1,000,000 owing to high turnover could easily save more than $100,000 by cutting the amount of turnover. Furthermore, comparable amounts of improvement in the two companies would probably save comparable percentages of the respective total extra costs. This is what is meant by the statement that returns should be proportional to the measure of the company involvement in the problem area. The measure of involvement here is the extra cost owing to the high turnover. And lest it be objected that this measure wouldn't be known let us hasten to add that the same conclusion would follow if total labor costs were used as the measure. The same kind of argument applies to most kinds of company problems. The solution of a marketing problem might increase sales by any of a considerable range of amounts but the increase would generally be proportional to the sales. A company with ten times the annual sales of another company that solved the same problem would probably get around ten times the amount of return in sales units, or about the same percentage return. It is reasonable to say that it is the exceptions to this statement that need explanation rather than the statement itself.

The second part of the answer is that the cost of solving a problem tends to be a fixed amount. This requires justification because it is certainly an overgeneralization and is false in some cases. Nonetheless, it is generally a reasonable approximation to the facts. The important word is "tends"—we are not stating an equation. The major reason why the cost of solving a problem tends to be a fixed amount is that the amounts of information and analysis required are more nearly a function of the problem than they are of the size of the organization that has the problem. Consider an analysis of an inventory problem as an example. A small firm may have two- or three thousand items in inventory whereas a large firm may have 200,000. But what will be typically required, in either case, will be a careful analysis of a relatively small selection of items. Once an inventory system has been worked out it will generally be up to the company personnel, with a little coaching, to get the system installed on all the items. Much of the total time spent in analysis will be used in careful studies of the company's special circumstances and needs. This represents a general cost of the study which will be applicable regardless of the number of items studied. Add to this the fact that a fair amount of the time will be spent in establishing the necessary working relationships and channels of communication. The result is that a large percentage of the cost of solving the inventory problem is fixed and only a small percentage depends on the number of items. This is the hallmark of an essentially fixed cost, which is exactly our thesis. Similarly, consider the case of a problem involving the allocation of salesmen's time. The fact that one company has ten times the number of salesmen another company has does not necessarily make the study of the first company's problem more expensive. The study of customer characteristics will be required in either case and the same mathematical models will be tried in both cases. The fixed costs, in short, are high. A great number of business problems are of this sort.

There are, of course, problems for which the cost of a solution is directly proportional to the size of the company. An outstanding example of this kind of problem is one in the area of information flow. These are the problems that prompt systems analysis in the hope of improvement by redesign of the company communication network. Fundamentally, a communication network in a company consists of links between various processors of information. If all possible links existed (between every pair of information-processors) the number of links would increase in proportion to the square of the number of information-processors. Generally this isn't the case, but the number of links certainly increases as fast as the number of information-processors. The work, and hence cost, of an analysis of such a system depends on the number of such links. Therefore, a larger company, having more information-processors and more links, can expect to have such a study cost more money. But despite such exceptions, it appears that a considerable majority of business problems are such that their solutions involve high fixed costs. This implies our statement, that solutions to problems tend to cost fixed amounts.

What will this imply in terms of company attitudes to problems? The main implication revolves around company size. Consider a problem in marketing for which a solution would involve a 2 per cent increase in sales for one year. In accord with our argument we will suppose that a solution will cost $50,000. If we assume a 10 per cent gross profit on sales it follows that a company's sales would have to be at least $25,000,-000 per year—since ($25,000,000) (0.02) (0.1) $=$ $50,000—before it would be profitable to undertake the study. Smaller companies would be equally delighted to gain 2 per cent of their sales by solving the given problem, but it is simply not economical for them to have it solved. Similarly, in the case of the two manufacturers of electronic equipment with which we commenced this section equivalent percentage improvements might result if the problem were solved in the two cases. But the difference in the amount of involvement in the problem area makes it economical for the larger company to undertake an expensive analysis of the problem which would be completely uneconomical for the smaller company.

This argument, then, serves to explain the reason behind the commonly observed difference in company responses to problems. Each executive can be acting with complete rationality but one initiates an extensive, and often expensive, search for a solution while the other essentially ignores the problem.

Some further ramifications of the same argument are worth discussing. First, we have assumed in the above discussion that the solution to the problem is assured if only the search is undertaken. This, of course, is a very bad assumption. An executive's life would be delightfully easy if he knew that each of his problems could be solved by retaining some suitable consultants or employing company specialists. Unfortunately, this is far from true. An executive may invest considerable sums in an attempt to solve a problem and may find no solution at all. In this event he still has his problem plus the realization that he has wasted some resources in a vain effort to solve it. We must now consider some of the implications of this fact.

In terms of the procedures we have been using this situation can be expressed by saying that a search for a problem solution has some probability of being successful. The possibility of making an immediate and realistic estimate of this probability must be questioned, but we will reserve our discussion of this intricate subject for subsequent sections of this chapter. For the present it will be sufficient that there is some probability of finding a solution, whether we know what it is or not. Now, since there is usually a continual succession of problems in any business, it follows that the company has a succession of choices to make. For any problem it can attempt to find the solution, or it can ignore the problem, or it can handle the situation by utilizing its executives' intuition (we shall discuss the various alternatives subsequently). At present let us note that there are two available possibilities: (1) undertake a search for the solution to the problem, which will cost some specified sum and which will have some specified probability of success, or (2) do something else that will not involve finding the solution to the problem. This choice is available for each problem and there is a constant succession of problems. So formulated, the situation of a company regarding its problems bears a striking resemblance to that of a gambler making wagers on some chance device. The problems are the successive wagers and, like the gambler, the company is not forced to make a bet. The sum required to search for the problem solution is the amount of the wager, and the return that results if the solution is found represents the amount won if the wager is successful. Finally, the probability that a solution will be found is the probability of winning. The analogy is complete and we might expect that probability theory, which has much to say about gamblers' chances, might have something to say about the company's policy regarding its problems. And in fact it does.

We have not yet taken account of two factors that must be introduced in order to have a reasonably realistic model of the company's situation regarding its succession of problems. However, it will be convenient here to discuss the main aspect of this situation which the probability-theory analysis suggests. In probability theory this problem is treated under the descriptive title, "The Problem of the Gambler's Ruin." Now the company that is establishing a policy for dealing with its problems is not a gambler, and it is not often in a position where it is really risking ruin by attempts to solve its problems. However, because of the analogies we have pointed out, it is possible to consider the company's situation in the light of the results available from an analysis of this intriguing comparison. The main result for the case of the gambler is that if he has C dollars and wagers one dollar each time with probability p of winning and probability $q = (1 - p)$ of losing, and if he intends to play the game until he has won some amount W, then his probability of ruin is

$$\text{Probability of ruin} = \frac{\left(\frac{q}{p}\right)^C \left[1 - \left(\frac{q}{p}\right)^W\right]}{1 - \left(\frac{q}{p}\right)^{C+W}} \qquad \text{(for } p \text{ not equal to } q\text{)}$$

where we are assuming he is playing against a gambling house or an opponent having essentially unlimited resources. The case where $p = q = \frac{1}{2}$, an even game, is much simpler. For this case, using the symbols as before, we have

$$\text{Probability of ruin} = 1 - \frac{C}{C + W}$$

As an illustration, a gambler who has $5 and wants to win $10 in the game of matching pennies for $1 per throw has a probability of ruin of $1 - 5/(5 + 10) = \frac{2}{3}$. In short, the probability that he will lose his $5 (ruin) is $\frac{2}{3}$ and, of course, the probability that he will win $10 is $1 - \frac{2}{3} = \frac{1}{3}$.

In analogy to the case of the company, however, suppose that the gambler has no set sum that he proposes to try and win. The company certainly is not going to stop attempting to solve its problems once it has succeeded in solving a given number of them. In other words, the gambler will play indefinitely. In the case where p does not equal q we find that the probability of ruin for the gambler becomes simply $(q/p)^C$. As would be expected, if q is greater than p (an unfair game) the gambler's ruin is certain (probability equals 1). However, somewhat surprising is the fact that when $p = q = \frac{1}{2}$ the probability of ruin is also 1. The basis from which this expression has been developed differs from the company's situation in two respects: first, we have assumed p was constant at every trial, which is not true for the company because the probability of achieving a solution will differ with each problem; and second, we have assumed a fixed stake at each wager, whereas for the company the amount risked by the attempt at a solution and the amount to be gained from a solution will differ for each problem. Despite these differences, however, we can still draw a conclusion from the parallel.

The company is not likely to put its entire resources into an effort to find the solution to a specific problem. But as a going enterprise faced with a succession of problems it will probably have a sum of money which it is willing to commit to such research activities. Any amount beyond that sum would require the utilization of funds needed for different purposes, and other company activities would suffer as a result. Furthermore, as a profitable enterprise it would ordinarily be the case that the problem-solving funds, if used in other company activities, could be expected to produce the average company rate of return. At the very least, such funds could be invested in short-term securities to return the going rate. In short, the company would want to get at least this large a yield from investment of these funds in problem-solving efforts. And, like the gambler, the company can be ruined by the exhaustion of the funds available for searching for problem solutions. Therefore, conservative executives could be expected to recognize, and take account of, the fact that the allocation of funds to a search for problem solutions bears a strong family resemblance to the problem facing a gambler with a limited capital. This does not mean that they need be experts in probability theory. The point is simply that their allocation of such funds should be weighted in the direction indicated by the theory. This direction is given by the probability of ruin for an indefinite number of plays, $(q/p)^C$. In our derivation C represents the number of dollars the gambler has at the start of the game. Nothing is changed if we let the amount wagered be the unit of dollars (instead of one dollar), in which case C is simply the number of units (such as units of \$100, \$1000, or \$100,000) the gambler has. The probability of losing, q, is ordinarily smaller than the probability of winning, p. Otherwise the executive would seldom commit his company's resources to the solution of a problem. For this reason the quantity (q/p) is generally less than 1. Therefore, as C gets larger and larger the quantity $(q/p)^C$ gets smaller and smaller. This is as it should be, since the probability of ruin would be expected to decrease as the initial capital, C, increases. But there are two implications which we want to stress.

First, for fixed initial capital, as a specific problem requires larger amounts of money for a search for its solution, then the probability of finding the solution must be larger in order to maintain a fixed probability of ruin.

Second, a larger initial capital can support more costly searches for problem solutions at the same probability of ruin.

To illustrate the first proposition, suppose that a company has available $100,000 (or 4 units of $25,000) for problem-solving. Assume it wants to allocate this sum so that its probability of ruin is always less than 0.05 (1 in 20). Then a search for a solution that required an expenditure of $25,000 would require a probability of about 0.68 or more of a return of $50,000 if solved, in order to keep the probability of ruin to the desired level [since $(0.32/0.68)^4$ is approximately 0.05]. Since the company is paying $25,000 whether it wins or loses, it is necessary that it should receive $50,000 if it wins, in order to have an even-money bet. More than, or less than, even-money bets require more complex mathematical treatment, but the essence of the idea of ruin would be the same. A search for a solution that required the expenditure of $50,000 would require a probability of about 0.82 of a return of $100,000, if solved [since $(0.18/0.82)^2$ is approximately 0.05]. A company with $1,000,000 available for problem-solving, however, could maintain the same probability of ruin on the $25,000 expenditure if the probability of a solution were only 0.52 [since $(0.48/0.52)^{40}$ is approximately 0.05]. Similarly, the $50,000 expenditure would require the probability of a solution of about 0.54.

Figure 12.1 depicts the relationship for a fixed probability of ruin between the capital cost ratio and the return cost ratio. These ratios are as follows:

$$\text{Capital ratio} = \frac{\text{capital}}{\text{cost}}$$

$$\text{Return ratio} = \frac{\text{return} - \text{cost}}{\text{cost}}$$

where capital = capital available for problem-solving,
    cost = cost of the search for a solution, and
    return = size of the return obtained if the problem is solved.

The capital ratio is placed on the ordinate scale. The return ratio is placed on the abscissa. Thus, a return ratio of 1 is the equivalent of an even-money bet. Lines of iso-p (equal probability for the successful

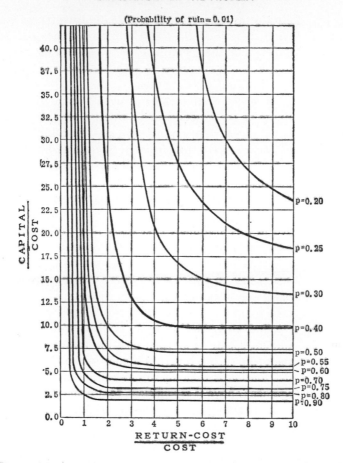

Figure 12.1   *Lines of equal probability of successfully solving a problem when the probability of ruin is fixed at 0.01 for different capital and return ratios.*

solution of the problem) are shown in relation to the capital and return ratios. It is important to notice how these lines are asymptotic to particular capital and return ratios. As the p value decreases, the asymptotes move to larger capital and return ratios. On the basis of this figure we can draw several conclusions in addition to the observations we have previously made.

1. For a fixed probability of success (p), there is a return ratio below which no amount of capital will suffice if a fixed probability of ruin is to be maintained. For example, when $p = 0.6$, then infinite capital would be required to maintain the probability of ruin at 0.01 when the return ratio is $\frac{2}{3}$ or below.

2. For any given capital ratio there is a probability of success that requires an infinite return ratio if the probability of ruin is to be maintained. For example, when the capital ratio is 5, an infinite return ratio is required to maintain the probability of ruin at 0.01, when $p = 0.6$.

Observation of Figure 12.1 reinforces our previous conclusion that there are even sharper limits on the expenditures a smaller company can undertake in order to find problem solutions as compared to a bigger company. The introduction of the fact that solutions to problems are not certain, results in sharper limitations on smaller companies, essentially because it introduces the possibility of a bad-luck streak against which companies must maintain protection in the form of control over their probabilities of ruin.

We have assumed in this argument that there is a probability of finding a solution but that the solution, if found, will permit a fixed gain (or avoidance of a loss). Actually, of course, this is an unlikely state of affairs. Far more usual will be a case where there is some probability distribution of returns if a solution to the problem is found. The range of possible returns would probably start at zero in most cases, since we certainly hope that finding a solution to a problem will not result in a loss beyond the amount spent. For each possible return there would be a probability of achieving such a return if a solution to the problem were found. Such a distribution is difficult to determine but it is not impossible. For our argument above it is sufficient to use the expected or average return of this distribution as equivalent to the fixed return there assumed.

Two other points remain to be mentioned in this discussion of the effect of company size on the approach to problems. First, most returns from solutions to problems are not lump sums received upon implementation of whatever is indicated by the problem solution. Instead they are in the form of some increment to income over a period of years. Ordinarily the number of years cannot be assumed to be too great because future changes in conditions will either require a new solution or will render the whole problem irrelevant. But, even so, the future income stream must be discounted back to present worth before any conclusions can be drawn concerning the advisability of searching for a solution. From the standpoint of the smaller company the effect is to require a greater margin of safety (as compared to the larger company) against the possibility of a bad-luck streak. The spreading of the possible return over a number of years means that there is less chance of one good solution's sustaining the available funds against several failures. Thus, the probability of ruin is increased. This requires a greater relative increase in the safety margin for the smaller company than it does for the larger company.

Second, as soon as probabilities of gains and losses enter the picture the question of the utility of money arises. The effect of the introduction of the utility of money was illustrated by our discussion of the self-insurance problem earlier in the book. The reader will remember that when due account was taken of differing utilities for money the company with larger resources could assume risks that a smaller company could not assume. Precisely the same effect results in the present case. The introduction of utilities for money will result in the smaller company's having to forego still more searches for solutions to problems which the larger company can easily undertake.

The net effect of all these various factors and influences is that there is a very strong relationship between company size and the problems for which the company can attempt to find solutions. We would not expect, then, to find smaller companies so often undertaking the solution of problems that have an indirect or smaller effect on their objectives. Only large companies can afford to assume the risk of undertaking solutions to problems for which the probability of return is low or that have an attenuated, indirect effect on primary objectives.

This is the general background to the question of the allocation of funds for a search for a problem solution. We must now turn to a discussion of some of the specific questions that must be considered in reaching a decision concerning the allocation of such funds.

101. PROBLEM-SOLVING: THE POTENTIAL GAIN

In the last paragraph we referred to the "decision concerning the allocation" of funds for problem-solving. It is, of course, a decision problem and one that is quite similar to the many others we have discussed throughout the book. One difference, however, is that this decision problem is one that the executive often has to block out for himself. It is not uncommon to have a preliminary analysis performed in order to determine the desirability of undertaking some particularly expensive search for a problem solution, but even in this case the executive must himself reach the first decision: to undertake the preliminary investigation.

Having recognized that this is a decision problem, let us try to identify the usual components of a decision problem. First, what are the strategies? This depends on the kind of problem that has arisen. On the one hand it may be some aspect of company operations that has never previously been considered as a problem. An example might be labor turnover in a small to medium-sized plant. In this case the strategies might consist of (1) continuing to ignore the problem or (2) investing various sums of money in an attempt to solve the problem. On the other hand, there are problems that have always been treated as decision problems but that are now being considered to be perhaps worthy of a more careful analysis. The past method of handling the problem may have been some established policy, or an executive may have decided each case on its merits. In this event, the strategies in the decision problem would include (1) the continuation of the previous procedure and (2) the allocation of various sums of money to the solution of the problem. The states of nature are the various possible situations that may pertain to the problem. The payoff is the return that results for the various combinations of strategies and states of nature. It is the payoff that we will now consider.

Many of the decision problems we have discussed have been of a kind in which something positive was definitely going to be done and it was a question of choosing the most profitable or the least costly "something" to do. For example, there will be an ordering policy of some kind in an inventory problem. The relevant decision problem is to choose the least costly one. But in the present decision problem the question is, essentially, whether to invest in a search for a solution or not. Since the required investment will ordinarily be fairly well fixed, it follows that we will never make the search unless it is possible that the return can be larger than the cost of the search. We may not attempt to find the solution even if the return can be larger than the cost, but we certaintly won't make the search if the return cannot possibly be larger than the cost. Therefore, a reasonable first step is to raise the question: What is the maximum possible return if this problem is solved?

The answer involves a comparison of how the company stands with regard to the objective affected by the problem and what the company might conceivably achieve if it tried. It is clear that the latter is more difficult to estimate than the former. But even knowing how the company stands with regard to some objectives is quite difficult. Any objective that has a natural quantified measure causes no difficulties. The company's position with respect to profit is simply the amount or percentage of profit it is making. How it stands with regard to labor turnover is some suitable measure of turnover like the percentage of new employees per month. But what the company's position is with regard to labor relations, for example, is hard to define. We have already discussed this problem extensively and we will not repeat our remarks here. In the present context, if the objective cannot be quantified then the approach we are developing here cannot be used. We intend to find some measure of the distance separating the actual position of the company from its conceivable position. Distance implies measurement and if the objective cannot be quantified we cannot measure the distance. Therefore, we will assume that the objective in question has a quantitative measure and that the company's actual position with regard to the objective can be determined.

The more difficult part of the question is that dealing with what the company might conceivably achieve. There are two major ways (three if we include executive experience and intuition) by which the best conceivable position of the company with regard to the objective might be determined. An analogy from a different field suggests the first method. An engineer who designs steam engines is interested in measuring their efficiency. He can do this very easily because the basic laws of thermodynamics imply a top efficiency beyond which no engine can possibly go. This, then, represents a theoretical maximum for any steam engine. Are there any such theoretical maxima for business organizations? If there are any such, then these would supply an upper (or lower) limit to the conceivable position of the company.

The answer is that there are such absolute maxima for companies as well as for steam engines. As a matter of fact, there are quite a large number of them. Some of them are tritely obvious but others are far from trite or obvious. Obvious ones come from areas where achievement can be measured in percentages of some total amount. Obviously, in this case, a percentage cannot be bigger than 100 per cent nor smaller than 0 per cent. For example, labor turnover, readers of a magazine who notice an advertisement, potential customers reached by an advertising campaign, percentage defectives in production, and many similar kinds of measures have theoretical maxima or minima of 100 per cent or 0 per cent. A less obvious theoretical optimum was discussed in our section on inventory problems. It was shown that it is possible to construct a curve that depicts the minimum total cost of an ordering policy for any given set of items and for any combination of carrying charges and order cost. This curve, then, shows the least possible costs associated with ordering and carrying a set of items, given the price and demand for each item. It is clear, therefore, that theoretical maxima or minima do exist for some business objectives.

Many times, there is no such theoretical limit and it is necessary to try the second method: use data that show the positions of other companies with regard to the objective in question. The maximum or minimum obtained in practice can be used as an approximation to the limit. Such data are often available from trade associations; sometimes they appear in annual company reports to stockholders, or they may be found in special studies. The more similar the other companies, the more reliable the extrapolation, but for many objectives it is possible to establish empirical limits on the basis of data from quite dissimilar companies. For such measures as inventory turnover, sales per dollar of advertising, labor turnover, and many measures of rates of return it is usually possible to determine practical upper and lower limits in this manner.

Finally, of course, if no other limit can be obtained the executive can use his own experience as a guide to estimating the limit of possible improvement. It is important to have some kind of estimated limit because of the obvious, but sometimes overlooked, fact that no search for a solution should be undertaken unless it is at least possible to gain a return from the solution that exceeds the cost of the search. Once a limit has been established, the distance separating the actual position from the limit gives the maximum possible improvement as a result of solving the problem. Of course, the problem may not be solved, and even if it is solved the actual improvement will probably fall far short of the maximum possible improvement. But the knowledge of the upper bound that exists to the return from a solution is, nonetheless, a necessary component of this decision problem. When the upper limit has been determined, it is then necessary to estimate the actual returns that may be achieved. We now proceed to a discussion of this difficult question.

102. WHAT IS A PROBLEM SOLUTION WORTH?

The question is obviously a complex one. But it is equally obvious that it is the key to a rational analysis of the decision problem whether or not to undertake a search for a solution. The main difficulty results from the large variety of ways in which the executive might profit from a search for a solution. Let us list some of them.

1. He may profit from the mere fact of a search for a solution even if no solution is found. For example, a study of productive efficiency sometimes results in greater efficiency purely because of the response of the personnel to the fact that their efficiency is being studied.

2. He may profit from a search that doesn't find a solution by discovering that some factor that he had been considering important is not so important. As a result, he will no longer have to worry about that factor. For example, a company that undertakes a study to minimize direct-mail duplication may not discover the solution, but as a result of the investigation it may learn that duplication is not large enough to warrant further attention.

3. He may profit because the range of the possible states of nature is narrowed. Any successful search for improved predicting methods is an example.

4. He may profit because the number of strategies that he needs to consider is decreased. Often this results because the complex system involved in the problem is found to depend on some key component. Only those strategies which affect this key part need be considered. For ex-

ample, the manufacturer of pens who shipped them to small retailers in quantities of 25 of each color discovered that he was shipping quantities that were too small. The size of the shipment was the key factor in his strategy (see p. 240).

5. He may profit by discovering a more suitable measure of effectiveness. As an example we can cite our earlier analysis of the decision problem of the number of repairmen needed to service a group of machines.

6. He may profit by obtaining good estimates of the probabilities of the states of nature. An example would be that of a company considering a sizable expansion in a foreign country. Such a company might undertake a study to ascertain the probabilities of war, revolution, socialization, and other relevant states of nature.

7. He may profit by discovering the correct evaluation of the payoff measure. As an example we can cite studies made of the optimal allocation of salesmen's time in which it has been found that the payoff measure (sales, for example) is related to the allocation of time in ways that are far from obvious.

Still other kinds of returns from solutions could be given. But it is not worthwhile to try listing all of them, even assuming that this could be done. We cannot discuss every possible gain that might be derived from a search for a solution. The important thing to note is that the process of searching for a solution can produce peripheral benefits that help to justify the decision to solve the problem. In other cases, the side effects may not be beneficial. This occurs, in particular, when an efficient process must be disturbed to collect information necessary for the solution of the problem. The decision-maker must consider the pros and cons of the side effects that might result from the decision to solve a problem.

Basically, the value of a solution can be treated in much the same way as any other value problem. We can distinguish at least three different types of value situations. In the first place, we have the situation in which the solution to a problem has a value determined by the supply and demand for solutions. For example, the demand for oil and the frequency with which varying quantities of oil are found permit us to specify the value of this solution. Similarly, the value of the solution to the problem of finding an adequate number of engineers depends upon the supply of engineers and the company's demand for them. The second type of value situation is the one in which there is an imputed value for the solution which is independent of the supply and demand for such solutions. For example, when an air-sea rescue operation is undertaken to locate a pilot downed at sea the combined cost of all of the equipment and personnel employed in the search provides at least a lower bound for the imputed value of the pilot's life. In business, imputed values must be used when a numerical equivalent cannot be found. This is the case for employee morale, company goodwill, community relations, and so forth. The third type of value situation we will mention is one in which the value of the solution is basically a measure of improved efficiency. As we have previously stated, it is sometimes possible to estimate an upper limit for efficiency, in which case, if the company knows its present efficiency it is able to estimate the probable value of a solution. The estimate depends upon the anticipated effectiveness of the strategies (techniques) that will be employed. Consequently, the appraisal of techniques is of great importance in the estimation of the value of a solution. (Chapter 13 presents such an evaluation of O.R. techniques.) With standard techniques and methods, and an evaluation of the data that are used, it is possible to estimate the degree to which the best possible result will be approximated. With nonstandard techniques, it is necessary to approach this problem in stages. At each stage, the previous results and additional information gained can be used to re-estimate the probable value of the solution that will result if the problem-solving procedure is continued.

It is not unusual for the solution of one problem to bring to light the value to be gained from solving another problem. For example, the solution of the work-pool problem in Chapter 11 clearly presents the value to the company of a solution to its absenteeism problem. Similarly, the solution of an inventory problem can establish the value of solving the forecasting problem. However, many problems are not involved in such mutual relationships and it is necessary to find still other means for estimating the worth of a solution.

The general procedure we would like to be able to follow is clear. We must attempt to estimate the payoffs that result from solutions. Since we will often have an estimate of the maximum possible improvement that could result, it may be most convenient to express the different payoffs as percentages of this maximum. Then by determining the effect of a percentage-point improvement on some convenient dollar measurement (sales, costs, profit, and the like) it will be possible to convert the payoff measures to dollars, which can be included directly with the dollar cost of the search in evaluating the expected returns of the strategies. This, of course, is far easier said than done, but it is quite straightforward for many problems. In estimating the payoffs it is often possible to utilize published studies showing the improvements that resulted from similar searches for solutions. In this context it may be noted that the smaller company has an advantage here. In accordance with our previous argument it is likely that the smaller company will be dealing with problems that have a direct and large effect on its primary objectives.

These are the problems which have most often been handled by other companies and, hence, for which the greatest amount of information on resulting improvements is available. The larger company may be dealing with a specialized problem that has never, or rarely, been dealt with before. This makes it more unlikely that any significant amount of information concerning improvements will be available.

One rule of thumb is worth noting. We mentioned earlier that a basic distinction between problems is that some of them have always been recognized as being decision problems, although no formal search has been made to find a solution. Others have not been considered to be decision problems. The first kind of problem, in short, will have had the attention of a decision-maker. If he has had the benefit of an accurate measure of the payoff from his decisions he will have had the opportunity to develop his own methods for approaching an optimal selection of strategy. Under usual conditions he will have done so—and with a fair degree of success if the problem is not exceedingly complex. Thus, a solution for a problem of this kind is not likely to produce nearly so much improvement as will a solution to the other kind of problem.

To illustrate the difference we will contrast three problems. First, consider a transportation problem involving factories and warehouses. Here the costs are given and the total cost of any shipping strategy is immediately available. Any conscientious decision-maker would approach the minimum-cost strategy for this problem, over a period of time, even for a large number of factories and warehouses. Second, consider an inventory problem. Here the decision-maker will rarely receive the information necessary to completely evaluate his own decisions. He will not, therefore, be so likely to improve his decisions with practice beyond a certain point. Third, consider a problem in plant location that has never arisen before. Clearly, there is no basis for improving performance on a unique problem. Generally speaking the relative improvements resulting from solutions will be smaller in the first case, larger in the second, and largest in the third. We must emphasize the word "relative." It means the improvement as a percentage of the cost of the decision-maker's unaided decision. We cannot say anything about the absolute improvements because this measure depends on the specific circumstances of the problems. The moral is simple: Never underestimate the ability of the decision-maker to approach the optimal strategy if he is given an adequate feedback of information.

In the attempt to evaluate the return from a solution one of the greatest difficulties results from the fact that a solution may be found but the determining factors may be outside the control of the decision-maker. This would essentially eliminate the possibility of a return from the solution. For example, the labor-turnover problem might be analyzed at considerable expense only to find that the main contributing factors were sociological conditions over which the company had no control. There is no certain way of handling this difficulty, but it is possible in many cases to estimate the hazard. Usually the decision-maker has reasonable knowledge of the factors that he controls. This being so, he may be able to discover, either from his company's experience or from that of similar companies:

1. That the quantitative measure of his objective in the past has varied while the factors under his control remained essentially constant, or

2. That the quantitative measure of his objective in the past has remained fairly constant while the factors under his control varied.

In either case, one can assume that the factors under his control are not sufficient to determine the objective measure (payoff). Hence, there is a good chance a solution will disclose that the important factors in determining his payoff are outside his control. However, we have observed that feedback systems can produce variation although a constant strategy is being maintained. In this case, the lack of sufficient information about the system could mislead the decision-maker into believing that he has no control over the situation, when in fact he does have control but he doesn't know how it works.

Similarly, there is a problem with respect to the second point. The quantitative measure of the objective may remain constant while the control factors are varied but the time lag may be so great that the effect of varying the controls cannot be observed. For example, changing advertising effort may not affect short-term sales but profoundly affect long-term sales. Consequently, the decision-maker must evaluate the kind of situation that prevails when he attempts to determine how much control he exercises in obtaining a solution. This question of control is examined at some length in Chapter 14.

Whenever a situation arises in which the decision-maker appears to have no strategy available that will permit him to utilize the results of a solution, the value of that solution would be nil. For example, the fact that a company knows who its potential customers are will be of limited value unless specific means are available for reaching these customers. If no medium exists that includes a larger proportion of potential customers in its audience than exists in the general population, the characterization of potential customers is valueless—at least for selecting optimal media. Sometimes persistence and imagination can succeed in devising a strategy that will give value to a solution. This depends on the calibre of the men who attempt to resolve the problem. It is not our intention to discuss such questions as the kind of men needed to provide creative and resourceful ideas with respect to the utilization of solutions. Still, the value of a solution will frequently increase because an ingenious way has been found for putting the result to work.

One additional factor should be mentioned that affects the value of a solution. Competitive incentives exist that are difficult to evaluate. Many times a value must be imputed for being the first to achieve something. Frequently, the company that is second benefits at the expense of the first. In many other cases, the advantage of being first gives the company that pioneers the solution a lead that cannot be overcome. The position of a company with respect to its competitors and the characteristics of the market must, therefore, be considered when attempts are made to place a value on a solution.

We can see that the value of a solution is a function of many factors. If it can be represented on a single scale, such as dollars, then a direct decision can be made between possible alternative problems to be studied. If it is not possible to estimate the value of a solution on a single scale, then it is necessary to use the methods that we have discussed for comparing outcomes in terms of the multiple objectives of the company.

PROBLEMS

1. A company has $100,000 available for research in problem solutions. Use Figure 12.1 to determine the returns it would have to receive, for each of the probability curves, to justify the investment of $10,000 in a search for a solution. Do the same thing for an investment of $20,000. How does the ratio of the returns necessary in the two cases change as the probability of a return decreases?

2. For a constant investment of $10,000 and a constant return of $50,000, what amounts of capital are necessary for each of the probability curves?

3. For a fixed return of $50,000 and capital of $100,000, what investment is justifiable for each of the probability curves?

4. A company with $100,000 available for research in problem solutions is willing to invest $10,000 in a search for a solution which will return $20,000 (its investment plus an equal amount) with probability of 0.574.
   a. What probability of ruin is the company accepting?
   b. What probability should this company expect for a return of $40,000 on an investment of $20,000 in order to have the same probability of ruin?

5. The reasoning we followed, based on the idea of the ruin probability, has a much more general applicability than the one we have emphasized in this chapter. Consider, for example, an investment in a small business. The business may be profitable over a long enough period of time but the earnings may be quite variable over any short period of time. We cannot reflect the actual situation very well with only the methods developed in this chapter but some of the characteristics of the situation can be approximated. We will

consider the monthly fixed expenses to be the investment and the gross profit (over fixed plus variable expenses) plus fixed expenses to be the return. Then we can reflect different amounts of variability in returns by taking a fixed expected return and varying the probability, and the amount, of the return. Thus, a return of $2000 with probability 0.5, a return of $1500 with probability 0.67, and a return of $1100 with probability 0.91 all have an expected return of $1000. Obviously, the variability is greater when the probability is smaller

a. Suppose fixed expenses are $1000 per month. Suppose that the expected return is $1200 per month (by our definition this means a gross profit of $200). How much capital would be required to maintain the probability of ruin at 0.01 in each of the following cases:

RETURN	PROBABILITY
$1333	0.90
1500	0.80
1600	0.75
1714	0.70
2000	0.60
2400	0.50
3000	0.40
4000	0.30

b. Suppose a single owner has $10,000 and suppose that fixed expenses are $1000 per month. If he wishes to maintain a probability of ruin of 0.01, what combinations of amount, and probability, of return are satisfactory for him?

Chapter thirteen

Evaluation of Operations-Research Methods

In this chapter we want to present an overview of the various methods and models of operations research. Many of these operations-research methods were used in our analysis of some typical decision problems in Part III, but we made no reference there to the fact that we were using operations research. One of the theses of this book is that operations-research methods can be understood only in terms of the broader subject of which they constitute a highly developed part. This broader subject is, of course, decision theory. We tried, in Part III, to show how the logic of the decision problem in question accounted for the specific method used to solve the problem. This has naturally resulted in a greater emphasis on the structure of the decision problem and a lesser emphasis on the method of a solution as a separate subject.

In the last chapter, however, we saw that any evaluation of the probable returns resulting from a search for a solution to a decision problem requires some estimate of the likelihood that the problem will be solved. The estimate can hardly be made without some understanding of the kinds of tools and techniques available. These tools and techniques are the methods and models of operations research; we will try to present a description of them here.

103. THE SIMILARITIES OF PROBLEMS

The reader has doubtless noticed some similarities among the various problems we discussed in Part III. In a few cases we explicitly noted some of the similarities. For example, there is an obvious similarity between the work-pool problem and the repairmen problem. Both of them involve finding the right number of men to handle some work load with a minimum total cost. And, for the same reason, these two problems are similar to the overtime problem. The similarities resulted in similar procedures in solving the respective decision problems. This, in itself, is a useful insight since it suggests that a procedure used in solving one problem may work for a different problem, provided it is "similar" in some sense to the first problem. It will be worth considering just what we mean by "similar" in this context.

It is clear that quite a great number of elements that distinguish one problem situation from another do not have any effect on the problem structure itself. For example, the inventory problem of one supermarket will be very similar to that of another supermarket, even though the second one is owned by a different company and is located in a different city, and it will be similar to the inventory problem of a large chain drug store, even though the items carried will be quite different. Furthermore, it will be similar to the inventory problem of a department store, or of a warehouse, or of a factory maintaining an inventory of its finished products. Yet the warehouse and the factory are not even meeting the demand of the ultimate consumer as all the others are. Despite the differences there is an underlying similarity in all the cases. On the basis of this similarity we would all unhesitatingly refer to each of these cases as an *inventory problem*. And it is this similarity that we would like to understand a little better.

In the example we are considering, the similarities among the various specific cases cited are apparent. In every case the problem is the maintenance of a supply of some item or items, where the item is a physical thing. The reason for maintaining the supply is to meet future demand for the item. These two statements seem to outline the problem. The reason such things as store location, kind of store, and kind of item do not affect the problem is that they are irrelevant to the two characteristics we have abstracted. The relationship of demand to the problem is somewhat different. Demand is mentioned explicitly in the second statement and is therefore directly involved in the problem. The difference in kind of demand in the cases of the warehouse and the factory will therefore be incorporated in the analysis of the problem in the form of assumptions, or empirically determined facts, about the nature of demand. In each of the cited cases, then, we find the same two characteristics: the maintenance of a supply of some physical item to meet future demand.

But do these two characteristics really describe the inventory problem? Those situations which have these two features appear to be inventory problems, but are there any inventory problems that do not have these two features? In mathematical terminology, we agree that the two characteristics in question are sufficient conditions (their occurrence is sufficient to ensure that we have an inventory problem) but are they necessary (must every inventory problem have these two features)? The answer to this question is mainly a semantic one. After all, we are only defining a term and we can define it pretty much as we please. But since we would like to be able to communicate ideas with other people it is desirable that our definitions of familiar terms, like "inventory problem," should not diverge too widely from accepted usage. With this in mind it appears that our two statements do represent necessary and sufficient features of an inventory problem. However, we can make one significant change in the first statement without distorting the usual conception of an inventory problem. We can remove the restriction that there must be a supply of some physical thing. Let us, instead, say that the problem may be one of maintaining a supply of anything at all. This change doesn't seem to affect the idea of an inventory problem in any significant way, but it does disclose the fact that there are a host of other kinds of situations that are inventory problems. As examples we can cite such things as a company's maintenance of liquid assets to meet future demand, the maintenance of an inventory of plant capacity, the maintenance of an inventory of able junior executives, the maintenance of an inventory of research projects, and many others. It immediately becomes evident, as another example already pointed out, that the hotel-reservation problem we considered in Part III was an inventory problem requiring the maintenance of a sufficient inventory of reservations. All of these diverse kinds of problems, together with the more usual ones mentioned earlier, fall into the general category of inventory problems.

Let us take another example of a class of problems with an underlying similarity. Consider the problem of having sufficient toll booths on a superhighway to receive the payments of all the drivers. First let us note that this is clearly an inventory problem: to maintain a sufficient supply of toll booths to meet the demand of the motorists. The reason for discussing separately this particular subclass of the inventory problem will be given later in this chapter. Now, the problem on the superhighway would certainly be essentially the same as the problem of having sufficient toll booths for a bridge or for a tunnel. Let us try to characterize the problem in general terms. Something (we aren't going to restrict it to motorists) comes to a facility at which the something in question is delayed for some reason. Then our something leaves the facility which is now free for any subsequent somethings. The problem is to determine the number of facilities necessary. Of course, the reason for the delay at the facility is that some kind of transaction takes place there. Since the transaction is often a service, this class of problems can be called *servicing problems*. Great numbers of problems fit our general description. As examples we can cite the supply of tables to restaurant customers, of teller windows to bank customers, of clerks to store customers, of landing strips to incoming airplanes, of docks to trucks, of berths for ships, of repairmen for broken machines, of telephone lines to callers, and many others. All of these problems have the general characteristics given above. In each case the "something" is different, the facility is different, and the service is different. Yet the underlying similarity remains. They are all examples of servicing problems.

The fact that we have shown two examples of classes of problems that are seemingly diverse and yet have an underlying similarity tells us very little about "similarity." How many other such classes of problems are there? How can we discover new ones? We would like to be able to answer questions such as these. But, to come right to the point, we cannot answer these questions. The two examples given above were chosen because analysis of these two kinds of similarity has led to large numbers of methods and procedures for handling the corresponding decision problems. And there are some other classes of problems with an underlying similarity that have also permitted the development of some methods for handling the related decision problems. But there are many other classes of problems that seem to have the same kind of underlying similarity but that have not proved at all fruitful in terms of discovering procedures for coping with the corresponding decision problems. Thus, we can say that many companies are striving to minimize costs, or we can say that many are trying to maximize profit, or we can say that many are trying to utilize their total resources in an optimal manner, and we could cite numerous examples of each of these kinds of behavior, but none of these similarities leads to any kind of procedure for dealing with the decision problems.

Of course, discussion in terms of any one of these statements may give rise to some useful insights, but it doesn't lead to any specific methods for dealing with the decision problems. It may be observed that all three of these similarities among companies are of the nature of objectives rather than problems. This is true, but it does not explain the difference. By rephrasing, an objective can be converted into a problem. Thus, how should we minimize costs? How should we maximize profits? How should we utilize our resources? There are many other kinds of underlying similarities that are not related to objectives and that have not been fruitful in leading to procedures for handling the decision problems. For example, some industries take a basic raw material and process it into a number of products. Examples are oil refining, the dairy industry, the meat packing industry, and the lumber industry. Other industries take a number of components and assemble them into a finished product. The automobile industry is a sufficient example. Now, these are certainly two very basic underlying similarities among industries. Yet this fact has not led to the development of decision-problem methods, however much it may contribute to the understanding of one of the industries.

Examples of this sort could be multiplied indefinitely. There is no way of telling in advance which similarities will be fruitful and which will not. The reason seems to be related to a famous rule which was much quoted by medieval philosophers and logicians. They observed that a concept, "dog" for example, had two inversely related aspects. First, it covered a number of specific examples (all dogs for our example). They called the number of specific exemplifications of a concept *the extension of the concept*. Second, there would be a number of things that could be said about the concept (all dogs are mammals, and so on). They called the number of things that could be said about the concept *the intension of the concept*. Now, their rule was: *the greater the extension, the less the intension and the greater the intension, the less the extension*. This is just another way of saying that if you talk about everything you can't say very much and if you say a great deal about something then you aren't covering very much. We can't say nearly as much about dogs in general as we can about the particular one at our heels (because everything we can say in general can be said about the particular dog) but what we say about the particular dog doesn't tell us about dogs in general (because that is what makes him particular). This little excursion in old-fashioned logic will serve to highlight the same kind of problem in our discussion of similarities. If we start with too general a similarity we can't say much about it. But if we start with too specific a similarity we don't cover many cases. The fruitfulness of an observed similarity depends on striking a happy medium (the medieval scholars would have called it a golden mean) between the extension and the intension of the similarity. And this depends on the creativeness of the observer and analyst of the similarity. What one person rejects as not being fruitful another person may use to develop a host of valuable insights and methods. We cannot hope to predict the kinds of similarities that may be found fruitful in the future. We must, therefore, be content to discuss those kinds of similarities which have been proven useful by considerable amounts of practice. And in Chapters 7 and 8 we attempted to catalogue these similarities according to their characteristics as qualitative and quantitative models.

This entire book is devoted to the development of one kind of similarity: the similarity among decision problems. This particular similarity covers an enormous range of cases (large extension) and yet a great deal can be said about it (large intension). It seems to have a very good balance between these opposing "costs" (extension and intension). This is why it can provide a unifying theory for so many different areas. But we now want to discuss some other similarities which have less extension but a correspondingly greater intension.

The most fruitful among such similarities are those which are at the roots of the best-known operations-research techniques. Each one is the nucleus from which have developed a number of specific techniques, methods, and models. We intend to discuss each of the major clusters of techniques with the dual purpose of providing a basic understanding of the techniques and of furnishing a basis for appraising the likelihood of successful applications of the techniques to specific decision problems.

104. INVENTORY MODELS

We have already discussed various aspects of inventory models in our analysis of some kinds of inventory problems in Part III, and we have considered other aspects in the preceding section. At the cost of some repetition we will summarize those earlier discussions here.

The underlying similarity of inventory models is that they all deal with problems associated with storing something to meet future demand. As we have seen, there is no need to restrict the application of these models to the storage of physical things, which is the most common kind of inventory problem. We can equally well talk of the storage of capital, of plant capacity, and of similar kinds of intangibles. The problem of inventory decisions is suggested by the following two questions. First, why store any of the things in question at all? Second, why not store an enormous amount, enough to meet any conceivable demand for a long period of time? The answer to these questions is that we can't act in either of these ways because there are costs associated with storing and costs associated with not storing. Either of these two extreme solutions would be too costly. Of course, in the general case the costs may have to be measured in utilities rather than in dollars, but the statement remains correct in either case.

The fact that there are costs associated with storing and with not storing immediately suggests that the decision problem of how much to store can be formulated in terms of the minimization of the sum of these two kinds of costs, which we can call the *total costs*. The costs associated with storing obviously increase as the amount stored increases. The costs associated with not storing decrease as the amount stored increases. The total costs are, therefore, a function of the amount stored, and the decision problem is to determine that amount to be stored which minimizes these total costs. Any specific inventory decision problem therefore requires the determination of the relationship between amount stored and these costs before it can be resolved. This requires three logically distinct steps: first, the identification of the relevant cost components; second, the measurement of the costs; and third, the determination of the relationship between the amount stored and the costs. We must now discuss these steps.

The identification of the relevant costs is not ordinarily difficult, but there is always a risk that one of them may be overlooked. This risk can be minimized by following a logical analysis of the costs and seeing which ones among the logical possibilities are applicable to a specific inventory problem. The basis of this logical analysis of costs is that one of the outstanding features of any inventory problem is its dependence on time. This much is implied by the very statement of the underlying structure: the maintenance of a supply to meet *future* demand. It is, therefore, always necessary in inventory problems to consider the effect of changes over time on the costs. The costs basically come in pairs: one increases as the amount increases, and the other decreases as the amount increases. There are two such pairs. We will phrase our discussion in terms of the usual kind of inventory problem.

The first arises from the fact that we have to maintain sufficient stock to meet demand, which may be either known certainly or else known only in the form of a probability distribution. Since demand occurs over time, we have a great number of ways in which to maintain stock. We could obtain small amounts very frequently, or we could obtain larger amounts less frequently. The two associated costs are the *procurement cost* and the *carrying cost*. The procurement procedure might be to produce the item in question, in which case we speak of the set-up cost involved in changing the production process to produce the item. Or it might be to order the item, in which case we speak of the ordering cost, which includes all the costs attendant upon processing an order. In either case, this cost increases as the amount ordered decreases since this requires more procurements per unit of time. The carrying costs include all costs of storage, insurance, depreciation, obsolescence, spoilage or theft, loss of interest on capital, and the like. These costs, and hence the total carrying cost, increase as the amount stored increases. Since loss of interest on capital is ordinarily expressed as a percentage of the amount invested it is important to consider any possible changes in price of the item in the future. It is also possible to decrease the amount invested by taking advantage of any quantity discounts or quantity savings on transportation charges. These, then, are the component costs of the pair of costs associated with the process of maintaining a supply to meet the demand over time.

The other pair of costs arise in those cases where demand is not known certainly. In this case two new possibilities arise. First, we may not have sufficient stock to meet the demand. Second, we may have too much stock, more than the demand. The first kind of cost is called the *back-order cost*, because in retailing any excess demand appears in the form of orders that cannot be filled until new stock is obtained by "ordering back" to get more stock. A variety of costs may be components of the back-order cost. First, the sale may be irrevocably lost with an attendant loss of the profit that could have been made. Second, there may be a considerable loss in the goodwill of the customer who was unable to immediately obtain what he wanted. Third, there is a cost associated with processing the special order required to get more stock and this cost, because of the speed required, may be greater than the usual order cost. Fourth, there will usually be expediting costs associated with trying to induce the supplier to act with more speed than usual. Fifth, there will usually be extra transportation costs. All of these costs enter into the back-order cost. This cost decreases as the amount of stock increases because there is clearly less chance of running out of stock in a period if there is a greater supply on hand.

The opposing costs here are the *carrying cost*, discussed before and still operative, and the *overstock cost* which results from having too much stock. Actually, we could achieve greater symmetry by defining the overstock cost to include the carrying costs but it is convenient to use the term "overstock cost" to designate a special, and important, cost which is not always relevant. For many items the only penalty for having too much stock is that it will be carried longer. The extra stock from one period can always be used in a subsequent period. However, for some items the demand is limited to a certain period of time and any stock on hand at the end of the period will have to be disposed of for a fraction of its cost. Examples are women's fashion goods, some kinds of children's toys, and the generator spare-part problem we discussed in Chapter 10. The cost associated with the disposal of such items is the overstock cost. Clearly, this cost increases as the amount carried increases. The two pairs of costs we have discussed include all the costs relevant to an inventory problem.

The next question concerns the measurement of the costs. Under ordinary circumstances the first pair of costs, carrying costs and procurement costs, can be determined from cost-accounting data. This means that for any inventory problem *where the demand is certain* the costs can be determined, since only these two costs are involved. Exceptions do occur, however. Thus, the value used to represent the loss of the use of the capital tied up in inventory can be difficult to measure satisfactorily because it is really an opportunity cost. Similarly, the procurement cost includes components that are opportunity costs. Since opportunity costs are defined in terms of the best possible use of resources it can be very difficult to estimate them if, as is usually the case, the best use of resources is not certain.   In this case we have available the method presented in Chapter 10 which permits the executive to directly select the combination of total carrying costs and total procurement costs that he believes is most suitable for the company.   In essence this procedure imputes a value to the ratio of the two costs but does not require direct estimates of the costs.

Let us consider the other pair of costs.   The overstock cost in many cases can be determined directly from the records of losses suffered in past disposals of overstock items.   Unfortunately, the situation with regard to the back-order cost is not so straightforward.   All of the elements of this cost can be determined from cost-accounting data except for the cost due to the loss of customer goodwill.   The lost goodwill is a highly important aspect of the back-order problem, and a good estimate of its cost is essential to the determination of the optimal amount of inventory to carry.   Sometimes ingenious methods can be devised to estimate this cost, but more often it is not possible to get a reliable estimate. In this case recourse must be made to the experience and intuition of the executive by methods analogous to those discussed in Chapter 10 for the other pair of costs.   This is not the ideal procedure, but it may be the only one available.

The last question concerns the determination of the relationship between the amount stored and the relevant costs.   This is essentially a mathematical problem and not too difficult, with one exception.   Carrying costs and procurement costs vary with the amount ordered in an obvious way and it is easy to express the relationship in mathematical terms.   The back-order cost and the overstock cost require the use of probability distributions to represent demand but there is no particular problem about handling these two costs mathematically.   The exception noted, and the real difficulty in this part of the analysis of an inventory problem, is that it is necessary to know the probability distribution of demand.   This requirement is a crucial one.   We will discuss the matter more fully below in our evaluation of the usefulness of inventory models in the related decision problems.

This discussion has been in terms of the most common kinds of inventory problems.   Later in this section we will briefly mention the additional difficulties that occur when we extend the inventory models to include supplies of intangible things.   We can summarize our discussion by saying that the inventory models will provide solutions to the decision problems involving inventories provided that the necessary information is available.   Further, the necessary information is usually obtainable with the exception of the cost due to loss of goodwill and the probability distribution of demand, both of which may cause serious difficulties.

Now let us turn to an appraisal of inventory models from the executive's point of view. The first point that must be made—and it is an important one—is that there is often a semantic confusion between the executive who talks of his inventory problem and the operations-research analyst who talks of his inventory models. They often don't refer to the same inventory at all. This sounds like a surprising statement but it is true and the explanation is simple. The executive considers his inventory problem to consist of the whole process of predicting demand, ordering, and so on, and he feels he has an inventory decision problem if his total inventory is too high or his back-orders are too high, for whatever reason. Not so the analyst. He includes all of the executive's components except one: predicting demand. He has excluded that one by assuming in his formulation of the problem that the probability distribution of demand is known. The implications of this fact for the executive are enormous and we must discuss them briefly.

In assuming that the probability distribution of demand is known we are assuming that the average demand during the given future period is known and that the probabilities of deviations from that demand are known. Now, to be blunt, this is assuming quite a lot. To know the average demand by itself requires nothing other than the prediction or forecasting of demand, and this is subject to all the usual hazards attendant upon the notoriously backward art of forecasting. In the many cases where good forecasts of demand are available the inventory models will work perfectly well. But where there are no good forecasts of demand the use of inventory models will do very little to rectify the situation.

Let us take an example. When breaks are going badly in a retail business, say a department store, the situation will arise in which total inventory is too high and there are simultaneously a great number of back-orders. Now, this seems almost a contradiction in terms since we have already seen that the back-order cost should decrease as the amount maintained in stock increases. But it happens all too frequently. Why? Because the too-large inventory is in items for which the demand is small while supplies were too low in the fast-moving items and so these have had to be back-ordered. There is only one explanation for such a predicament: bad forecasting. If the harried executive of our department store were told that inventory models assumed demand forecasts, he would be likely to respond with a few choice expletives as preface to some such statement as: "If someone will give me some good forecasts I can manage the inventory myself!" The moral is simply that not all of an executive's inventory problems are solvable by the use of the inventory models we have been discussing.

It is necessary, then, to be certain of the nature of a given inventory problem before deciding to utilize inventory models in helping to solve it. It is not difficult to discover what aspects of the inventory procedure are at fault. For this purpose it is convenient to consider the actual inventory on hand to be the sum of three components:

1. The amount carried to meet average demand, assuming it to be known certainly in advance.
2. The amount carried as reserve stock to meet fluctuations in demand.
3. The excess amount that has resulted from forecasting errors.

For example, a typical inventory policy (before the utilization of inventory models) might be to order every item once a month and to maintain two months' supply as reserve stock. Consider an item with actual monthly demand of about 100 units. According to company policy there would be an average year-round inventory of half a month's demand, or 50 units, simply to meet the average demand. This is our first component. According to company policy there should be 200 units continually in stock to meet fluctuations in demand. This is the second component, reserve stock. The application of inventory models to this item might change the order period and it might change the amount of reserve stock maintained; any such change would be rationally based on the relevant costs and would save the company money. Further, such savings on hundreds or thousands of items can add up to very large amounts. But suppose that an inspection of the stock card for our item shows that the actual inventory is 1100 units. This could only have resulted from a forecasting error, and inventory models can do nothing to avoid such errors. It is particularly important to be aware of this difference because very many inventory problems in the executive's terms are forecasting problems in the terms of inventory models.

With this major provision about forecasting errors it appears that inventory models applied to the usual inventory decision problems can result in very significant savings. The formulation of the models is realistic, and due account can be taken of special circumstances such as storage space or capital limitations. The necessary information is usually available; if it is not there are procedures that can still produce significant improvements. It is, of course, the executive's problem, and responsibility, to estimate whether the total saving will justify the search for a solution. But in the case of inventory problems there is a high degree of likelihood that the solution will be found.

What about the application of inventory models to the supply of intangibles such as plant capacity, research projects, and the like? In these cases the fact that inventory models assume a forecast of demand is much more limiting. In such problems the forecast of demand is often, if not usually, the major obstacle. How, for example, does one forecast demand for liquid assets? And in the case of intangibles there is an additional difficulty because the relevant costs are not generally known and often can only be estimated within rather wide ranges. What, for example, is the cost of maintaining a supply of liquid capital, and what is the cost of being out of stock? Difficulties such as these rather sharply circumscribe the indefinitely wide applicability of inventory models. Nonetheless, when forecasts and costs can be had, the inventory models can be applied with good promise of success. We hope that our examples of the work pool-problem, the hotel-reservation problem, and the overtime problem (all in Chapter 10) have served to illustrate some of the possible applications of inventory models to decision problems other than those dealing with inventories of the more usual kinds of things.

105. WAITING-LINE MODELS

In the first section of this chapter we discussed an underlying similarity which we suggested could be called the "servicing" problem. This is the problem of providing sufficient facilities to meet the needs of persons or things that arrive at the facility, are given some "service," and then depart. An unexpectedly large number of processes meet this description, and there are a correspondingly large number of decision problems that depend upon the analysis of this kind of situation. We mentioned that this kind of problem is really a special case of the inventory problem, since it is obviously a question of maintaining a supply of facilities to meet future demand. However, the analysis differs sufficiently from that of other inventory problems to justify considering it to be a separate subclass. We must first attempt to discover the reason for this difference.

It will be instructive to compare three problems that were discussed in Part III. These are the repairmen problem, in Chapter 10, and the work-pool problem and the overtime problem, both in Chapter 11. All three of these problems are inventory problems where the thing being stored is time (in the form of men). Yet the work-pool problem and the overtime problem were handled by straightforward applications of inventory models, while the repairmen problem required analysis in terms of waiting lines. Why the difference?

The explanation in the case of the overtime problem is fairly obvious. In that problem the out-of-stock cost (equivalent to the back-order cost) is simply the extra labor costs required because the personnel have to work overtime in order to complete the day's workload. There is no cost caused by the fact that some of the workload had to wait until the overtime period before being completed. In short, in the overtime problem there was no waiting-time cost. Therefore it could be handled directly as an inventory problem. However, this is not true of the other two problems. In both cases the out-of-stock cost is a penalty cost caused by not having a man available. In the repairmen problem this is the amount per hour that it costs to have a machine not working, and in the work-pool problem it is the amount per day that it costs to have a position unfilled. At this level the problems are similar, although one is based on hours and the other on days.

The difference between these two stems from the fact that in the work-pool problem the positions can be filled the next day by the absent employees of the day before, whereas a broken machine must wait until it is repaired. In the work-pool problem an absent employee corresponds to a broken machine in the repairmen problem. In terms of this correspondence we can say that in the work-pool example "the machine can repair itself" by an employee's returning to work. The machines in the repairmen problem cannot repair themselves so they must wait until a repairman is available. Hence this problem requires analysis in terms of waiting lines. In any case where something requires some kind of service from one of a limited number of facilities and where there is a cost associated with any delay caused by the something's having to wait for a facility we will have to use waiting-line analysis rather than the other inventory models.

A great variety of waiting-line models have been developed to handle the different cases that arise in practice. All of them are developed in terms of two measurable quantities: (1) the *arrival rate* of the things or persons to be serviced and (2) the *service rate* at the facility. The service rate is commonly called the *departure rate*, since at the conclusion of the service the thing or person departs from the facility. Both of these rates can be directly measured by an observer with a stop watch or some suitable recording device. Such measurements can be readily converted to probability distributions showing the probability of a given number of arrivals per time unit and the probability that a given time will be required to complete the servicing. These two distributions were given directly in our repairmen problem. As might be expected, it is the ratio of the average arrival rate to the average departure rate that governs the behavior of the waiting lines. Mathematical analysis which is sometimes of great complexity is used to determine various characteristics of the resulting process. Two of the more important measures of the behavior of the process are (1) the average number of things or persons in line waiting for service and (2) the average waiting time required in order to get service. The great variety of models that exist is required to handle all the variants of the fundamental waiting-line process that occur in practice. Some of the major variants are:

1. *Different probability distributions for arrivals.* For example, an assembly line delivers parts to a specific worker at a constant rate. Motorists arriving at a toll booth will have some probability distribution of arrivals.

2. *Different probability distributions for service times.* For example, a vending machine will service each customer with a constant service time but a doctor will require differing times (a probability distribution) to service his patients.

3. *Number of facilities.* For example, a single repairman must service all broken machines but a large airfield has several landing strips to service incoming planes.

4. *Servicing order.* This refers to the way in which the facility selects the next customer to be serviced. For example, a ticket office services the next customer in line, but a telephone operator chooses one of the waiting calls at random.

5. *Waiting-line discipline.* This refers to whether the waiting customers can switch to a shorter line (in the case of more than one facility). For example, a customer in line at a bank teller window will switch to a shorter line if he sees one, but a motorist in line for a toll booth usually cannot switch lines.

6. *Priorities.* There may be a set of priorities giving precedence to some customers over others. For example, broken machines might be repaired in the order of the cost of their being out of operation or in such order that shorter repair jobs are always done first.

Each combination of these variants, and of others not mentioned, requires separate mathematical analysis, so the profusion of waiting-line models is a necessity. The purpose of the mathematical analysis is, of course, to discover the important characteristics of the resulting waiting lines. It is worth noting that it is possible to determine the waiting-line characteristics by direct observation in the form of Monte Carlo samples. Any waiting-line process can be Monte-Carloed. Enormous samples may have to be taken in order to get reliable results, but the use of computers makes this necessity less of a handicap than it would otherwise be.

Granting, then, an adequate description of the process being considered, it is possible to obtain either through mathematical analysis or through Monte Carlo methods the average waiting time that will result with various numbers of facilities. It is this waiting time that constitutes one of the two opposing costs of waiting-time problems. The average service time is one of the facts of the process and is accepted as such in the analysis. But the average waiting time decreases as the number of facilities increases and can, therefore, be controlled by management. The other cost is, evidently, the cost of the facility. For any given number of facilities the average waiting time can be determined. Given the cost per unit of waiting time and the cost of operating each facility, it is then simple to find the total cost for each number of facilities. The minimum such total cost then determines the optimal number of facilities.

The procedure outlined above is straightforward, and usually the only difficulty in obtaining the necessary data is in determining the waiting-time costs. Generally the cost of operating the facility is obtainable from accounting data, which may also yield the waiting-time cost. However, in the many cases where the waiting line consists of prospective customers it is difficult, or virtually impossible, to estimate the waiting-time cost. The possible cost of loss of customer goodwill is a major component which can only rarely be determined. However, in cases where the waiting-time cost cannot be estimated it is still possible to provide the decision-maker with the average waiting time that will result for any selection of number of facilities. This provides him with a quantitative basis for exercising his judgement as to acceptable waiting times.

Evaluated from the decision-maker's point of view there is no question whatsoever concerning the value of waiting-line models in analyzing decision problems involving this kind of situation. The necessary techniques are well developed and relatively easy to apply to specific problems, and no unrealistic assumptions or data requirements are involved. Further, waiting-line behavior is often contrary to an inexperienced intuition, so it is not easy to find the optimal strategy by judgement alone. The very nature of the waiting-line process implies that waiting lines can only be shortened by increasing the over-all idle time of the facilities. In order to have the facilities busy most of the time it is necessary to have waiting lines most of the time. Casual observation of such a process will generally lead to the wrong conclusions. A supervisor who walks repeatedly through the machine shop of our repairmen problem, for example, will find the two repairmen idle 75 per cent of the time. He might well decide to fire one of them because of this. Nonetheless, this was the optimal strategy, and firing one of the repairmen would increase total costs considerably. Only a careful analysis of the total costs of such situations in terms of waiting-line models can unequivocally determine the best strategy.

In our problem section we included only one problem involving waiting lines, the repairmen problem of Chapter 10. The reason was not that this kind of problem is unimportant. On the contrary, as our remarks above should show, problems of this kind are frequent and important and the models are very valuable tools in resolving them. However, many of the most interesting of the waiting-line models are of a degree of complexity that puts them beyond the range of our discussion.

106. ALLOCATION OF RESOURCES

A large number of important decision problems involve the allocation of resources to various activities in such a way as to maximize profit or to minimize costs. Typically, there are a number of things to be done and there are not sufficient resources available to do each of them in the most effective way. This second fact is the demonstration that a problem exists and a hint suggesting the way to solve it. If there were sufficient resources to do everything in the best possible way there could be no problem; one would simply do everything in the best way. The problem arises because the limitation of resources requires that some things be done in a less-than-best way. The decision problem, then, is to assign the things that must be done to the available resources so that the total cost is minimized or the total profit maximized. The fact that some things must be done in a less-than-optimal way means that opportunity costs arise and suggests that one method for finding the best allocation would be to minimize these opportunity costs.

The simplest example of such a problem is the assignment problem, treated in Chapter 10. In the problem considered there it was necessary to assign a group of jobs for simultaneous processing to a group of machines, any one of which could do any one of the jobs. The cost of processing each job differs according to which machine processes it. The decision problem is to assign the jobs to the machines so that the total processing cost is minimized. The problem results from the fact that one machine does several jobs most cheaply but only one job can be assigned to it. The method of solution for this kind of problem is based on the determination of the opportunity costs of the various possible assignments. The problem used as an example in Chapter 10 typifies the assignment problem. The defining characteristic of this kind of problem is that each activity (job in our example) must be assigned to exactly one resource (machine in our example) and each resource must be assigned to exactly one job. Other examples of this kind of problem are: the assignment of salesmen to sales regions, the assignment of executives to positions, the assignment of consultants to clients, and similar ones. The procedure for determining the optimal assignments is so simple that there is no possible excuse for not using this model when it is applicable. However, its applicability is sharply limited by the difficulty of determining the necessary costs or other measures of utility. It is necessary to know the cost or measure of utility for each of the possible assignments. These data can often be obtained from cost-accounting reports in the case of assignments of jobs to machines, but it will usually be extremely difficult to determine the utilities involved in the other examples cited above.

A more frequently occurring kind of allocation problem is the transportation problem. An example of this kind of problem was given in Chapter 10. In a transportation problem there are a group of origins (the factories in our example) and a group of destinations (warehouses in our example). Each origin has a limited quantity (factory capacity) of the commodity that it can ship and each of the destinations has a requirement for a certain amount of the commodity (the warehouse requirements). Generally any origin can ship to any destination, but this is not a requirement of the model. The cost of shipping a unit amount from each origin to each destination is fixed. The decision problem is to determine the minimum-cost shipping schedule that meets all the requirements of the destinations while remaining within the capacities of the origins.

The method of solution depends on an iterative process which evaluates the opportunity costs involved in specific shipping schedules and changes the schedules until a schedule is found that has an opportunity cost of zero. This, of course, is by definition the lowest-cost shipping schedule. The method of solution illustrated in our example requires that the total cost of any specific shipment should be simply the cost per unit times the amount shipped. In other words, quantity transportation discounts cannot be included if this method is to be used. However, in this case the procedure to be discussed below can be used. The simplicity of the method of solution and the fact that all the necessary cost data are easily available make this model an extremely useful one. Many actual transportation problems are far too large to be solved by hand, but the method of solution is well adapted for computers so the size of the problem is not an obstacle. This technique has been used repeatedly and has in many instances produced large transportation-cost savings.

Each of these two kinds of allocation problem is actually a special case of a far more general formulation of the allocation problem. This is the *linear programming model,* one of the most widely used of all operations-research models. We have given two examples of it (apart from the assignment and transportation examples which, as mentioned above, are special kinds of linear programming models). These examples were the media problem of Chapter 9 and the problem concerning the optimal utilization of plant capacity in Chapter 10. Linear programming models, in common with the other allocation models, are useful in situations where restrictions on the use of resources render it impossible to perform each activity in the same way it would be performed if it were the only activity to be performed. There is a conflict between activities; some of them must be performed, therefore, in less-than-optimal ways. Thus opportunity costs are involved, and there is a problem of determining the best allocation of resources to activities. This kind of conflict is expressed in the model in the form of equations showing the limitations on the combinations of amounts of the various activities. For the problem involving the optimal utilization of plant capacity these limitations arose because of the limited capacities of the various plant departments. In other cases the limitations may take the form of minimum (or maximum) amounts prescribed because of space limitations, money limitations, or any other.

Essential, however, for a linear programming model is the requirement that the expression showing each of the restrictions should be linear with regard to each of the activities in question. This is another way of saying that each additional unit of the activity must add a constant amount to the quantity being restricted. In our plant-capacity example an increase of one unit in the amount produced of either of the products required a constant amount of departmental capacity. Similarly, the expression that shows the relation of the activities to the objective must be linear with regard to the activities. That is, returns from the activities must be "to scale": twice as much of an activity produces twice as much profit, if the objective is to maximize profit; or twice as much of an activity costs twice as much, if the objective is to minimize costs. The fact that the restrictions and the objective function have to be linear with regard to the activities accounts for the name of the model, linear programming.

The decision problem is solved by finding the levels of the various activities that maximize (or minimize) the objective function while satisfying all the restrictions. Naturally, all the activities must occur either at a zero level or in some positive amount, since there is no meaning to a negative amount of an activity. It is usually the case that most of the restrictions in linear programming problems take the form of inequalities. In this event it is necessary to add one variable to each inequation to convert it to an equation. These variables are called *slack variables* and are activities just as much as the other activity variables in the equations. In our example, if a slack variable had occurred at a positive level in the optimal solution it would have meant that the corresponding productive facility was not utilized to its full capacity. One of the important conclusions of the mathematical analysis of this kind of problem is that the maximization (or minimization) of the objective function can be achieved with no more activities at positive levels than there are restrictions. For our example of the allocation of plant capacity we had two restrictions (for the two departments) and two activities (the two products). In our optimal solution some of each product was produced. However, we could equally well have started with 3, 5, 10, or any number of activities (products). The mathematical conclusion which we mentioned assures us that, no matter how many products were involved, we would never need to produce more than two in order to get maximum profit (since there are only two restrictions).

Where there are less than four activities it is possible to solve the decision problem geometrically. We used this method in our example dealing with media since it provides some insight into the algebraic procedure followed when there are four or more activities (the procedure can equally well be used instead of the geometric solution for less than four activities). We used this algebraic procedure in our example dealing with plant capacity. The procedure is an iterative one. Starting with a specific set of activity levels that meet the restrictions we use a simple criterion to determine whether the solution can be improved. If the answer is affirmative we use another criterion to discover which activity should be replaced in our solution. We then replace it by the activity, which changes the objective function value in the desired direction. This series of steps is repeated until no further improvement is possible, which means that the optimal solution has been found. The best-known procedure for accomplishing this iterative process is called the *simplex* process. The procedure we followed in the plant-capacity example is equivalent to the simplex process, but the simplex process requires a lesser amount of pencil work. The cost of this saving of muscular effort, however, is an increase in the time required to learn the elements of linear programming, so we have not given an example of the simplex process. Since many linear programming problems that arise include large numbers of activities and restrictions it is, in practice, necessary to take advantage of the saving in effort afforded by the simplex process—especially since the simplex process is well suited for use in computers.

A highly important mathematical fact concerning linear programming problems is that they really come in pairs. To every linear programming maximization (or minimization) problem there corresponds a linear programming minimization (or maximization) problem. The two problems thus paired are called *dual problems*. The dual of any linear programming problem is formed from the same data as the original but arranged in a different order. For example, any problem of the allocation of plant capacity that has two products and two departments, as did our example of Chapter 10, can be formulated thus:

To maximize $\qquad$ Profit $= p_1 x_1 + p_2 x_2$

Subject to $\qquad a_{11}x_1 + a_{12}x_2 \leqq 100$
$$a_{21}x_1 + a_{22}x_2 \leqq 100$$
$$x_1 \geqq 0$$
$$x_2 \geqq 0$$

In this formulation a_{11} represents the percentage of capacity of Department 1 that the production of one unit of x_1 (the first product) requires,

a_{12} represents the percentage of capacity of Department 1 that the production of one unit of x_2 requires, and so on. This formulation is precisely equivalent to the one we used in our example. Since this is a maximization problem the dual will be a minimization problem. The dual is written with the same constants but different variables.

To minimize $\qquad\qquad Z = 100W_1 + 100W_2$

Subject to $\qquad\qquad a_{11}W_1 + a_{21}W_2 \geqq p_1$
$$a_{12}W_1 + a_{22}W_2 \geqq p_2$$
$$W_1 \geqq 0$$
$$W_2 \geqq 0$$

A little study of how the constants have been rearranged in the dual will disclose the pattern better than will a lengthy verbal explanation, so we forego the latter. The main conclusion of the mathematical analysis of the relationship between the duals is that Z, the objective function of the dual, will have, for the optimal solution, the same value as the final value of the objective function in the original problem, profit in our case. A little dimensional analysis now suggests what the variables in the dual (W_1 and W_2) represent. Since Z is in dollars it follows that the right-hand side of the objective function ($100W_1 + 100W_2$) must be in dollars too. But we know that the coefficients (100 and 100) are capacities, and not in dollars, so it follows that W_1 and W_2 must be in dollars. In fact, they represent prices and, hence, are called "shadow prices." The shadow prices are the values that must be assigned to a unit of capacity in each of the departments in order to minimize the value of the output, the two products. In general, shadow prices represent the economic value per unit of the scarce resources involved in the restrictions of the problem.

Linear programming models are not the only models available for dealing with decision problems involving the allocation of resources. On the one hand there are various models that deal with cases where the linearity requirements cannot be assumed to hold. The quadratic programming model is an example, and there are other nonlinear programming models. On the other hand are models that attempt to represent situations in which the allocation of resources is made in a sequence of decisions over time and the objective is to obtain the maximum return over the entire sequence of decisions. The best-known model of this kind is the dynamic programming model. We used dynamic programming in our example of dividend payout in Chapter 11.

The linear programming model, however, is the one that has been most used in practice. There is an extraordinary diversity of decision problems to which the linear programming model has been applied. A representative sample of such problems includes the optimal blending of gasoline, minimization of trim losses in the manufacture of paper, the minimum-cost diet meeting certain nutritional standards, smoothing production patterns, the optimal scheduling of airline flight crews, determination of an executive compensation plan, and even problems of structural design. All of these problems together with those previously discussed and many others not mentioned have the required linear programming structure: (1) a conflict between activities because of limited resources and (2) linearity of the restrictions and the objective function with regard to the activities.

From the executive's point of view linear programming models are of tremendous value. They provide expeditious means for solving decision problems of such complexity that it is almost impossible to find the optimal strategy by any other method. Two questions can be raised concerning the applicability of these models. First, can the costs that enter into the equations be reliably determined? The answer is that in the majority of frequently occurring linear programming problems, and particularly in those dealing with production, the cost figures can be determined from cost-accounting data. However, even if the cost figures are not really reliable, the linear programming procedure will still be based on the same data that management would use if it selected a strategy by some other means. Therefore, the use of linear programmig will at least ensure the selection of the optimal strategy on the basis of the data management would use anyhow. When linear programming is applied to problems that arise in areas where cost data are not usually collected on a regular basis there can be considerable difficulties in determining the relevant costs. Under these circumstances linear programming can be used with each of a range of sets of costs and the effect of changing assumptions concerning costs can be determined. This in itself can provide the executive with a much sounder basis for handling his decision problem.

The second question is: What is the effect of the linearity assumptions that are required? Do these assumptions sharply limit the kinds of decision problems to which linear programming methods can be applied? The answer is a definite, but qualified, no. First, a great number of practical decision problems involve activities that are linear within the feasible range of levels of the activities. Second, when the activities are not linear over their entire feasible range it is very often possible to split the activity that is not linear into several activities, each of which is linear. Such a procedure can be used, for example, in handling transportation problems where there is a quantity discount. Thus, instead of having one activity that consists, say, of shipping from a specific factory to a specific warehouse we have two activities. The first is the activity of shipping any amount up to the amount at which the discount applies, and the second is the activity of shipping any amount to which the discount applies. But if the nonlinearity cannot be remedied by this means it will be necessary to use some nonlinear programming model. The best proof of the applicability of linear programming methods remains the great number of highly successful uses of these models in actual business decision problems.

107. COMPETITIVE MODELS

The study of the decision problems underlying competitive strategies has been very highly developed under the title of the theory of games. Ordinarily we think of games as being purely recreational and not of importance to our more "serious" activities. In this sense, then, the name, "theory of games," is misleading. Actually, the essence of a competitive situation is that two or more persons or organizations are competing for some objective for which there is a conflict of interests. A game is the prototype of this kind of situation; for this reason the study of competitive decision problems is called the theory of games. The same theory underlies the playfulness of the decision problems in card games and the deadly seriousness of a struggle between two companies for greater shares of the market.

Despite the considerable body of theoretical results in the theory of games there have been few successful applications of the theory to practical decision problems involving competitors. As a result we have included only two examples of decision problems dealing with competitive behavior. The first was the problem concerning the advertising of two department stores in Chapter **9**. This was a genuine "game" and was analyzed as such. The second was the competitive bidding model, also in Chapter **9**. This was not handled as a "game" because all the game-like features were missing. The reason was that the situation was viewed as one company against a group of essentially anonymous competitors. The situation was, therefore, of the kind analyzed in classical economic theory, where no one buyer and no one seller has any influence on price. Game theory does not produce any new results or insights in this kind of situation. Our main question in this section must, therefore, be: Why hasn't game theory been found to be of greater usefulness in competitive decision problems? The subsidiary question will then be: What does game theory contribute to the executive who is faced with such decision problems?

We will be better able to answer these questions if we first discuss the main outlines of game theory as it is presently known. For our purposes it will be sufficient to note two main dichotomies in game theory. First, there are two kinds of games distinguished by the relationship that exists among the payoffs to the various players. Zero-sum games are those in which the sum of the payoffs to all the players is zero. In other words, what one player wins another, or others, must lose. A typical example is the game of poker.   The other kind of game is one in which the sum of the payoffs to all the players need not be zero.   This kind of game is called, for obvious reasons, a nonzero-sum game.   Examples will be given below.   It may be noted that any nonzero-sum game can be converted to a zero-sum game by adding another hypothetical player, "Nature," who always receives a payoff calculated to make the sum of the payoffs equal to zero.   This fact is important theoretically but it doesn't help in the analysis of any specific nonzero-sum game.   The second dichotomy has to do with the number of players.   Specifically, we want to distinguish between games with exactly two players and games with any number of players greater than two.   We will now try to explain why these two dichotomies are important in understanding the present sharp limitations on the usefulness of game theory in competitive decision problems.

Let us consider the case of the two-person zero-sum game.   In this case there is a complete conflict of interest; what one person gains the other losses.   Analysis of this kind of game has led to a number of important conclusions.   First, the decision criterion must be the maximin or minimax criterion.   The use of any other criterion can lead only to a smaller payoff if the opponent uses the maximin criterion.   Second, the value of the game to one player is the negative value to the other player if both of them use their maximin and minimax strategies.   Third, to obtain this value it may be necessary to use a mixed strategy consisting of the random selection of one of several possible strategies.   The method by which the optimal strategy is determined is known, and it may therefore be said that the theory of two-person zero-sum games is essentially complete.

What happens when we try to extend this analysis to some number of players greater than two, still assuming a zero-sum game?   A major difficulty immediately arises.   As soon as there are three or more players it becomes possible for coalitions of players to form.   In a game of three players, for example, two of them may form a coalition against the third and by agreeing to their own selections of strategies may guarantee themselves payoffs greater than those which would result from their maximin strategies.   Naturally, this gain is at the expense of the third player.   Further, a coalition may be able to increase its total payoff by including a player who would sustain a loss by selecting the strategy desired by the coalition.   In this case the coalition can offer him a side payment which may induce him to join.   So coalitions, countercoalitions, and countercountercoalitions can form in ways as numerous as they are fascinating and bewildering.   The net effect of all these possibilities is that there is no generally accepted theory of zero-sum games with more than two players, although there are several extremely ingenious efforts in this direction.

Finally, consider a two-person nonzero-sum game. Here the difficulties are equally severe. First, the two players can form a coalition against "Nature," if necessary with side payments, since there may be specific strategies for which they both receive positive payoffs (since the game is nonzero-sum). It may profit one of the two players to desert the coalition. Whether he does so or not will depend on whether the game is to be repeated and on the amount of retribution his opponent can subsequently inflict upon him. Finally, and most important, one player may be able to inflict large losses on his opponent at the cost of small losses to himself. He can then use this possibility as a threat to force his opponent to select strategies that afford him greater payoffs. This feature of two-person nonzero-sum games has led to extensive analysis of threats, bargaining positions, arbitration procedures, and so on. The results are usually of great interest but it seems that, for any general theory, games can be constructed for which the theory gives a solution that is contrary to common sense. As a result there is as yet no generally accepted theory of these games.

Now let us return to practical competitive decision problems. First, they usually have more than two opponents. Second, they are generally nonzero-sum. As a result, there is no general theory competent to analyze these problems. The fact that most competitive decision problems have more than two opponents is obvious, but the statement that they are usually nonzero-sum requires some defense. There are two reasons. First, the actual situation may be such that the payoffs do not sum to zero. For example, an advertising campaign may expand the whole market so that all opponents get larger amounts. Second, a competitive situation can only be zero-sum if all the opponents' utilities are measured by the same payoff measure. If they have different utilities for the various payoffs the game is automatically a nonzero-sum game. Yet, as we have noted before, there is good reason to believe that the utilities will be different for the different opponents. Finally, it may be noted that if the utilities are different it is necessary for each opponent to know the utilities of the other opponents for the various possible outcomes in order to even have a nonzero-sum game. If the utilities are unknown the situation becomes a game against nature with decision-making under uncertainty. These various reasons explain why game theory has found few applications in practical competitive decision problems.

Nonetheless, game theory does provide some useful insights into competitive situations. One such is the fact that the decision criterion in competitive situations should be the maximin criterion. Another is the idea of mixed strategies. It is not at all obvious that it is sometimes necessary to randomly select a strategy in order to gain the maximum possible payoff. Yet this turns out to be the case in competitive situations. This realization can be of considerable value in competitive decision problems.

108. TWO OTHER MODELS

The four models discussed in the preceding four sections are, without doubt, the major models of operations research. There are, however, other models that are worthy of mention. Obviously, the question of what is a sufficiently general model is to a considerable degree a matter of taste. The models discussed above each cover a remarkable range of seemingly different problems. On the other hand, some models have been developed to handle a single decision problem arising for one company at one specific time. In between these two extremes are a great number of models covering differing numbers of separate decision problems. We have selected two of these for brief comment.

The first one is known as the *replacement model*. This model is concerned with decision problems arising with reference to the replacement of parts or components of some complex system. Such problems arise in connection with things as diverse as light bulbs, machines, and executives. In any population of similar elements such as these an item that fails must be replaced by a similar item. Problems arise as to the expected number of replacements needed at various times in the future, the optimal replacement procedure, maintenance policies, and so on. In the case of a population of executives a desired age distribution may be an objective. What should be the hiring policy in order to achieve this age distribution? These and a variety of similar questions can only be answered on the basis of replacement models, which analyze precisely these kinds of problems. The models generally demand advanced mathematical treatment, so we have not included any examples of replacement problems here. The models are, however, available for the analysis of these kinds of decision situations.

The last model we will mention is the *search model*. It is less well developed than any of the other models we have discussed but it has promise of becoming very useful for a great variety of decision problems. People search for many different things: scientists search for hypotheses, decision-makers search for optimal strategies, advertising agencies search for customers, personnel departments search for good potential executives. All of the various searches have similarities, and the search model undertakes to determine and analyze the common elements. The first such model was developed during World War II to solve decision problems connected with air patrol searches for enemy submarines. The result of the application of the model was a considerable improvement in the effectiveness of the search system. There are a number of difficulties connected with the attempt to incorporate into the model the essential features of the kinds of searches mentioned above and, as a result, the model is not yet sufficiently developed. However, there appears to be no intrinsic reason why this model cannot eventually be further developed and applied to these other kinds of searches.

109. OPERATIONS RESEARCH: AN OVERVIEW

The preceding sections of this chapter have attempted to give a general picture of the various models of operations research together with some remarks about the value of the various models to the decision-making executive. The various models discussed were used in many of the problems we considered in Part III, and the more general discussion in this chapter has been intended to supplement the more detailed analyses of Part III. We will devote the final section of this chapter to some conclusions that may be drawn about the use of operations research in solving decision problems.

The reader perhaps noticed that the problems discussed in Chapter 9, on Marketing, seemed more complicated and generally somewhat less precise than those treated in Chapter 10, on Production. This difference is no accident, and its explanation will give some insight into the process of evaluating the economics of a search for a solution to a specific decision problem. We will focus our discussion on two aspects of operations-research solutions.

First, all the solutions depend on some set of costs, whether measured in dollars or in utilities. The solutions generally depend on the accuracy with which these costs are measured; and as more costs are involved, the greater will be the cumulative effect of inaccuracies in the costs. In the case of the inventory model we were able to develop a procedure for describing all optimal solutions—for any carrying costs and ordering costs. But the usefulness of this procedure depends fundamentally on there being three or less costs. For larger numbers of costs it would not provide any assistance to the decision-maker. Now, generally speaking, operations research does not have any magical means of estimating costs. Sometimes an ingenious method for estimating a specific cost is discovered but this is the exception rather than the rule. We would expect, then, that operations-research solutions would be most frequent in those areas where reliable cost estimates are most often available. This is exactly what we find. Cost estimates are readily available wherever cost-accounting systems have been used and, hence, most frequently in the areas of production and the clerical side of administration. In the area of marketing there are generally not any good estimates of the relevant costs. Therefore there is either the additional problem of trying to estimate the costs or the problem of trying to avoid them. In either case the solution to the decision problem is one step further removed.

Second, solutions depend on the number of factors that must be taken into account. This statement does not refer to a simple count of the factors. Any large linear programming problem is sufficient to show that the mere size of the problem is no insurmountable obstacle, at least as long as computers are available. Rather, we have reference to the inter-relationships among the factors. And, again, we do not mean a simple count of the number of interrelationships. If a mathematical equation can be written that describes all the interrelationships some method will be found to use it. The problem is to write the equation. In order to do this we must know the form the interrelationship takes. And the form the interrelationship takes is not, to put it bluntly, generally known in the marketing field. It is much more likely to be known in the production area. The major reason is simply the question of control. Most of the relevant factors are under the decision-maker's control in production, whereas many crucial factors are outside his control in marketing. Even when the factors are under control it can be an extremely onerous task to disentangle the interrelationships. A case in point is the lengthy re-search effort required to determine the interactions among the umpteen factors that affect the growth of penicillin. Yet virtually any major marketing decision has as many, or more, factors and many of them are not under the control of the decision-maker. He cannot set their level and then run experiments varying the factors one by one, two by two, and so on. Thus, in the marketing area a solution will often depend on laborious attempts to disentangle the interactions of the various factors and will, even then, usually require some rather ruthless assumptions.

Both of these differences in the two areas act to make operations-research solutions less likely and less reliable in the marketing area than in the production area. Other factors operate in the same direction. One major one, the difference between physical systems and behavioral systems in terms of stability, will be discussed in Chapter 14. Now, none of these difficulties is intrinsically insuperable, but the resolution of them requires the accumulated experience of many different efforts to solve them. But here the argument of Chapter 12 enters the picture. Since the probability of a return from a search for a solution in the mar-keting area is smaller, it follows that fewer companies can afford to un-dertake the search. Thus, experience accumulates more slowly in the development of suitable marketing models.

The same reasoning, however, has a happy side. The converse of all these arguments is that the models of operations research are particularly well developed in the production area. For decision problems in this area, and in others where the above arguments are less relevant, there is a very high probability of a return from a search for a solution, and many models are available ready-made for the solution of these problems. Even small companies can profitably utilize these models in their decision problems. And, as experience accumulates, we can expect a steady increase in the number of adequate models available in the more difficult fields.

PROBLEMS

1. In our discussion of problems in the allocation of resources we stated that the transportation problem was a special case of this more general kind of problem. This suggests that the transportation problem might be solved by means of linear programming and, as a matter of fact, this is true. Consider the following simple transportation problem:

	FACTORIES			
WAREHOUSES	I	II	III	REQUIREMENTS
A	$5	4	6	600
B	6	7	8	400
C	8	7	6	500
CAPACITIES:	300	500	700	1500

  a. Determine the minimum cost transportation schedule by the method used previously.
  b. Set up the equations which express this problem in linear programming form.
  c. In "b" we refer to "equations." Shouldn't this be "inequations"? (Note that there are six restrictions but the answer to "c" implies that only five of them are necessary since if any five are fulfilled the sixth will be also. In mathematical terminology we say that only five of the equations are independent.)
  d. Use the solution obtained in "a" and see whether the linear programming objective function shows that this is an optimal solution.

2. A company which manufactures dog food has a great number of different ingredients which it could use in mixing the final product. The final product must meet certain minimum nutritional requirements such as percentage of protein, percentage of fat, amount of vitamins, etc. The objective is to minimize the cost of the final product.
  a. What information would be needed in order to formulate this as a linear programming problem?
  b. Introduce whatever symbols you need and put this problem in linear programming form.
  c. What does the requirement that the restrictions and the objective equation must be linear mean in this problem?

3. An oil company can mix its blending stocks in a variety of ways to make a corresponding variety of final products. There are a fixed number of different blending stocks and the total available amount of each blending stock is fixed. Per unit profits for the various final products are different. The company objective is to maximize profit.

    a. What information is needed in order to formulate this as a linear programming problem?

    b. Introduce whatever symbols you need and put this problem in linear programming form.

    c. What does the requirement that the restrictions and the objective equation must be linear mean in this problem?

4. A company has large retirement plan funds which it invests. Top level policy has been established which places percentage limits on the amounts which can be invested in bonds, preferred stocks, and common stocks. The manager of the funds wants to obtain the maximum possible returns from the investments.

    a. Formulate this as a linear programming problem.

    b. Why isn't this really a linear programming problem?

5. A company maintains inventories on 500 items. The average cost (total cost divided by total number of items used) to the company of these items is $2 per unit and the average monthly demand per item is 100 units. The company estimates its carrying costs at 10 per cent per year and its ordering costs at $10 per order. Over the last year the average inventory has been $250,000 and it is felt that this is too high. Company policy is to order each item once each month and to maintain a reserve stock of one month's demand for each item. What improvement do you think can be achieved through the use of inventory theory?

6. We have emphasized four kinds of costs, which can be involved in inventory problems. Most inventory problems involve only these four costs or some subgroup of them. However, there are exceptions. One such is a department store inventory of women's fashion dresses. In this case the department store does not maintain an inventory of dresses in each style, color, and size combination. Instead, the store will use its "inventory" to increase the number of styles and colors which it has on its racks. In other words, an increase in "inventory" means an increase in variety rather than an increase of the number of each variety. The reason for this is that the variety and, hence, the inventory attracts customers. In our terms we can say that the inventory serves to create demand. How would you analyze this problem?

7. As an example of some of the difficulties involved in the analysis of two-person nonzero-sum games we can use the following:

	A'S PAYOFFS			B'S PAYOFFS	
	B1	B2		B1	B2
A1	1	−4	A1	1	5
A2	5	−2	A2	−4	−2

a. What are the players' maximin strategies? Should they use them?
b. Consider the difference if the game is only played once or if it is going to be played a number of times.
c. Consider the difference if communication is allowed between the players before the game is played.
d. Suppose A and B are competitors and the first strategy in each case is to leave price unchanged. The second strategy is to lower price. Do you think payoff matrices such as these might be reasonable representations of this situation?

Chapter fourteen

Implementation and Control
of Operations-Research Solutions

We have discussed the conditions that lead an executive to use operations research to help him resolve his decision problems. We would then expect that, having obtained a solution, the executive would proceed in his accustomed manner to implement the solution, observe the results, and make further decisions as they were required. However, as we observed in Part I, deciding and doing can be quite closely related to each other. We concluded, at that time, that it was entirely reasonable to consider decisions apart from actions for the purposes of formulating the decision framework. In this way, we were spared the problems that arise when a theoretical solution conceived on paper or in the mind of the executive must be converted into practice. We now want to consider what happens when the executive transforms solutions into decisions and decisions into actions.

110. FORM OF THE SOLUTION

1. *The degree of specificity of the strategies.* Depending upon the nature of the problem solved, the executive may find that the strategies are completely explicit with respect to what actions he should take. However, this circumstance would be unusual. More often, the solution specifies a strategy that is stated in general terms. For example, the solution to an inventory problem might list the minimum amount of each item to

keep in stock. The solution does not tell the decision-maker how he should go about maintaining the required levels. It does not tell him what kind of records to keep, how the level should be measured, what companies to order from. Similarly, the solution to the media problem does not specify the form of the message, the dates on which each medium should be used, the page on which the advertisement should appear. We can distinguish these multitudinous elements that produce the strategy as *tactics*.

It is inconceivable, in most circumstances, to include all relevant tactical factors in the decision problem, and it is generally not necessary to include them all since the assumption is made that the decision-maker has enough tactical means at his disposal to enable him to fulfill the strategy. However, at the point of implementation the decision-maker must reconsider the validity of this assumption. He could not detail all possible tactical approaches for each of a great number of alternative strategies. But now that the solution has indicated one particular strategy he must concentrate his attention on fulfilling that strategy. We must always bear in mind that deciding what to do is not the same thing as deciding how to do it. The solution to a decision problem can be to increase the variety of flavors sold under a single brand name. But the choice of which additional flavors may not be specified. Implementation of this decision requires tactical decisions having as their objective the fulfillment of the strategic decision. It is clear that what may be a tactical decision in one case may be a strategic decision in another. Referring to our example of flavors, if the decision problem were conceived as the optimal selection of a set of new flavors then the strategies would be the various combinations of flavors that could be used. Many tactical problems would still remain after this decision was reached, such as what color, what sweetness, what strength. Nevertheless, the form of any solution can be examined in terms of the extent to which the strategies offer explicit instructions for carrying out the decision.

2. *The degree of certainty of the outcome.* Another aspect of the form of the solution concerns the specificity of the outcome. When a solution is obtained under conditions of certainty, then the decision-maker knows exactly what will happen if he chooses to implement a specific strategy. On the other hand, if the solution is derived for conditions of risk or uncertainty, then the decision-maker does not know exactly what will occur. That is why he must utilize a decision criterion in order to produce a solution. Degree of certainty, we know, is the direct result of the way in which Nature takes part in the problem. States of nature, by definition, are not under the decision-maker's control—but they play a vital part in his evaluation of the solution. We will have occasion to go into this subject in much greater depth as this chapter progresses.

3. *Repetitive and nonrepetitive solutions.* From a purely theoretical point of view, we have not had to distinguish between decisions that are made once and decisions that are made many times. Expected values provide the solution to risk problems whether the problem arises once or frequently. However, when a solution must be implemented, the question of how often the decision will be made becomes important. In this regard, we can further differentiate the solution as to whether it will be the exact same decision that is made each time or a different solution based on the use of a general model. For example, the decision with respect to the location of a new plant is made only once. The decision of what level of inventory to carry is made only once but it is used over and over again, without change, until costs, demand, or some other factor is altered. The decision of how much stock to order can change at each order point, based on previous demand and forecasts of future demand. We will see that the repetitive character of the form of the solution influences the implementation phase.

4. *Degree of reversibility.* When something can be done that can be undone without any loss whatever, the form of the solution is completely reversible. In some cases, the tactics used to put a decision into effect can vary widely in the way that they affect the reversibility of a decision. For example, if the decision is made to increase the warehouse facilities of a company, renting additional space has a greater degree of reversibility than building a new warehouse. Similarly, renting computer equipment permits the decision-maker to return to the previous methods of data-processing if his decision to use computer equipment was not the best one. Temporary assignments to executive positions, test markets for redesigned products, and inventory test periods in which larger stocks are maintained until the reduced stocks required by the inventory decision have proved themselves to be adequate, are further examples of tactics with some degree of reversibility. In most of the cases, the decision-maker is willing to accept a lesser gain in the long run in exchange for increased security with respect to the soundness of his decision. The loss in his gain that the decision-maker is willing to take is related directly to his degree of belief in the solution and his degree of control in applying the solution. These two subjects will be treated in separate sections in this chapter.

5. *Degree of permanence of the solution.* The states of nature that exist at the time of the solution can change to other states at a later time. For example, an unexpected technological break-through can rapidly alter production and market conditions. The change does not have to be this extreme. It can occur gradually, escaping detection unless adequate means are set up to watch for this eventuality. In still other cases, because of feedback, strategies result in outcomes that alter

the state of nature.   For example, the decision to introduce variety will in all likelihood produce a number of responses that will permanently alter competitive strategies and states of nature.   The decision-maker will, of course, try to predict the changes, but his predictions may be poor for a number of effects other than his immediate profit.   Consequently, the decision-maker must take appropriate steps in his implementation to allow for the lack of permanence in states of nature.   In this respect, the executive problems of long-range planning tend to emphasize the uncertainties that exist with respect to the permanence of states of nature, while short-range plans are based on a relatively stable nature.

When states of nature change, such that states that had zero probability of occurring take on a larger probability of occurring, it is almost implicit that different strategies will provide the optimal solution.   For this reason, the decision-maker will consider the relative permanence of strategies.   In fact, that is what is generally meant by long- and short-term planning.   Long-term planning strategies are meant to provide relatively permanent strategies in the face of less permanent states of nature.   Short-term plans are not intended to remain for long periods of time and are expected to be replaced when, for example, the likelihood of a specific state of nature shifts from .10 to .50.   While these issues exist throughout the entire problem-solving phase, they gain most importance when the solution must be implemented.   There is no question that the problem-solving effort can be directed to provide solutions with more or less permanence.   But it is the decision-maker at the point of implementation who must contend with the problem.

There are, of course, still other ways in which the form of the solution can be characterized.   But we can consider the ones that have been given to represent the points of major interest to the executive when he thinks about the problem—and its solution—in terms of implementation.

111.   DEGREE OF BELIEF

The fact that a solution has been obtained does not mean that the decision-maker will always have equal faith in the essential correctness of the solution.   The word, solution, has a very final sound.   It is the end point of a search process that has attempted to investigate all relevant factors and to combine them in such a way as to simulate the outcomes that would occur if the factors were actually combined.   "Solution" implies that the outcomes have been transformed into payoffs reflecting the utility of the outcome to the decision-maker.   "Solution" also connotes that a decision criterion has been employed to select the "optimal" strategy.   The degree of belief that the decision-maker has for the soundness of the solution will vary.   It will depend upon how many factors were investigated and combined—and how many were left out. The degree of belief will be affected by the extent to which the payoff measures actually reflect the decision-maker's utilities. His degree of belief will further depend upon the extent to which the decision criterion expresses his intuition and attitudes. We have shown that a number of different decision criteria exist, and we now want to emphasize that many more could be created. Since a choice must be made between different decision criteria, it is to be expected that frequently the decision-maker will not be 100 per cent satisfied with any of the available criteria. This dissatisfaction must be expressed in a lower degree of belief in the solution.

We can make the general statement that the executive's degree of belief in the goodness of a solution will always be affected by the assumptions that he knows have been made in order to reach the solution. Many times, they will be his own assumptions—and for these, he will know better than anyone else how much faith he places in them.

The extent to which error could influence the solution is another point on which the executive evaluates the "answer" to his problems. Errors can arise in many ways, but in general, the executive does not include computational or technical mistakes as errors. Most important are errors of estimation and errors of prediction. For example, if the problem requires an estimate of the number of people between the ages of 25–40 who are blue-collar workers, the executive knows that the figure used will not be exact. As far as predictive errors are concerned, the forecasts of expected demand for a particular product are certain to include error. But the important point is how much error—and how sensitive is the solution to error? If the solution is very sensitive to error, and a small amount of error is likely to exist, then the executive will place less belief in the solution. On the other hand, if the solution is relatively insensitive to error, and only a small amount of error is likely to exist, then the executive can place a higher degree of belief in the solution. For example, in the competitive-bidding problem, we observed that for the specific example used, a large error in the estimation of the cost of fulfilling the contract could be tolerated before the solution shifted to a different bid. Similarly, in linear programming problems, the shape and orientation of the solution polygon with respect to the payoff function can, at times, permit an entire range of optimal solutions (when the payoff function falls along a line of the polygon rather than first intersecting with a corner). In the same way, mixed strategies can result in which the minimax (or the maximin) is not a point but a line. Any combination of strategies that falls along such a line meets the requirements of the solution.

One of the most important factors influencing the decision-maker is his ability to control the solution. In other words, the problem-solvers will have told him that if he will use strategy x he should obtain the best possible payoff, y. The solution may contain all of the elements of control that the decision-maker deems necessary. But he will come to his conclusion after a careful evaluation of the solution. Generally, the degree of belief the decision-maker has for a solution will increase with the amount of control he is able to exercise.

112. DEGREE OF CONTROL

The subject of control is complex. The reason is, partly, that "control" means many things to us. To begin with, we will distinguish between two kinds of control. First of all, there is the kind of control that depends on the degree to which the decision-maker can control his instruments. The instruments may be executives, machines, money, or others. This kind of control is associated with tactics and with the skill of the executive in handling his instruments. In essence, control of the first type concerns the ability of the decision-maker to fulfill his strategy.

The second kind of control we shall consider in some detail. It is independent of the executive's skill in carrying out a plan by means of the instruments and tactics available to him. It is the degree of control that is inherent in the solution to a problem. In other words, it is the manner in which a strategy and states of nature combine to yield a solution. Up to this point we have shown how an optimal strategy can be chosen subject to an objective such as maximize profit, minimize cost. But the decision-maker, being aware of the implementation phase, has an additional objective at all times—to maximize control. He will, therefore, examine the solution that is optimal with respect to cost, profit, or whatever and evaluate it with respect to control. He may decide that a less optimal solution offering greater control should be preferred to the optimal solution.

Frequently, the executive will evaluate a solution intuitively, but we shall attempt to explain what is involved in this evaluation and to indicate what methods are available for performing this task. Let us look at the following decision matrix.

	0.5	0.5	
	$N1$	$N2$	EV
$S1$	11	90	50.5
$S2$	50	50	50.0
$S3$	30	69	49.5

If we could control states of nature we would select $N2$. But we have always said that we cannot control states of nature and, in this case, we see that each of the two states of nature is assigned a probability of 0.5. The states occur with equal likelihood, but which state will occur is no better known than whether a coin toss will result in a head or a tail. Then the only kind of control we can exercise is by the choice of a strategy. However, our objective is to maximize the payoff, and strategy $S1$ accomplishes this end. We have met this same type of situation before, when the farmer was trying to decide which strategy to use—asparagus or peas.

To restate the problem, strategy $S1$ offers the greatest expected value for the payoff, but if $N1$ should occur, then the decision-maker must accept a very low payoff. Perhaps it would mean ruin for him. In our present case, we see that $S2$ offers almost as good an expected payoff as $S1$. No rational decision-maker is going to choose $S1$ with its great extremes in preference to $S2$ which produces just 0.5 less expected payoff. As in the farmer's case, we know what the difficulty is and we know how to resolve it. Utilities must be substituted for the payoffs that are presently being used. Before we do this, let us slightly rearrange the decision matrix so that the basic quandary can be posed.

	0.5	0.5	
	$N1$	$N2$	EV
$S1$	10	90	50
$S2$	50	50	50
$S3$	30	70	50

On the face of it, no strategy is preferred—a ludicrous conclusion to any experienced executive who would immediately choose $S2$ because it offers him complete control. His payoff with $S2$ is independent of the state of nature. No matter what happens he will always get 50 with $S2$. His control if he chooses $S2$ is perfect. With $S1$ or $S3$ it is less than perfect.

We will convert to utilities by means of the standard-gamble technique. We let the smallest value 10 equal zero. We take the largest value in the entire matrix, which is 90, and replace it with 1. We then ask, for what probability that 90 will occur in a lottery between 10 and 90 would we be willing to accept either 50 with certainty or the lottery. Let us assume that the answer is $3/4$. We ask the same question for 30 with certainty or the lottery, and 70 with certainty or the lottery. Let us presume that the resulting matrix is as follows:

	0.5	0.5	
	$N1$	$N2$	EV
$S1$	0	1	0.50
$S2$	0.75	0.75	0.75
$S3$	0.625	0.875	0.75

It is clear that strategy S1 has been eliminated. But the problem remains. The expected values of the utilities for S2 and S3 indicate that they are equivalent. Again, the executive knows that this is not reasonable. Without question he prefers S2 to S3. It could be argued that the decision-maker did not properly choose his utilities. But this argument is relatively fruitless from an operational point of view since it can be demonstrated that the values assigned to the utilities are consistent and logical. That is, the decision-maker can hardly assign a value of ½ to 50. Were he to do so, it would mean that he considered 50 with certainty to be the equivalent of a 50–50 lottery between 10 and 90 with an expected value of 50. He would, in other words, be placing no utility on control.

Obviously the executive wishes to express his preference for a stable situation over an unstable one. Therefore, the utility of 50 is greater than ½, and ¾ is a reasonable choice. In other words, the reason that the executive assigns a utility of ¾ to 50 is precisely because he prefers certainty or control rather than uncertainty or lack of control. The distortion of the utility upward from ½ is a function of the decision-maker's lack of certainty. Furthermore, the selection of ¾ instead of ½ is implied by the diminishing utility of money. The utility sacrificed by foregoing $50 with certainty is greater than the utility gained by an additional $40 with uncertainty. Even in the case of an even-money bet, no rational person governed by diminishing utilities would ever participate. As for the other utilities, it is completely consistent that if 50 has a utility of ¾ or ⅝ that 30, which is less than the expected value, will be worth a bigger gamble. Therefore, we have assigned it ⅝. Similarly, to forego 70 with certainty we require more certainty. Therefore, we have assigned it a utility value of ⅞. Although we have created this example with just the right values to illustrate our point, the fact remains that they could have been the executive's assignment of utilities.

Now, several things can be said about this problem. We will concentrate our remarks on the implications of the example to control. We can say that the decision-maker has not estimated his utilities correctly. If he is willing to re-evaluate his utilities then the tie between S2 and S3 may be broken. The executive with the job of implementation will say that the decision-maker's revised utilities are correct only if S2 is chosen in preference to S3. But how can we be sure that the decision-maker's corrected utilities are the right ones? As in all problems of estimation, we can expect some amount of error. As we have previously stated, the solutions of different problems have various tolerances for error. But in the case of utilities, if the decision-maker insists that he has made no errors, then it is impossible to contradict him. What we can say, however, is that his utilities indicate that he has different objectives and different values from ours.   If, for example, the decision-maker insists that the matrix with equal expected utilities for $S2$ and $S3$ is correct—then the conclusion can be drawn that he is not interested in the degree of control.   The evaluation of the solution by the executive in charge of implementation will, in all probability, reject the decision-maker's solution.

Unfortunately, the situation is not always as clear as it is in this simple example.   If the chosen utilities do not express the multiple objectives of obtaining the best possible combination of payoff and control, it is difficult to detect this fact.   When the executive does not have the rare situation of choosing between two strategies that appear to offer equal expected utilities, but that have clearly different outcomes, how is he to know whether similar distortions have not appeared in the assignment of utilities?   That is, how is he to tell whether the problem-solvers have included his objective of control?

In the problem section of Chapter 4, the reader was asked to use the standard-gamble technique.   In that example, we suggested that comparisons should be made between the smallest and the largest values— but also with ranges falling between the extremes.   In so doing, the reader was able to check his consistency in assigning utilities.   If the elements of this comparison are now extended to the utility matrix, we will eliminate the 0 and 1 of $S1$ from our consideration.   In other words, we will use the standard gamble to evaluate the utilities of $S2$ and $S3$. Then matrix 1

	0.5	0.5	
	$N1$	$N2$	EV
$S2$	0.75	0.75	0.75
$S3$	0.625	0.875	0.75

becomes matrix 2

	0.5	0.5	
	$N1$	$N2$	EV
$S2$	0.625	0.625	0.625
$S3$	0	1	0.50

We have taken the maximum and minimum values in the matrix and have set them equal to 1 and 0, respectively, as the method requires. Since 0.75 lies an equal distance from both 0.625 and 0.825, the probability that 0.875 will occur in a lottery with 0.625 should be greater than 0.50 to produce indifference between that lottery and 0.75 for certain.

The reasons are the same as those given above for assigning more than 0.50 for the utility of 50. However, in order to obtain equal expected utilities as indicated by the original (Matrix 1, above), we should have obtained Matrix 3 (below) instead of Matrix 2.

	0.5 N1	0.5 N2	EV
S2	0.50	0.50	0.50
S3	0	1	0.50

But Matrix 3 is not reasonable since it assigns a utility of 0.50 to the value 0.75, and we have explained why a value of 0.50 for 0.75 is not justifiable. Why does this occur? Because the supposition of the standard gamble is that we can express any utility in terms of the two extremes. Using the standard-gamble method assumes that the individual, evaluating his utilities, is capable of assessing the multiple objectives that are involved in the problem—one of which is control. If the executive does not share this assumption, believing that it is beyond the realm of bounded rationality, then there is a means available for systematically including the control objective in the selection of a strategy. We have previously discussed this means—which is the use of the logarithmic measure of utility—but we must now express its importance in the area of control and implementation.

113. CONTROL AND THE LOGARITHMIC MEASURE OF UTILITY

Let us replace the outcomes in the decision matrix with the logarithms of the outcomes.

REPLACE			0.5 N1	0.5 N2	EV	APPROXIMATE EQUIVALENT EV
10 90		S1	1.000	1.954	1.477	30
50 50		S2	1.699	1.699	1.699	50
30 70		S3	1.477	1.845	1.661	46

We observe that the logarithms produce the highest expected value for S2—which is in keeping with the rational requirements for control. The tie between the expected values is broken by means of this measure of utility. The use of the logarithm insures the selection of the strategy with the best possible control whenever a tie occurs for the outcomes. Thus, the following relationship holds for any pair of values with the expected value of 50:

$$\log 99 + \log 1 < \log 98 + \log 2 < \log 97 + \log 3 < \ldots < \log 50 + \log 50$$

Using logarithms the general form of the decision matrix can be written:

	p_1	p_2
	$N1$	$N2$
$S1$	$\log O_{11}$	$\log O_{12}$
$S2$	$\log O_{21}$	$\log O_{22}$
$S3$	$\log O_{31}$	$\log O_{32}$

The expected value is then derived by the equations:

$$EV_1 = p_1 \log O_{11} + p_2 \log O_{12}$$
$$EV_2 = p_1 \log O_{21} + p_2 \log O_{22}$$
$$EV_3 = p_1 \log O_{31} + p_2 \log O_{32}$$

The largest EV_i, so calculated, determines the strategy to be selected, i. If we convert from this logarithmic form, we get

$$EV_1 = \log (O_{11}{}^{p_1}O_{12}{}^{p_2})$$
$$EV_2 = \log (O_{21}{}^{p_1}O_{22}{}^{p_2})$$
$$EV_3 = \log (O_{31}{}^{p_1}O_{32}{}^{p_2})$$

This is a form we certainly recognize. It is the logarithm of the relationship that we developed, at some length, when we were discussing dimensional analysis and multiple objectives. The fact that it is the logarithm of this familiar expression is of no particular consequence since the logarithm is simply a convenient way of evaluating the expression, $O_{11}{}^{p_1}O_{21}{}^{p_2}$, and so on. The greatest value of the logarithm will also be the greatest value of the expression. However, the form of the expression itself suggests an approach to the meaning of control.

The values p_1 and p_2 are the probabilities that the states of nature will occur. In our former discussion of dimensional analysis the corresponding powers represented the importance the decision-maker placed on the individual objectives. The interpretation of the present case can be made in those same terms. We observe that O_{ij} is raised to the p_j power, where the strategy is i and the state of nature is j. This implies that the objective is the state of nature and the importance of the objective to the decision-maker is the probability that the state of nature will occur. This is reasonable since the importance of the state of nature increases as its frequency increases. The value that the objective takes on is, in each case, the result of the strategy employed. Since the value is the utility of the outcome, the logarithm of the outcome is multiplied by the importance, p_j, of the state of nature that produced the outcome. In this way the utilities of the outcomes express the multiple objectives of wanting to maximize the payoffs and wanting simultaneously to maximize control.

When the decision-maker wishes to include control in his appraisal of the decision matrix he can use the logarithms of the outcomes as his measure of utility. The extent to which an individual approximates the values of the logarithmic utilities in his estimates of utility by the standard gamble, or by whatever means he uses, is evidence of the importance he places on control. This leads to the important question: How does the decision-maker exercise this control? States of nature have repeatedly been defined as falling outside the domain of the decision-maker's control. The answer to this question requires a careful inspection of states of nature.

114. STATES OF NATURE AND CONTROL

States of nature were introduced at the very start of this book. At that time we presented a simple definition which adequately covered a great number of cases—but not all. The reader will have noticed that in a number of instances states of nature have been, in some sense, transformed into outcomes. We propose, now, to explore this kind of transformation and to explain what it means in terms of control.

The decision matrix, which we have studied at great length, can present situations where the states of nature appear under conditions of certainty, risk, or uncertainty. All three conditions require specific assumptions. First of all, with respect to certainty and risk, we must assume that the probabilities assigned to the states of nature are correctly chosen —which precludes the possibility that other states that are unknown could exist. In the second place, with respect to all three decision conditions, we must assume that the probabilities assigned to the states of nature will not change. The implications of these assumptions are far-reaching.

Let us consider decision-making under conditions of uncertainty. In a formal sense we know that our method guarantees we will obtain the best possible decision that our choice of a decision criterion permits. This selection of a decision criterion is, in a very real sense, a control decision. In other words, the decision-maker's choice of a criterion can be represented as a selection of p values. In this case the decision-maker is really rating the importance of the various states of nature but without the benefit of frequency observations. An executive faced with the problems of implementation could hardly be blamed for placing a relatively low degree of belief on a decision made in this fashion.

Because states of nature are, in many cases, difficult or impossible to determine—still less to place probabilities on their likelihood of occurring—an important transformation is used. In this transformation, states of nature are replaced by outcomes. Outcomes are usually much easier to observe. Furthermore, it is frequently possible to describe the complete universe of outcomes—an accomplishment which is much more difficult for states of nature. The transformation is used most often when the problem is one of uncertainty. That is, we do not know the states of nature but we can observe the outcomes. We can distinguish these transformed outcomes by calling them *outcome-states*. To illustrate, we will transform the matrix we used before.

	OUTCOME-STATES										
	0	10	20	30	40	50	60	70	80	90	100
$S1$	—	0.5	—	—	—	—	—	—	—	0.5	—
$S2$	—	—	—	—	—	1.0	—	—	—	—	—
$S3$	—	—	—	0.5	—	—	—	0.5	—	—	—

The payoff entries are the probabilities that each outcome-state will result from a specific strategy. Now, in this sense we see that although the decision-maker cannot control the state of nature, he has some control over the outcome-states. $S2$ gives him perfect control over one outcome-state. He may not like this particular outcome-state, and he can indicate this when he expresses his utility for it. But from the point of view of control, he could ask for nothing more.

Information theory tells us something about this aspect of the decision-maker's control. It will be remembered that H_{Max} was the condition of equally likely states—and that this represented complete disorder. In other words, it represents no control at all. When H was equal to zero—only one outcome-state possible—there would be complete order and perfect control. The information measures for this matrix would be (using bits):

$$H(S1) = -0.5 \log 0.5 - 0.5 \log 0.5 = 1.0 \text{ bit}$$
$$H(S2) = -1 \log 1 = 0.0 \text{ bit}$$
$$H(S3) = -0.5 \log 0.5 - 0.5 \log 0.5 = 1.0 \text{ bit}$$
$$H_{Max} = -\log (1/11) = 3.5 \text{ bits}$$

The redundancy value, R, gives a reasonable measure of control on the scale zero to one. Zero represents complete lack of control, while the value one, stands for complete control.

$$R(S1) = 1 - 1/3.5 = 0.7$$
$$R(S2) = 1 - 0/3.5 = 1.0$$
$$R(S3) = 1 - 1/3.5 = 0.7$$

Using information theory gives us a "pure" measure of control. For this reason it suffers from the same defect—but at the opposite pole—that we previously observed when maximization of the payoff was accomplished without full consideration of control. In other words, information theoretic measures tell us nothing about which outcome-states appear. They do not permit the decision-maker to express his preference for one outcome-state over another. That is why $S1$ and $S3$ have the same redundancy measures. H_{Max} is based on the eleven outcome-states. If unit divisions had been employed, i.e., 0, 1, 2, ... 50, ... 98, 99, 100, there would have been 101 outcome-states. In this case, H_{Max} would be 6.6 bits. This would not have affected the R measure for $S2$, but the R measures for $S1$ and $S3$ would have been increased to 0.85. On the face of it this might seem absurd, but from a purely control point of view it is understandable. The number of possible outcome-states has increased. Therefore, more control would be required to maintain only two equally likely states out of a greater number of possibilities. This further illustrates the fact that although information measures are descriptive of control, they are not well suited for the executive's evaluation of control.

We have explained how the outcome-state transformation allows for the possibility that we do not know or cannot observe all relevant states of nature. The transformation to outcome-states permits the decision-maker to encompass all of the reality with which he is concerned. For example, profit can be represented dollar by dollar between whatever bounds appear reasonably certain of containing all experience. Even more definitive are outcome-states given in percentages which range from 0 to 100. The brand-share model was an example of a transformation from states of nature to outcome-states. It would have been inconceivable to attempt to list, observe, or know all of the states of nature that affect brand share.

The outcome-state matrix can be used to obtain the logarithmic utility comparison by expressing the outcome states as logarithms. In the example given below, it should be noted how states $N1$ and $N3$ produce the same outcome, 3, when strategy $S3$ is used. This fact, which might be difficult to observe, is not required information for the outcome-state matrix.

	0.3	0.2	0.5		OUTCOME-STATES			
	$N1$	$N2$	$N3$		2	3	4	5
$S1$	5	4	3	$S1$	—	0.5	0.2	0.3
$S2$	2	5	3	$S2$	0.3	0.5	—	0.2
$S3$	3	4	3	$S3$	—	0.8	0.2	—

For the decision matrix, we have

$$EV(S1) = 0.3 \log 5 + 0.2 \log 4 + 0.5 \log 3$$
$$EV(S2) = 0.3 \log 2 + 0.2 \log 5 + 0.5 \log 3$$
$$EV(S3) = 0.3 \log 3 + 0.2 \log 4 + 0.5 \log 3 = 0.8 \log 3 + 0.2 \log 4$$

For the outcome-state matrix, we observe

$$EV(S1) = 0.5 \log 3 + 0.2 \log 4 + 0.3 \log 5$$
$$EV(S2) = 0.3 \log 2 + 0.5 \log 3 + 0.2 \log 5$$
$$EV(S3) = 0.8 \log 3 + 0.2 \log 4$$

And, in this sense, these forms are equivalent, even though we cannot retransform the outcome-state matrix back to the form of the usual decision matrix. Information is lacking as to which states produced which outcome-states.

The outcome-state transformation takes care of the first problem we mentioned—that is, the difficulty of assigning probabilities to states of nature and the possibility that unknown states exist. We will now consider the second problem that we raised, namely, the assumption that probabilities assigned to states of nature will not change.

115. STABILITY AND STATES OF NATURE

One of the most fundamental requirements of decision-making is that stability exist with respect to the states of nature. In its simplest form stability refers to stationary probabilities for the states of nature. Stationary probabilities will not change values and, therefore, when we talk about decision-making under risk we assume that the probabilities for the states of nature are forever the same. Let us consider the following decision matrix, which applies to only one strategy, observing the probabilities of the states of nature over two periods of time.

	0.2	0.3	0.1	0.2	0.1	0.1
	$N1$	$N2$	$N3$	$N4$	$N5$	$N6$
$S1(t_0)$	10	4	10	4	8	10

	0.1	0.2	0.2	0.3	0.1	0.1
	$N1$	$N2$	$N3$	$N4$	$N5$	$N6$
$S1(t_1)$	10	4	10	4	8	10

We see that stability for the states of nature does not exist in this example. However, purely from the point of view of outcome states, the process appears to be stable. As long as only this kind of interchange takes place, we can consider the outcome-state distribution to be stable.

	OUTCOME-STATES										
	0	1	2	3	4	5	6	7	8	9	10
$S1(t_0)$	—	—	—	—	0.5	—	—	—	0.1	—	0.4
$S1(t_1)$	—	—	—	—	0.5	—	—	—	0.1	—	0.4

A most important statistical method exists that determines whether or not an in-time process is "under control" or stable. This is the method

used in quality control.   Because it is so difficult to observe states of nature—to find out how many states exist, to describe all of the states so
that they can be identified and recognized, to observe which states produce the same outcome, and so on—quality control is based on the outcome-state matrix.   Quality control enables the decision-maker to detect
nonstationary probabilities for the outcome-states.   Since so many decision methods require stationarity, such as all decision-making under
risk, standard-gamble or logarithmic evaluation of utilities, it is of the
greatest importance that the decision-maker consider this aspect of control.

Statistical quality control is based on the sampling of outcome states.
Each sample is examined to determine how much variability occurred
within that sample.   After a reasonable number of samples are taken, the
average variability is determined.   This average variability is then converted to an estimate of the variability of the population from which the
samples were drawn.   The measure of variability is used to establish control limits.   Outcome-states that lie within the control limits are expected
to occur.   Ouctome-states that fall outside of the control limits are unexpected events that appear to have so low a probability of expected occurrence that when they do appear it is taken as a signal that changes in
the process may be taking place.   Figure 14.1 shows a control chart in
which outcome-state 90 appears.   Since this outcome-state lies above the

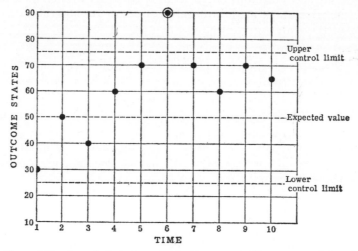

Figure 14.1   A control chart on which outcome-state 90 appears and signals
that the process may not be under control.

upper control limit, its occurrence is unexpected and improbable unless a
change in the process has taken place.   Another sign that leads to the
same conclusion appears on the chart.   Starting with the fourth observa-

tion, all of the outcome states lie above the expected value. This is called a *run*. When a large number of successive values fall entirely on one side of the expected value, an improbable occurrence has been observed. Again, it is taken as a signal that a fundamental change may have occurred in the process.

It has not been our intention to develop the statistical methods of quality control except as they relate to the decision-maker's problems of evaluating his control. The most significant consideration, in this regard, is the fact that the conclusion that a process is out of control is not taken as an indication that the probabilities of the states of nature have changed. Instead it is interpreted as the fact that the definition of the strategy is incomplete. In other words, the conclusion is drawn that the decision-maker either lacks control over his instruments or else he has failed to consider an element that he could control if he found out what it was. Why is it that the assumption is made that no change occurred in the probabilities of the states of nature?

The answer is that quality control is applied mostly to physical processes. The assumption is far less applicable to behavioral processes. In a physical system Nature tends to exhibit constancy and consistency. When such a system does not exhibit constancy, then the most rewarding conclusion is the one we have drawn above. Under most circumstances it is possible to locate that element in the strategy which was either forgotten or changed. Clearly these sequential methods cannot be used when the strategy is changed at each decision (such as changing the settings on a machine as each new part is made), or when nonrepetitive decisions are being made. However, for repetitive decisions, this approach to control epitomizes the notions of an automatic decision-maker. The knowledge that a process is under control, and that an unknown change in strategy will be detected, adds immeasurably to the degree of confidence the decision-maker can place in the solution.

But what happens when the constancy of nature cannot be relied upon? As we have pointed out, this is particularly characteristic of behavioral systems, but not limited to them. It can be argued that if we could recognize the basic elements in economic, market, and personnel problems then we would be able to complete our strategies and thereby remove the apparent differences between physical and behavioral systems. Practically speaking, however, the point is purely philosophical but the problem is real. The area that we are calling "behavioral" includes the greatest number of high-level decision problems.

First of all, we find a contradiction. States of nature, by definition, cannot be controlled. But in feedback systems, an input leads to an output which is fed back and causes a change in the state of nature. In that case, by selecting an input the decision-maker can indirectly control the state of nature, within whatever limits the system allows. For example, in the work-pool problem of Chapter 11, the decision-maker changed the probabilities of absenteeism by changing the size of the work pool. Further, it can be recognized that a stochastic process produces continual changes in the probability distribution of the outcome-states. But in this case, we will also observe that the matrix of transition probabilities could be constant. In that event, we would treat the transition probabilities as the outcome-states, and the decision-maker would be in a position to evaluate the degree of control in these terms. However, we have had occasion to suggest the use of the transition matrix of the transition matrix.

It is evident that lacking a stable system, we must hunt indefinitely through a maze of interdependent probabilities without ever finding our stable system upon which everything else could be based. Under these circumstances, lacking a permanent solution, the decision-maker can utilize the various methods available for reaching short-term decisions. His long-term decisions are achieved in a step-by-step process which continually evaluates what has happened—what can now be achieved—and how much control is available at each step along the way. If a limiting distribution is available, the stepping process can benefit from this information. However, states of nature with variable probabilities do not necessarily come to equilibrium. Some states oscillate continually in a periodic form, while others enter states from which there is no return and from which they lead to an entirely new set of companion states of nature. We can represent some of these conditions in the following way:

	$N1$	$N2$	$N3$	$N4$	$N5$	$N6$
$S1(t_0)$	0.10	0.50	0.40	0.20	—	0.80
$S1(t_1)$	0.20	0.40	0.40	—	0.20	0.60
$S1(t_2)$	0.30	0.50	0.40	—	0.20	0.45
$S1(t_3)$	0.20	0.40	0.40	—	0.20	0.34
$S1(t_4)$	0.10	0.50	0.40	—	0.20	0.26
$S1(t_5)$	0.20	0.40	0.40	—	0.20	0.20
$S1(t_6)$	0.30	0.50	0.40	—	0.20	0.15
.	.	.	.	.	.	.
.	.	.	.	.	.	.
.	.	.	.	.	.	.
$S1(t_i)$	—	—	0.40	—	0.20	0.08

The outcomes shown are the probabilities that the states of nature will appear. Each of the matrix columns is intended to represent a different type of condition for states of nature. $N1$ and $N2$ are periodic, but oscillate with different frequencies. The periodic states may behave in this fashion because of feedback. A different strategy could produce different periods of oscillation or even stable states. $N3$ is an example of a stable state. Solutions for conditions in which all the states are stable can be regarded as relatively permanent. $N4$ and $N5$ are intended to represent a nonreversible change in the states of nature. We might suppose that under $S1$, $N4$ becomes $S5$ by means of some feedback connection. If, after $S1$ is removed, $N4$ does not reappear, then the implication is that some kind of threshold has been crossed from which there is no return. The issue of reversibility is an important one from the point of view of control. Catastrophy and ruin represent extremal situations from which the smallest chance of return exists. $N6$ is an example of a process that has a limit. Long-range decision-making can be based on predictions of such an equilibrium state.

Another control characteristic of repetitive decision-making is worthy of mention. We have previously indicated how a mixed strategy changes the value of the payoff for both parties in a competitive situation. When the decision matrix does not have competitive strategies but only states of nature, the decision-maker can obtain complete control of a large range of outcomes by using a mixed strategy. For example,

| | 0.5 | 0.5 | |
	$N1$	$N2$	EV
$S1$	10	30	20
$S2$	70	90	80

If the decision-maker decides to use $S1$ exclusively, over a great many repetitions, he will obtain the expected value of 20. If he uses $S2$ exclusively, he will get 80. But suppose that the value he wishes to obtain is 50. Then, if he uses $S1$ half of the time and $S2$ half of the time, he will obtain an expected value of 50. Suppose that he would like to get 35. The answer is simply to use $S1$ three-fourths of the time and $S2$ one-fourth of the time. In this way, the decision-maker exercises control over the entire range of values between his minimum and his maximum expected values. If he knows how the probabilities of the states of nature will vary in the future, he can apply the same kind of mixed strategies in time. In all cases, this approach requires that the effects of the decisions should be cumulative over time. Repetitive decision-making allows for a learning process, and increased control can be gained by the decision-maker as he improves his knowledge of the situation.

These are some aspects of the problem of control which the decision-maker is faced with when he considers the solution in implementation terms. We are now in a position to answer the question: How does the decision-maker exercise control? Whether or not he can in any way affect states of nature, the decision-maker's control is a function of the information he has about the problem and the solution. The decision-maker's choice of a strategy—if predicated solely on some analytical maximization device—cannot include all of the elements pertinent to implementation. All of the elements cannot be included in a single maximization technique. On the other hand, there are a variety of analytical methods that can produce useful information with respect to this problem. The decision-maker who puts full faith in his intuition alone is turning his back on information that could substantially assist him in resolving his control problems. For we see that the control problem is a question of comparing complex multiple objectives under a variety of restrictive conditions imposed by nature. The decision-maker's only means of exercising control is by his choice of a strategy. Modifications of the strategy can be made, based on information that went into obtaining the solution. Further modifications will result from additional information derived by auxiliary techniques. The decision-maker can then select that strategy which promises the most rewarding degree of achievement of the multiple objectives involved.

PROBLEMS

1. An executive has a choice of two alternative sets of tactics, x or y. His objective is to achieve the state of the system "E." The system has six states, A, B, C, D, E and F and no matter which tactics he uses he must begin with A. The executive's ability to control the system is represented in matrix form for each set of tactics. (That is, in x for example, there is perfect control, (1), in changing F to B but only 0.2 chance of changing D to C with an 0.8 chance of changing D to E.)

	x							y					
	A	B	C	D	E	F		A	B	C	D	E	F
A	0	0	0	0	0	1	A	0	0.5	0	0	0.5	0
B	0	0	0	1	0	0	B	0.2	0	0	0	0.8	0
C	0	0	0	0	0.6	0.4	C	0.1	0	0	0	0	0.9
D	0	0	0.2	0	0.8	0	D	0.1	0	0.9	0	0	0
E	0	0.3	0	0	0.7	0	E	0	0	0	0.5	0.5	0
F	0	1	0	0	0	0	F	0	0	0	0	1	0

a. What is the relative permanence of the outcome in each case?

b. What is the relative degree of reversibility with respect to the starting point A in each case?

c. Which set of tactics offers greater control?

d. Which set of tactics should the executive choose?

2. An executive is faced with the following decision problem under uncertainty:

	$N1$	$N2$	$N3$	$N4$
$S1$	2	8	16	8
$S2$	8	8	8	4
$S3$	4	4	16	8

a. What decision will he come to if he uses expected values?

b. What will be his decision if he considers the control aspects of the problem? How can he resolve the problem which arises?

c. Transform this matrix to an outcome-state matrix and obtain the entropy and redundancy of each strategy.

3. In what way can we interpret the four situations described below? $\bar{S}$ is the expected sales per week. S_u is the upper control limit so chosen that sales per week are greater than S_u less than 1 per cent of the time.

a. $S_u = .4.2, \bar{S} = 4.0, S_L = 3.8$
b. $S_u = t/2 + 6, \bar{S} = t/2 + 2, S_L = t/2 - 2$
c. $S_u = 2t/3 + 6, \bar{S} = t/2 + 2, S_L = t/3 - 2$
d. $S_u = 4/2^t + 4, \bar{S} = 4.0, S_L = 4 - 4/2^t$

4. Assume the following repetitive decision situation:

| | 0.5 | 0.5 | |
	N1	N2	EV
S1	2	8	5
S2	4	8	6
S3	2	16	9

a. If the executive's objective is to achieve outcome values closest to 8 as often as possible what is his optimal procedure?

b. If the objective is to obtain the expected value closest to 8 by following a pure strategy what then is the optimal procedure?

c. If the objective is to obtain the expected value of 8 by following a mixed strategy what is the best plan of action?

5. An executive makes n_i decisions per day where i stands for the day of the year. Over a period of time the executive collects enough a posteriori data concerning the correctness of each decision which he has made to determine that his expected fraction of incorrect decisions, $\bar{p}$, is 0.02. The executive prepares a control chart on which he marks the expected value. For each day he determines the control limits by using the equations:

$$(\text{Upper control limit})_i = \bar{p} + 3\sqrt{n_i\bar{p}\,(1 - \bar{p})/n_i}$$
$$(\text{Lower control limit})_i = \bar{p} - 3\sqrt{n_i\bar{p}\,(1 - \bar{p})/n_i}$$

What is the greatest fraction of incorrect decisions per day that the executive is prepared to accept as a chance possibility before he re-examines his own decision-making practices

a. If he makes one decision per day?
b. If he makes nine decisions per day?
c. If he makes 100 decisions per day?
d. How would you interpret the lower limit?

Bibliography

DECISION THEORY:

Bross, Irwin D. J.: *Design for Decision;* The Macmillan Co.; New York, 1953.
Luce, R. Duncan and Howard Raiffa: *Games and Decisions;* John Wiley & Sons; New York, 1958.
Wasserman, Paul with Fred S. Silander: *Decision-Making, An Annotated Bibliography;* Graduate School of Business and Public Administration, Cornell University; Ithaca, New York; 1958.

OPERATIONS RESEARCH:

Case Institute of Technology Operations Research Group: *A Comprehensive Bibliography on Operations Research;* John Wiley & Sons; New York, 1958.
Churchman, C. W., Ackoff, R. A. and E. L. Arnoff: *Introduction to Operations Research;* John Wiley & Sons; New York, 1957.
Saaty, Thomas L.: *Mathematical Methods of Operations Research;* McGraw-Hill Book Co.; New York, 1959.
Sasieni, M., Yaspan, A. and L. Friedman: *Operations Research, Methods and Problems;* John Wiley & Sons; New York, 1959.

O.R. CASE STUDIES:

McCloskey, J. F. and F. N. Trefethen (Eds.): *Operations Research for Management, Volume 1;* Johns Hopkins Press; Baltimore, 1954.
———— and J. M. Coppinger (Eds.): *Operations Research for Management, Volume 2;* Johns Hopkins Press; Baltimore, 1956.

INVENTORY:

Magee, John F.: *Production Planning and Inventory Control;* McGraw-Hill Book Co.; New York, 1958.
Whitin, Thomson M.: *The Theory of Inventory Management;* Princeton University Press; Princeton, 1953.

QUEUING:

Morse, Philip M.: *Queues, Inventories and Maintenance;* John Wiley & Sons; New York, 1958.

PROGRAMMING:

Bellman, Richard E.: *Dynamic Programming;* Princeton University Press; Princeton, 1957.

Vajda, S.: *The Theory of Games and Linear Programming;* John Wiley & Sons; New York, 1956.

Vazsonyi, Andrew: *Scientific Programming in Business and Industry;* John Wiley & Sons; New York, 1958.

GAME THEORY:

McDonald, John: *Strategy in Poker, Business and War;* W. W. Norton & Co.; New York, 1950.

Williams, J. D.: *The Compleat Strategyst;* McGraw-Hill Book Co.; New York, 1954.

MATHEMATICS:

Kemeny, J. G., Snell, J. L. and G. L. Thompson: *Introduction to Finite Mathematics;* Prentice-Hall, Inc.; Englewood Cliffs, N. J., 1957.

PROBABILITY THEORY:

Feller, William: *Introduction to Probability Theory and Its Applications, Volume 1;* (2nd Ed.), John Wiley & Sons; New York, 1957.

STATISTICS:

Schlaifer, Robert: *Probability and Statistics for Business Decisions;* McGraw-Hill Book Co.; New York, 1959.

ECONOMICS:

Allen, R. G. D.: *Mathematical Economics;* The Macmillan Co., Ltd.; London, 1956.

Dean, Joel: *Managerial Economics;* Prentice-Hall, Inc.; New York, 1951.

INFORMATION THEORY:

Goldman, Stanford, *Information Theory;* Prentice-Hall, Inc.; New York, 1953.

Shannon, C. E. and W. Weaver: *The Mathematical Theory of Communication;* The University of Illinois Press; Urbana, 1949.

COMMUNICATIONS:

Cherry, Colin: *On Human Communication;* The Technology Press of Massachusetts Institute of Technology; 1957.

CYBERNETICS:

Ashby, W. Ross: *An Introduction to Cybernetics;* John Wiley & Sons; New York, 1956.

Beer, Stafford: *Cybernetics and Management;* John Wiley & Sons; New York, 1959.

de Latil, Pierre: *Thinking by Machine, A Study of Cybernetics;* (Tran. Y. M. Golla) Houghton Mifflin Co.; Boston, 1957.

MEASUREMENT:

Campbell, Norman R.: *Foundations of Science;* Dover Publications, Inc.; New York, 1957.

Torgerson, Warren S.: *Theory and Methods of Scaling;* John Wiley & Sons; New York, 1958.

LOGIC:

Langer, Susanne K.: *An Introduction to Symbolic Logic;* Dover Publications, Inc.; New York, 1953.

COMPUTERS:

Stibitz, G. R. and J. A. Larrivee: *Mathematics and Computers;* McGraw-Hill Book Co.; New York, 1957.

SYSTEMS:

McKean, Roland N.: *Efficiency in Government through Systems Analysis;* John Wiley & Sons; New York, 1958.

ORGANIZATION:

March, James G. and Herbert A. Simon: *Organizations;* John Wiley & Sons; New York, 1958.

Seidenberg, Roderick: *Post-Historic Man, An Inquiry;* Beacon Press; Boston, 1957.

Whyte, William H., Jr.: *The Organization Man;* Simon & Schuster; New York, 1956.

MANAGEMENT:

Drucker, Peter F.: *The Practice of Management;* Harper & Brothers; New York, 1954.

Newman, William H.: *Administration Action;* Prentice-Hall, Inc.; Englewood Cliffs, N. J., 1950.

SCIENTIFIC METHOD:

Wilson, E. Bright, Jr.: *An Introduction to Scientific Research;* McGraw-Hill Book Co.; New York, 1952.

THE HUMAN ELEMENT:

Dixon, W. Macneile: *The Human Situation;* Oxford University Press; New York, 1958.

Hebb, D. O.: *Organization of Behavior;* John Wiley & Sons; New York, 1949.

Simon, Herbert A.: *Models of Man;* John Wiley & Sons; New York, 1957.

GENERAL:

Eiseley, Loren: *The Immense Journey;* Random House, Inc.; New York, 1957.

Index

An asterisk * following a page reference indicates an end-of-chapter Problem. A **boldface** page number indicates an illustrative figure.